THE BIRDS OF THE BRITISH ISLES

VOLUME FIVE

FALCONIDAE	AEGYPIIDAE
ACCIPITRIDAE	PANDIONIDAE

BLACK JESS.

PLATE I

BLACK JESS

INTERMEWED EYASS FALCON

The term " Falcon " here indicates the female as distinct from the Tiercel : " Eyass " that she was taken as a young bird from the eyrie, and " Intermewed " that she has gone through the moult and has attained adult plumage.

Reproduced by permission of Miss Brenda Lodge from *Memoirs of An Artist Naturalist*.

THE BIRDS OF THE BRITISH ISLES

BY

DAVID ARMITAGE BANNERMAN

M.B.E., M.A., Sc.D., F.R.S.E.

HONORARY ASSOCIATE, BRITISH MUSEUM (NATURAL HISTORY). PAST VICE-PRESIDENT
OF THE BRITISH ORNITHOLOGISTS' UNION. HON. FELLOW OF THE AMERICAN
ORNITHOLOGISTS' UNION AND OF THE SOCIÉTÉ ORNITHOLOGIQUE DE FRANCE

ILLUSTRATED BY

GEORGE E. LODGE

PAST VICE-PRESIDENT OF THE
BRITISH ORNITHOLOGISTS' UNION

VOLUME FIVE

OLIVER AND BOYD

EDINBURGH: TWEEDDALE COURT
LONDON: 39A WELBECK STREET, W.1

FIRST PUBLISHED . . 1956

PRINTED IN GREAT BRITAIN BY
OLIVER AND BOYD LTD., EDINBURGH

PREFACE

I<small>N</small> a *Postscript* to the Preface of my fourth volume I recorded with deep sorrow the death of my artist partner in this work—George Lodge—on 5th February 1954, and there stated that it was my intention to pay a brief tribute to his memory with the appearance of Volume V. A note therefore follows this Preface. To do his life's work justice would have required many pages and has not been attempted, but it is hoped that some day—while his memory is still fresh in their minds—one of his intimate friends will undertake to write his biography. It would make absorbing reading.

I have to thank the editor of the *Ibis* for allowing me to quote extracts from the obituary notice which I wrote for that journal at the time of Mr. Lodge's death.

The volume which is now published continues my account of the non-perching birds and deals entirely with the diurnal Birds of Prey. The life histories of many of the species are, if anything, treated more fully than are most of the birds in the earlier volumes, for it has been my aim to make this a super volume, the one in which George Lodge would have taken the greatest personal interest. I have consequently cast my net wide to enable much in the life histories of the Accipitrine birds which have a place on our British List to be included from observations made by naturalists in other lands, for it is a sad fact that several of our most noble birds of prey can no longer be studied in what were once their native haunts. Three—the osprey, the goshawk and the sea-eagle—have long since vanished as nesting species, while others, like the kite, are hanging on by a thread. It remains to be seen if the new Wild Birds Protection Act will enable them to regain their lost footing, but for some at least the Act has come too late while in the case of others the changes wrought by over-population of our islands have had the inevitable results which no Act of Parliament could have prevented.

Quite a number of the Raptores on our British List have their breeding places in the far north, others again nest in Mediterranean countries or in eastern Europe or Siberia and are but chance visitors to our shores. I have been fortunate indeed in having good friends in these distant lands as well as at home who have put their knowledge, their writings and their experiences at my disposal, and to one and all I tender my grateful thanks.

Madame Elizabeth Kozlova of the Academy of Sciences, Leningrad, has been a special source of help in sending me notes on the birds of the U.S.S.R. both from personal experiences and from those of Russian ornithologists whose work she has collated.   Many field notes from Norway have also been included, thanks to my good friend Doctor Hugh Blair who has taken a large share in the preparation of the essays on the Norwegian gyr-falcon, the goshawk, the rough-legged buzzard and the sparrow-hawk, and has furnished me with notes on the breeding habits of both the black and the red kite in Spain, and of the sea-eagle in Norway, to single out his most important contributions.   Doctor Blair's knowledge of the Norwegian language has proved invaluable, enabling the excellent work of Doctor Yngvar Hagen of Oslo on the predatory birds of his country to be utilized in an English work for the first time.   My debt to Doctor Hagen, Curator of Vertebrates at the University Museum, Oslo, for his permission to quote freely from *Rovfuglene og Viltpleien* is a great one.

In preparing my essays on the gyr-falcons, especially that on the Greenland falcon, I have made particular use of Doctor Finn Salomonsen's *Grønlands Fugle*, and when dealing with the hobby and the peregrine of Mr. Nethersole-Thompson's specialized knowledge.   I must also express my indebtedness to Doctor L. Horváth of the Hungarian National Museum for sending me a résumé of his investigations on the life of the red-footed falcon, in advance of publication—a courtesy of which I am fully sensible.

Mr. Seton Gordon, C.B.E., of the Isle of Skye, has done me the honour to write a special article in this volume on the golden eagle, upon which grand bird he is our greatest living authority.   His contribution will be found under his name on page 113.

To Major Anthony Buxton of Horsey Hall, Norfolk, I am indebted for the latest news of the marsh and Montagu's harriers breeding on his or adjacent estates and for permission to quote from his writings, especially *Fisherman Naturalist* (Collins, 1946).   Many other names of naturalists to whom I am indebted will be found in my text.

The specimens from which Mr. Lodge made his paintings, when not in his own collection, were borrowed mainly from Colonel R. Meinertzhagen, D.S.O. ; others from the British Museum.   I am also indebted to Dick Meinertzhagen for allowing me to quote from his valuable new book, *Birds of Arabia*, and to his publishers, Messrs. Oliver and Boyd, for similar permission.

Other recent works which I have found especially helpful have been *The Birds of Scotland* by Miss Rintoul and Miss Baxter, *The Birds of Ireland* by Colonel Scroope and his collaborators, *The Birds and Mammals of Shetland* by Mr. and Mrs. Venables, *The Birds of Lancashire* by Mr. Clifford Oakes and *Lakeland Natural History* by Mr. E. Blezard, to the authors of all of which I wish to make full acknowledgment for the advantages I have gained through these books.

Finally I must express my thanks to Professor Doctor Gladkow of the Zoological Museum of the University, Moscow, for presenting me with a complete set of *The Birds of the Soviet Union* written by various Russian specialists under the able editorship of Professors Gladkow and Dementiev : a monumental work, opening the door to much fresh knowledge.

In this, our fifth volume, I have again made use of Mr. Jourdain's egg measurements from *The Handbook of British Birds*, but have taken little else from that compilation without special acknowledgment, preferring to go to the source of many of the statements contained therein and to seek fresh inspiration from other fountainheads.

My wife, Mary Bannerman, has again helped me in countless ways with the preparation of the text and by her gift for languages has enabled me to make use of scientific papers and works—even those in Russian—which would otherwise have been closed to me.

Mr. Thomas Jenkins of Oliver and Boyd has once again been a tower of strength in the production of this book, especially in the supervision of the coloured plates.

Last, but not least, I would like to say thank you to my generous reviewers who have given me such encouragement to continue what is indeed a gigantic task.

BORELAND OF SOUTHWICK
    BY DUMFRIES
        October 1955

G. E. LODGE

3rd December 1860 — 5th February 1954

GEORGE EDWARD LODGE, to whose exceptional skill as an artist these volumes owe so much, died on 5th February 1954 in his ninety-fourth year, to the lasting grief of his many friends and countless admirers, and not least to the sorrow of his partner in this work, the writer of this notice.

To have collaborated with Lodge in the production of *The Birds of the British Isles* has been one of the greatest honours which have fallen to my lot, for Lodge's reputation as an artist-naturalist was world-renowned.

That he lived to paint practically every bird on the British List, for what was planned to be a standard work, fulfilled a crowning ambition of his life, and had it not been for the war years, when all writing work had to be put aside, it is probable that this volume, the one he had looked forward to beyond all others, would have been published in his lifetime. Alas ! that was not to be.

" For the sake of scientific accuracy "—to quote his own words—Mr. Lodge asked me before he died to correct the impression given in my Preface to Volume I that he was the instigator of this work, and in order to fulfil his wish I will quote from a letter which he wrote to me from Hawkhouse, Camberley, dated 23rd February 1942—a letter which had escaped my memory when preparing the original Preface. It reads as follows :

" Your idea of us two collaborating in a book of British Birds does appeal to me rather strongly. As you say I have always wanted to identify myself with a book on the subject and I now look upon it in rather this light—that the time has come when I might find myself with the leisure to be getting on with such an idea. . . . I am getting old, having gone eighty-one, but I do not think that my work is deteriorating yet. If such a book could be completed, with your name as writer and mine as illustrator, I feel sure that it would at once become a ' best seller '. . . . I have a very definite idea of what the illustrations ought to be."

Lodge came to stay with me in London on 1st July of that year and together we decided the plan of the book.

Despite his advanced age Lodge completed his share of the work and lived to see Volumes I and II published ; he was greatly pleased by their reception both by the public and by the scientific world, and especially by the unstinted praise given to his pictures. Of Volume I Canon C. E. Raven, F.R.S., wrote in *The Sunday Times* : " Mr. Lodge's pictures have never reached a higher level : they are among the very best

Photograph by Harry Savory

G. E. LODGE
3rd December 1860 — 5th February 1954

that have ever been published." Similar admiration for his work was expressed on all sides.

Lodge was at his best when depicting the birds of prey and those which are generally classed as " game birds ", and in the volume now issued some of the finest examples of his work in the former group will be found. Some of these pictures were already in his studio between the two great wars ; the others, with five exceptions, were finished and safely stored in an Edinburgh bank before the last war had ended.

The originals will be sold and the proceeds placed to the credit of the George Lodge Trust, which he founded in his lifetime, and thus used to further the project which was so near to his heart.

It was some time after all his pictures had been completed—384 plates depicting 426 different species—that, at the age of ninety-one, he asked permission of our publishers to include five extra plates, depicting the immature plumages of the gyr-falcon, Greenland falcon, Iceland falcon, peregrine and goshawk. By that time he had almost lost the sight of one eye and it was with some trepidation that we awaited these five paintings, fearing that they would not come up to his earlier standard. We need have had no fear ; the pictures submitted for our approval are reproduced in this volume as Plates 3, 5, 7, 9 and 26 respectively—proof, if proof were needed, that in his ninety-second year and with one eye impaired, his brush had not lost its delicate touch.

In his earlier life Lodge was a keen falconer, and in the only book which he wrote—at the age of 85, *Memoirs of An Artist Naturalist*—he devoted the first part of the book to " Hawks and Hawking " upon which he was a foremost authority.

The notice which I had the honour to write for the *Ibis* at the time of his passing gave some details of his early work and life. His character was summed up in these words :—

" Lodge was not one of those artists who sat at home in his studio. He travelled widely in his younger days and was also a great sportsman. A fine shot with gun or rifle, he was a welcome guest on numerous estates and deer-forests, and the walls of many country houses in England and Scotland are adorned with pictures of sporting scenes from his brush. He loved especially the grouse-moors and deer-forests of Scotland and the salmon rivers of Norway, and had an exceptional knowledge of the wild creatures which lived amidst such surroundings, for, in addition to his love of birds, Lodge was an all-round naturalist and a very keen oberver."

" A man of great simplicity of charm, with a keen sense of humour, Lodge made many friends. He was always ready to help others, particularly young artists."

"George Lodge was essentially a field naturalist ; his love of birds in their natural surroundings enabled him to portray them faithfully in his pictures, and his gentleness and love for them in some way communicated itself to the feathered inhabitants of his garden. It became a sanctuary for all the birds in the neighbourhood. Chaffinches, robins, sparrows and blue-tits would fearlessly perch on the arm of his chair and accept crumbs from his fingers without a trace of fear."

" George Lodge was a wonderful example of the best which Britain can produce, a sportsman, a naturalist and a very fine gentleman. No one could meet him without feeling the kindliness of his nature and his great integrity, and all who came in contact with him learned to love and admire him. The B.O.U. has lost a great bird-artist and his many admirers a wonderful friend."

The many tributes to his work which appeared in the Press and in scientific and sporting journals at the time of his death were accompanied by various excellent photographs of the artist in his studio, taken for the most part during the last years, or even months, of his life. I have chosen to reproduce in this volume one taken by his friend Harry Savory, showing George Lodge still in great form, at the age of seventy-five. One of his young friends at Avebury that year (1935), seeing that his photograph was about to be taken, had slipped a hooded sparrow-hawk on to his shoulder.

David A. Bannerman

CONTENTS

IN this list when a species is represented by *one race only* the English name is followed immediately by the Latin trinomial, or by the binomial if the species is monotypic.

If more than one race is represented in Britain, the species name is first given binomially, below which the recognized races follow in sequence, each with its English name and Latin trinomial.

As the majority of the species in the British List are illustrated, only a few great rarities not being depicted, a separate list of plates is unnecessary. On the left are given the plate numbers, and on the right the page numbers of the birds described. The plate numbers are placed opposite the *actual races* which are illustrated. As far as practicable the plates have been placed in the text facing the species which they depict.

CONTENTS

CONTENTS

Order FALCONIFORMES

Sub-Order FALCONES

Family FALCONIDAE

Genus *FALCO* Linnaeus

GYR-FALCONS   PLATES 2 TO 7

Falco rusticolus Linnaeus

1. Norwegian Gyr-Falcon

Falco rusticolus rusticolus Linnaeus

A rare Accidental Visitor
Discussed separately on p. 2

2. White Greenland Gyr-Falcon

Falco rusticolus candicans Gmelin

An Occasional, almost Annual Visitor, mainly to Scotland and Ireland
Discussed separately on p. 13

3. Grey Greenland Gyr-Falcon

Falco rusticolus obsoletus Gmelin

An immature female taken on the island of Stroma, Orkney, is practically indistinguishable from dark Labrador examples, but it is impossible to determine its origin, as equally dark birds occur in south-west Greenland. Discussed separately on pp. 13-15.

4. Iceland Gyr-Falcon

Falco rusticolus islandus Brünnich

An Irregular Visitor
Discussed separately on p. 20

SOME CHARACTERS OF THE RACES : In this puzzling group, which it has taxed the best ornithological brains of the world to attempt to unravel, there is considerable difficulty in setting down on paper the characters by which one race may be recognized from another.

Broadly speaking, there are four, if not five, races with which we may possibly be concerned in Britain, depending on whether we choose to ally the dark birds (plus the grey birds) which inhabit southern Greenland with the Labrador-Alaska race *F. r. obsoletus* Gmelin, or whether we retain the south Greenland population as a separate race under the name *F. r. holboelli* Sharpe, on the grounds that they have a slightly longer wing measurement than Labrador examples. Doctor Salomonsen would ally the south Greenland population with *F. r. obsoletus*, and with this I concur.

Of the gyr-falcons listed above the population in Iceland and Greenland exhibits bewildering phases of plumage which have nothing to do with age. These may be described briefly as follows :

1. A dark race, *F. rusticolus rusticolus* Linn., described from Sweden and ranging from Norway to Russia, consisting of dark birds only, the adults of which are slaty-brown above, with the underparts white, having drop-shaped streaks of dark brown on the throat and upper breast which become larger on the lower breast and belly ; the flanks and sides are broadly barred with dark brown. In this race there is an indication, sometimes well marked, of a moustachial streak and the cheeks are mostly dark brown.

2. A paler race, *F. r. islandus* Brünn., inhabiting Iceland, has more white on the head than Norwegian birds and paler upperparts, the barring being ashy-grey ; there is no moustachial streak and the underparts are usually less heavily spotted and barred. In this race the cheeks are mostly white.

Occasionally dark examples occur in Iceland which cannot be satisfactorily distinguished from the Swedish-Norwegian bird, but the darker crown of *rusticolus* is generally indicated.

Exceptionally pale examples of the Iceland bird are even more difficult to distinguish from some examples of the Greenland bird. Mr. George Lodge had in his possession a dark and a light bird which were taken in the same eyrie.

3. An almost entirely white race, *F. r. candicans*, inhabits the high Arctic regions of Greenland and ranges to Alaska, possibly also to northernmost Siberia.

4. There is another gyr-falcon which comes into the picture, *F. r. obsoletus* Gmelin, a very dark bird which the Americans distinguish as the black gyr-falcon. It was formerly supposed to be confined to Labrador, but is now recognized as having a much wider range south of that of *F. r. candicans*. It is with this subspecies that the birds of southern Greenland are now united. These birds exhibit two phases of plumage: (*a*) a dark phase very close to *F. r. rusticolus*, the Norwegian bird, and (*b*) a grey phase which in appearance approaches *F. r. islandus*. These Greenland gyr-falcons are discussed more fully hereafter. See p. 13-15.

PLATE 2 (adult)
PLATE 3 (immature)

NORWEGIAN GYR-FALCON[1]

Falco rusticolus rusticolus Linnaeus

A rare Accidental Visitor

IDENTIFICATION : Of the three northern falcons known to occur in Britain, the Norwegian or—as it is sometimes called—the *true* gyr-falcon is the darkest. Above it is more deeply and more uniformly coloured than the

[1] The notes on the Norwegian gyr-falcon have been supplied by Doctor H. M. S. Blair, from personal knowledge of the species in its native land and from wide experience of Norwegian authors.

PLATE 2

PLATE 2

NORWEGIAN GYR-FALCON (Adult)

Falco rusticolus rusticolus Linnaeus

Iceland falcon, the contrasts between the shades of grey on its broadly barred plumage being less striking, and it particularly differs from its ally in its darker—in some cases, practically black—crown. Individual Norwegian birds show considerable variation in the breadth of the slate-coloured moustachial marking. With some this is no more than a fleck of colour, or it may be lacking; but it can easily be seen on many, and on a mature male it often appears as a broad stripe. In appearance the Norwegian falcon bears more likeness to the peregrine than to the Iceland bird, as several naturalists and falconers have remarked. Writing to Canon Tristram, Lord Lilford summed up the first he ever saw alive as " most decidedly a very different bird from *islandus* and *candicans*. This falcon has much more of the peregrine about him in make and appearance." [1] In Bowdler-Sharpe's estimation too " the adult male of the gyr-falcon is wonderfully like an adult peregrine ". [2] The resemblance between the species becomes more striking from the extreme north of Norway eastwards, for in those regions the peregrine is represented by a pale form with a very slight moustachial stripe (*Falco peregrinus caeruleiceps* Stegm), which Norwegian ornithologists have aptly named the " tundra falcon " (tundra-falk). Young " tundra falcons " especially, with their almost white heads, could easily be mistaken for gyr-falcons by the novice. Aloft, the actions of a gyr-falcon differ but little from those of a peregrine. All one can say is that the gyr-falcon's wing movements *appear* the slower, but so fine a distinction will only be appreciated by an observer well versed in the ways of the more familiar bird. Close at hand, a difference in silhouette becomes noticeable to a practised eye, the tail of the gyr-falcon being proportionately larger and its wings broader and blunter—not so " willowy ", to borrow from the author of *In Search of the Gyr-Falcon*. The length of the tail feathers alone suffices to establish the identity of a perched falcon. In a peregrine these are almost covered by the closed wings, but in a gyr-falcon they project beyond the tips of the primaries for at least two inches. The gyr-falcon is besides the paler bird, the greys of its plumage approaching stone-colour, compared with the darker blue-greys of the peregrine.

On the falconer's block, a gyr-falcon, be it Norwegian, Iceland or Greenland, can always be recognized as such by its kestrel-like foot, the inner toe equalling the outer in length. In the peregrine—representative of the group sometimes described as the " true " falcons—the outer toe without its claw is longer than the inner toe and claw together. A further structural difference between the gyr-falcon and the peregrine appears in the shape of the big quills. Only the first of these shows any emargination in the peregrine, whereas in the gyr-falcon the second also bears a notch.

In a typical mature Iceland falcon the crown and nape are several shades lighter than the mantle, being creamy-white streaked with black,

---

[1] *Lord Lilford on Birds*, by A. Trevor-Battye, 1903, p. 86.
[2] *A Hand-book to the Birds of Great Britain*, vol. iii, p. 198.

and the whole plumage is much paler than that of a Norwegian gyr-falcon. But some Iceland examples have quite dark heads only slightly touched with white, and these can be confused with birds from Norway. Juveniles of the two forms are generally indistinguishable in the field, and at times even in the museum. In structure the Norwegian and Iceland falcons differ sufficiently to suggest to some that they should receive specific rank. Although the larger and longer-winged, the Iceland bird has the shorter tail. It is also distinctly the heavier in the skull, and Yarrell [1] tells us that " in modelling the hoods of trained birds of the two kinds, falconers use different blocks ". A still more important anatomical difference between the two northern falcons is that first brought to the attention of biologists by the late Professor Newton. He found that the sternum and attached coracoid bones of an Iceland falcon exceeded those of its Norwegian ally by nearly half an inch, the difference in measurements resulting chiefly from the elongation of the coracoids in the former bird. Yet in a series it is the Norwegian bird which will be found to have the broadest sternal apparatus, as Yarrell first pointed out.

OCCURRENCES IN GREAT BRITAIN : The typical subspecies *F. r. rusticolus* Linn. is the rarest of the three races to occur in these islands. In the latest B.O.U. List (1952) only two are recognized as having been correctly identified, agreeing with Howard Saunders' *Manual* (3rd edition) and *The Handbook*. The first of these was an adult obtained at Mayfield, Sussex, in January 1845,[2] which is figured in Borrer's *Birds of Sussex*. It passed as an Iceland falcon until 1884, when the error was discovered by John Henry Gurney. In the meantime a second example—a young bird—was procured at Sudbourne, near Orford, Suffolk, on 14th October 1867.[3] There is some doubt as to whether a bird captured at Westerfield, near Ipswich, date unknown, and recorded in *The Field*, 1875, p. 38, is a Norwegian gyr-falcon or an Iceland gyr-falcon. It was examined by Mr. Witherby. Yet another Suffolk example killed on Thetford Warren in the spring of 1883, and considered by Professor Newton to have been probably, but not certainly, *F. r. rusticolus*, may equally have been an Iceland falcon.

We are left therefore with but two records about which there appears to have been no question.[4]

DISTRIBUTION ABROAD : According to Scandinavian authorities, the gyr-falcon has been found breeding as far south as the 60th parallel— these are the Telemark heights in Norway. In the sub-Arctic districts

[1] *A History of British Birds*, by William Yarrell, 4th ed., vol. i, p. 47.

[2] Preserved in the Dyke Road Museum, Brighton.

[3] Preserved in the Ipswich Museum, Ipswich.

[4] Doctor Blair informs me that passing notice should be taken of a falcon trapped at Hatfield Broad Oak, Essex, in December 1891 ; this record has found its way into more than one textbook. The specimen was examined by the late George Lodge, an authority on falcons, who proclaimed it to be " nothing but a dark female peregrine in immature dress ".

of that country this hunting falcon must be sought high above the forests, at altitudes over 3000 feet, on the great ranges such as Dovre and Langfjeld. If never very plentiful, these powerful falcons were certainly once more numerous than they are to-day. Most of those flown in the heyday of hawking came from Finmark but the older writers on hunting all speak highly of the birds supplied from the southern ranges— Romsdal, Dovre, Osterdal and Telemarks fjelds. Even eighty years ago, Captain Dugmore, a professional falconer commissioned by Lord Lilford, succeeded in trapping fifteen or sixteen examples in a very short while on Dovre. Since then many breeding stations appear to have been deserted, perhaps as a consequence of the indiscriminate persecution to which birds of prey were so long subjected in Norway, and to-day the gyr-falcon must be accounted rare and local in the south of the country. Some accounts of its status may, however, be unduly pessimistic, as the uplands it frequents are often difficult of access until well into June, by which time the young have taken wing. While few eyries have been located of late, adult falcons —presumably breeding birds—have been seen in several places, in particular about the willow-grouse country at the heads of the western fjords, on Hardanger Vidda, in Dovre, and in Rondane. Further to the north, gyr-falcons are more frequently encountered, and in the Arctic province of Finmark they may almost be described as common. There eyries occur down to sea-level, and about the coasts as well as in the interior. The fell country around Kautokeino, at the source of the Alten, has been known as a stronghold since John Wolley procured the first authentic eggs there a century ago.

Beyond the frontier, the Norwegian gyr-falcon breeds in some numbers, both in Sweden and in Finland, amongst the fells around the remote lake Kilpisjarvi, and more sparingly along the upper reaches of the highest tributary of the Tornea, the Konkämä. Westwards of the Konkämä valley, it ranges down through the Swedish highlands into Jämtland, nearly 200 miles without the Arctic Circle. Much of Finland being thickly forested and comparatively low-lying, the gyr-falcon does not there penetrate so far south as it does in Scandinavia. From Kilpisjarvi scattered pairs breed downstream to the neighbourhood of Wolley's old headquarters at Muonio, and eyries could at one time be found a little further to the south, at Kittila, and in West Sodankyla. In north-east Finland too there are a few breeding stations around Lake Enare, on the Saariselka fells, and in the country eastward of the Pasvik. Most ornithologists visiting the adjacent Russian territories have met with gyr-falcons, either along the Murman coast or on the high ground inland. According to Pleske, the Russian ornithologist, Professor Menzbier, received three adult males of *rusticolus* from the bleak Kanin peninsula, whence Meves, the Swedish explorer, obtained eggs.[1] *F. r. rusticolus* is also the gyr-falcon of Siberia

[1] *Birds of the Eurasian Tundra*, p. 301.

eastwards at least to the Petchora. Beyond the Urals, it is replaced by the paler *Falco r. uralensis*, the Asiatic gyr-falcon of American ornithologists, which is distributed through northern Asia and across the Baring Strait into Alaska. So far, *rusticolus*, which Pleske distinguishes as the *Continental* form of the gyr-falcon, has not been identified on any of the great islands of the Polar Sea.

While *islandus* is commonly regarded as the only race of the gyr-falcon breeding in Iceland, it is interesting to note that two of the eyasses brought home by Ernest Lewis moulted into a plumage indistinguishable from that of the adult *rusticolus*.[1]

Even in districts remote enough to afford gyr-falcons security against molestation well-known haunts often remain untenanted for two or three years. Doctor Yngvar Hagen has given an account of one site in a recent paper.[2] Here a pair of falcons had young on the wing when Doctor Hagen visited the valley in June 1945, but a most painstaking search failed to discover any trace of them either in 1946 or in 1947. Falcons occupied the site in 1948 and again in 1949, broods being reared each season. The birds did not return in 1950, nor could any evidence of their presence in the neighbourhood be obtained in 1951 or 1952. Of an eyrie on the Seven Islands off the Murman coast it is recorded that falcons took possession in 1938 and 1940. In 1939 and 1941, on the other hand, the birds were never once encountered either about the islands or on the adjacent mainland.[3] Records all go to show that occupied eyries became most frequent in "lemming" or "vole years". In one such season—that of 1910—eight pairs of falcons took up their quarters on one Swedish fell-tract which normally holds only half as many.[4] "Lemming years" commonly happen to be also "grouse" or "ptarmigan" years, and in some districts at least it is with the abundance of feathered rather than of furred prey that the increase in the number of falcons should be correlated.

In winter the Norwegian gyr-falcon ranges from the North Cape throughout Scandinavia, and, further east, to the Gulf of Finland and into central Russia. Some birds of the year, with an occasional adult, spend the colder winters about Lister and Jaederen in south-west Norway, where under favourable conditions they become comparatively common. Yet very few visit the neighbourhood of the Oslo fjord, and in the southern districts of Sweden and Finland a gyr-falcon is always a rarity. Beyond the Kattegat and the Baltic, which may be regarded as marking the limit of the normal range in the west, gyr-falcons have been identified in Denmark, Belgium, Holland, Germany, Poland, the Baltic States,

[1] G. E. Lodge, *Memoirs of an Artist Naturalist*, 1946, p. 19.
[2] *The Gyr-Falcon (Falco r. rusticolus) in Dovre, Norway*, Oslo, 1952.
[3] G. P. Dementiev and N. N. Gortchakovskaya, "On the Biology of the Norwegian Gyrfalcon", *Ibis*, 1945, p. 559.
[4] Kolthoff and Jägerskiöld, *Nordens Fåglar*, p. 164.

Switzerland and Austria. There are also some winter records for southern Russia.

MIGRATION : Adult gyr-falcons, like ravens and eagles, are mostly resident in Scandinavia. Even those breeding in the interior of Finmark rarely move further from their summer quarters than the nearby coasts, and that only in the hardest weather. Immature birds, like other young falcons and hawks, undertake somewhat more extensive journeys than their parents. From August onwards until November, yearling gyr-falcons, in numbers varying from season to season, descend from the fells of southern Norway to pass along the lower-lying valleys on their way to the coast. Collett believed that a fair proportion actually left the country, and it is quite possible that these falcons winter more frequently in the Netherlands and central Europe than appears from records. In the colder climate of Russia, the gyr-falcon is perhaps more of a migrant than it is in Scandinavia. Unfortunately, we have very little data from that country. Birds breeding on the Seven Islands, off the Murman coast, did not appear to winter there, and in 1941 they were noted no earlier than 11th April.[1]

HABITAT : Like its near allies in Iceland and Greenland, the Norwegian gyr-falcon is largely a bird of the open. A very characteristic resort lies far up on one of the great watersheds of sub-Arctic Norway, 3500 feet and more above sea-level, and a clear 600 above the last outliers of the great pine forests. Much of the falcons' hunting-ground is fit only to pasture reindeer—a stone-littered wilderness devoid of cover other than a few stunted willows and junipers growing under the lee of the larger boulders. Lichens predominate amongst the Alpine plants. Some of the more lowly give touches of colour—greys and greens chiefly, but including a striking brick-red—to stones and rock-faces, while others, and in particular the white-tufted reindeer-moss, grow so thickly as almost to conceal the interlacing shoots of crowberry and creeping-birch. Amongst such surroundings nest those characteristic birds of the high fjeld, the ptarmigan, dotterel and golden plover, with occasional pairs of shore larks and purple sandpipers, and wheatears everywhere amongst the boulders. Meadow pipits are common on the lower slopes, and Lapland buntings sing about the little patches of willow-grown scrub. In the more sheltered valleys of the streams that rise in this waste, bluethroats and willow wrens haunt the scrub, ring-ouzels the screes of the defiles. Yet further downstream the falcons' hunting takes them into the upper birch woods, where the blackcock lek. Some of the little rivers leave the plateau through narrow cliff-flanked gorges, to one of which the falcons resort whenever they intend to breed. Other gyr-falcons' eyries overlook large marshes or lakes, which afford more varied hunting. Within the Arctic Circle these falcons will be found in very similar haunts, though at lower altitudes. Some breed by

[1] G. P. Dementiev and N. N. Gortchakovskaya, " On the Biology of the Norwegian Gyrfalcon ", *Ibis*, 1945, p. 565.

salt water, either along one of the great Finmark fjords or on a precipice
overhanging the Arctic Ocean itself, and usually conveniently near a
sea-bird colony.   In the interior of Lapland, a few have their eyries on
steep hills rising above the pine forests, and records of prey taken by such
birds show that they habitually forage amongst the evergreens.   As John
Wolley found, a pair of gyr-falcons will occasionally so far depart from the
normal habit of their kind as to settle in forest, occupying the old nest of
some tree-building Raptor, rough-legged buzzard or osprey.[1]

A ravine tenanted by gyr-falcons is often shared with ravens, or the
two species may breed there alternately.   More frequently, one or perhaps
two pairs of rough-legged buzzards will build in close neighbourhood to
the falcons, occasionally less than a hundred yards away.   Kestrels besides
sometimes nest hard by their more powerful allies, and the slopes below the
latters' eyrie may attract a pair of merlins.   Such communities of raptorial
birds cannot, of course, be regarded as in any way exceptional.   Less usual
is the association between falcons and buzzards in autumn observed by
Perr Höst on Hardanger Vidda.[2]   At that time of year the ptarmigan,
already packed, tend to change their ground daily.   The larger packs at
least can soon be located anew by the sportsman who takes the birds of
prey as his guides.   Rough-legged buzzards, up to as many as half a dozen
together, will be soaring over the hillside where the game have taken up
their temporary quarters, while where the birds lie thickest, a gyr-falcon
sits on a boulder or ledge.   Seemingly almost sluggish, the falcon is in
reality keenly alert for the least movement amongst the game, and
sportsmen have seen it kill a grouse rising before the dogs.

HABITS :   According to Norwegian observers, the gyr-falcon is most
likely to be seen on the wing in mid-morning and mid-afternoon.   In
flight it is a typical falcon, gliding over a considerable distance on still
pinions, generally between thirty and forty feet from the ground, and then
regaining momentum in a succession of winnowing wing-beats ;   now and
then it will pause to hover like a kestrel.   As mentioned earlier, the gyr-
falcon's wing-beats are—or, at least, seem to be—slower than those of the
peregrine, and many falconers concede the latter superiority in grace and
agility.   Yet the larger bird's turn of speed enables it to overhaul a fleeing
grouse after a long stern chase, while the force with which the death blow
is dealt can send the prey plunging deep into the snow.   The falcon may
strike as it overtakes its victim in level flight, or it may gain height for a
stoop.   In falconers' parlance, the gyr-falcon does not " bind " to its prey
so frequently as the peregrine, but circles around and then alights beside it.
Unlike peregrines also, gyr-falcons often take prey on the ground.

After handling the remains of " kills " Doctor Hagen decided that a
successful gyr-falcon's first action is to bite off the head of its capture.[3]

[1] *Ootheca Wolleyana*, vol. i, p. 95.   [2] *Trekk av Dyrelivet på Hardangervidda*, p. 58.
[3] *The Gyr-Falcon (Falco r. rusticolus) in Dovre, Norway*, p. 28.

If the prey is to be carried to the eyrie, the legs and intestines are also removed.   Hagen further discovered that the gyr-falcon's mode of " dressing " a feathered prey differed considerably from that of the peregrine.   While the peregrine leaves the shoulder-girdle intact with the primaries, and often some secondaries, still attached, the gyr-falcon with its more powerfully muscled bill removes all the larger feathers, including the toughest and strongest quills.   It can even bite through bones as solid as the humerus and femur of a fully mature grouse.   Fragments of these and other thick bones, such as the central part of the pelvis, can usually be found in pellets, and a casting frequently contains a whole foot, or even both, of a willow grouse or ptarmigan.   Around a sea-bird colony a gyr-falcon will smash and partly eat the sternum of a guillemot.

Gyr-falcons can, and do, overpower birds as large as male caper-caillies, lesser white-fronted geese, and even, though rarely, snowy owls. Yet they will not despise such humble quarry as snow buntings and meadow pipits.   Otherwise willow grouse and ptarmigan figure promin-ently in lists of prey taken by these birds, which include, besides ducks, waders and thrushes, particularly fieldfares.   Gyr-falcons also readily attack mammals—leverets, lemmings and, it is said, squirrels—differing in this from peregrines, and sharing affinities with the so-called " desert falcons ", such as the lanner and the American prairie falcon.   Some writers go so far as to suggest that when lemmings become very abundant the falcons feed largely upon them.

The prey chiefly taken by individual gyr-falcons varies, it need hardly be said, according to season and locality.   In winter willow grouse and ptarmigan are the commonest victims, supplemented in coastal districts by sea-birds.   Blackgame are recorded amongst winter kills in Sweden, and in the extreme south partridge also.   Given the opportunity, a sharp-set falcon will raid a poultry yard, and one of the two recorded in England was feeding on a hen at the time it was killed.

As showing the variety of prey killed by gyr-falcons in summer, it will suffice to compare records from three resorts of widely differing character. The first is above the tree-line on a Norwegian fjeld.   Here Yngvar Hagen, in the course of two visits, distinguished in pellets and the remains of kills 214 victims.[1]   These included one golden plover, two leverets, three lemmings and a vole, all probably captured on the open fell near the eyrie. A blackcock showed that the falcons now and then foraged in the birch woods below, where a wood pigeon had also been killed.   The remaining 205 preys—roughly 96 per cent. of the total—were either willow grouse or ptarmigan, the latter being greatly in the majority where the species could be named with certainty.   As Doctor Hagen points out, the analysis of his material goes far to prove that the gyr-falcon in this particular habitat takes grouse in preference to all other prey, and that even in " rodent

[1] *The Gyr-Falcon (Falco r. rusticolus) in Dovre, Norway*, pp. 18-25.

years " the proportion of small mammals amongst the " kills " remains trifling. On Kharlov Island, off the Murman coast, on the other hand, a pair of gyr-falcons hunted lemmings very regularly.[1] Many of their pellets were gathered about lemming colonies, and of 117 birds and mammals whose remains were found, thirty-five were lemmings. Seventy of the feathered quarries were distinguishable. These coastwise falcons, it seems clear, lived mainly on the sea-fowl about them. Besides twelve auks of undetermined species, they had struck down twelve puffins, eight black guillemots, as many kittiwakes, and three examples each of the guillemot, razorbill and little auk. The local eiders had likewise suffered, traces of nine being found, besides one Steller's eider. Of three small waders, one was a purple sandpiper, as were probably the others. One pellet contained the remains of two snow buntings, the only Passerine bird represented. The willow grouse is always scarce on the island and the nearby mainland, but even so it seems very poorly represented by only five examples. Apart from the lemming, the only mammal identified was the stoat (one example). Material collected by Russian naturalists about the third eyrie, in the Lapland forests, shows that the owners resemble the birds of the Norwegian high fjeld in their preference for game. Of 126 creatures, furred and feathered, recognized amongst their leavings and pellets, sixty-five were game birds—forty-seven willow grouse, three blackcock, one hazel grouse and two capercaillies (one a male), besides twelve birds whose specific identity remained undetermined, but which were probably willow grouse. But the falcons had also shared the Murman coast birds' taste for small rodents ; indeed, the proportion of voles and lemmings amongst their prey, forty-four, or 35 per cent., seems even higher. Besides the hazel grouse and capercaillie, a surprising variety of woodland birds had been accounted for, which suggests that a gyr-falcon can hunt the forest as successfully as a goshawk. The solitary examples of waxwing, fieldfare and cuckoo might be surprised on the forest fringe but the three Siberian jays, the pied wood-pecker, the Tengmalm's owl and the pigmy owl could, one would think, be found only amongst dense timber. Three waterfowl appear in the list, the only one recognizable being a teal, but at an eyrie in another of the wooded Lapland valleys, Schaanning found, besides willow grouse, a pintail and a whimbrel.[2]

Falcons generally are rather silent birds throughout most of the year, and the gyr-falcon forms no exception. In the breeding season, however, they can be as noisy as peregrines, particularly when their eggs or young appear to be in danger. Wheeling and dashing above the eyrie, first one and then the other of the pair breaks into a rattling *kek-kek-kek*, very like the peregrines' anxious complaint. Yngvar Hagen, timing one protesting

[1] G. P. Dementiev and N. N. Gortchakovskaya, " On the Biology of the Norwegian Gyrfalcon ", *Ibis*, 1945, pp. 559-565.
[2] *Jegerliv Nordpå*, Oslo, 1916.

PLATE 3

NORWEGIAN GYR-FALCON (Immature)
Falco rusticolus rusticolus Linnaeus

PLATE 5

NORWEGIAN GYR-FALCON (Ornamate)

Falco rusticolus rusticolus Linnaeus

bird, found that the hoarse notes followed each other at intervals of half a second, and was reminded of the cackling of an angry barnyard fowl. The voices of the fledgling gyr-falcons can hardly be distinguished from those of their parents. One of their notes, heard by Hagen from a brood unaware of his presence and therefore at ease, seemed as gruff as the croaking of a raven.[1]

BREEDING : While in some places the one cliff has held a gyr-falcon's eyrie " time out of mind ", in others the birds, like many peregrines, shift their quarters from year to year. The rock from which, in 1854, John Wolley took the first authentic eggs of this species held a raven's nest in the following spring, and again twelve months later, while the falcons reared a brood, each season, in a gully nearby. In 1857 the original site was once more taken over by falcons, nothing being seen of the ravens.[2] A cliff overlooking the Pasvik forests was likewise tenanted by falcons and ravens alternately during the years Schaanning knew it. By the sea, gyr-falcons often have their eyries in the midst of the sea-bird colonies on which they depend for food. One pair, on the Murman coast, had as close neighbours a crowd of herring gulls, besides a small company of shags.[3]

A gyr-falcons' stronghold may be a formidable cliff as much as 300 feet high, but the birds occasionally select a ledge no more than twenty or thirty feet up on some insignificant rock. Usually the cliff can be scaled only with the aid of a rope or by felling a nearby tree against the rock face— a device to which John Wolley resorted [4]—and one eyrie visited by Pearson proved inaccessible.[5] The eggs are commonly laid under an overhanging ledge, which affords some cover against snow and winter during the early days of incubation, and as often as not the recess has earlier been the nursery of a family of ravens. While normally too exposed to the weather, and more easily reached than ravens', rough-legged buzzards' nests are some-times put to use by gyr-falcons. Rough-legged buzzards too have generally been the original architects where these falcons have been found nesting in trees. More rarely the falcons' eggs have been laid in old osprey's nests.

A gyr-falcon, like a peregrine, makes no attempt at a nest beyond scratching out a hollow on the ledge, or in the mould that has accumulated amongst the bleached remains of the former tenants' nest, perhaps adding a little grass, willow-down or moss as a lining. John Wolley put one bird off a " very large " structure of " fresh sticks ", lined with " a few green willow twigs and several tufts of sedgy grass," and another nest appeared to him to " have been quite freshly made ", and therefore by the falcon,

---

[1] *The Gyr-Falcon (Falco r. rusticolus) in Dovre, Norway*, p. 14.
[2] *Ootheca Wolleyana*, vol. i, pp. 89-90.
[3] G. P. Dementiev and N. N. Gortchakovskaya, " On the Biology of the Norwegian Gyrfalcon ", *Ibis*, 1945, p. 560.
[4] *Ootheca Wolleyana*, vol. i, p. 92.
[5] *Three Summers among the Birds of Russian Lapland*, p. 124.

but the former at least seems more likely to have been the work of a raven.[1]

Gyr-falcons are amongst the first of the northern birds to set about nesting. The cliff will be the only spot bare of snow when the first eggs are laid, and the fell often receives a fresh covering while the falcon is sitting. Eggs have been found in Finmark as early as 6th to 8th April, a full clutch upon the former date. The majority of birds, in south Norway and Lapland alike, lay in the latter half of the month. Further north, as on the bleak Murman coast, falcons do not have eggs much before the second week of May, and some Norwegian birds are a week or more later. Four eggs are more frequently laid than three but clutches of five are very rare.

Typical eggs of the gyr-falcon are blunt-ovate in shape, and many specimens show a varying number of nodules on their thick shells. In colour they are creamy white, often washed with yellowish or tawny brown, and freckled and spotted with rufous or brick-red, with here and there shell markings of violet-grey. Sometimes the superficial markings are so evenly and thickly distributed as to become confluent, the egg then appearing uniformly coloured. A few examples are very sparingly marked with rufous, and Jourdain recorded unpigmented specimens. These eggs are much darker than those of either the Iceland or Greenland falcon, and in a large series only a minority of about one in eight shows the ground colour to an appreciable degree. Like those of all falcons, gyr-falcons' eggs have a delicate roseate or violet bloom when first laid, but this most attractive feature soon fades. Norwegian specimens vary in length from 55 to 63 mm., and in breadth from 44 to 49·5 mm. (Collett).[2] The largest measured by Jourdain were 62·6 by 46 mm. and 57·3 by 48·5 mm.; the least 55 by 45·7 mm. and 56 by 43 mm.; with an average in a series of a hundred of 58·69 by 45·65 mm.[3]

As commonly happens with birds of prey, gyr-falcons settle down to brood before their clutches are complete, the eggs following each other at intervals of three days. Some observers have surprised the tiercel incubating but he never takes more than a trifling share in the task. Even when she is still laying, and particularly in stormy weather, one falcon will persist in her brooding as the climber scales the rock, while another leaves her eggs before he has come within gunshot. All become more reluctant to take wing as the incubation period advances. At one eyrie visited by John Wolley the tiercel settled on the eggs after the falcon had left, and remained there until Wolley had reached the foot of the rock, a bare ten yards below.[4] When disturbed, gyr-falcons rarely show their resentment in more than a

[1] *Ootheca Wolleyana*, vol. i, pp. 89 and 92.
[2] *Norges Fugle*, vol. ii, p. 213.
[3] Witherby's *Handbook*.
[4] *Ootheca Wolleyana*, vol. i, p. 91.

hoarse, challenging complaint as they wheel overhead. The few can at times be very demonstrative, and the stoops of a particularly aggressive bird in Finmark became close and vicious enough to be intimidating. Any raven, crow or fox straying too near the eyrie is vigorously mobbed. Two of Wolley's assistants followed the progress of one such scuffle through the snow beside an eyrie they visited. The trespasser had been a fox, and the men could see how, when hard pressed, it had backed into the cover of a small willow the better to fend off the angry falcons.[1]

A young gyr-falcon breaks the shell after an incubation period of twenty-eight days. At first the female spends her whole time beside the brood, receiving the food from the male and breaking it up, but as the young grow she leaves the nest to supplement the male's hunting. The eyasses keep to the nest for at least forty-five days, the males developing more rapidly than the larger females. Doctor Hagen found that these young birds react to a threat of danger just as eyass peregrines will, leaning backwards with half-open wings and slashing out with their talons. Those he handled surprised him by their strength, and he ruefully comments on the painful impression their powerful beaks left on his gloved hands. Sometimes, after he had left the nest and the birds had settled down, the whole brood " seemed possessed by sudden gaiety " for a few seconds, running about the nesting platform, flapping their wings, and calling eagerly.[2]

REFERENCES : Original Description. *Falco rusticolus* Linnaeus, Syst. Nat., 10th ed., 1758, p. 88 : Sweden.

GREENLAND GYR-FALCONS

PLATE 4 (adult)
PLATE 5 (immature)

White birds—*Falco rusticolus candicans* Gmelin
Grey and dark birds—*Falco rusticolus obsoletus* Gmelin

White birds (*candicans*) are almost Annual Visitors ; for status of others see p. 16.

IDENTIFICATION : It is not possible to give field notes on this falcon by which it can be readily identified from the other races of *F. rusticolus* unless the bird happens to be in the almost pure white dress assumed by these birds which breed in the high Arctic regions. Some of the characters exhibited by the three races *rusticolus*, *islandus* and *candicans* have already been discussed on p. 2 under the Family heading.

The gyr-falcon of Greenland and Arctic North America is trimorphic ; the three phases of plumage (which have nothing to do with age) are connected by intermediates, but nevertheless are clearly defined by Doctor Finn Salomonsen,[3] as follows :

[1] *Ootheca Wolleyana*, vol. i, p. 90.
[2] *The Gyr-Falcon (Falco r. rusticolus) in Dovre, Norway*, p. 14.
[3] *Grønlands Fugle*, part iii.

DESCRIPTION OF THE THREE PHASES OF PLUMAGE (after Salomonsen):

Dark Phase (*obsoletus* type) : Crown and nape as dark as or darker than rest of upperparts. In all young birds and many adults the upperparts are almost uniform brownish ; in the adult birds, however, they often have paler greyish spots or transverse bars. The general aspect is dark. Many specimens in this phase are identical with, or very near to, the typical Scandinavian bird *F. r. rusticolus* Linn., but the variation exhibited is greater, many young birds being distinctly darker, while some adults have the barring of the upperparts more pronounced and more extended than in any Scandinavian bird.

Grey Phase (*holboelli* type) : Crown and nape mixed with white, or predominantly white with dark shaft-streaks, always lighter than the rest of the upperparts. All adult birds have barred upperparts, with their bars paler greyish-white than in the dark phase ; young birds usually have light spots and feather edges on the upperparts, giving them a variegated appearance ; the remiges,[1] in both the adult and the young birds, have the light barring considerably more extended than in the dark phase ; the striation of the underparts is paler and finer (narrower) ; the under tail-coverts always exhibit more or less barring or streaking. The general aspect is greyish.

This grey phase is nearest to *F. r. islandus* Brünn. of Iceland, but can usually be distinguished by the distinctly more spotted or barred upperparts.

White Phase (*candicans* type) : Crown and nape pure white, with only very fine shaft-streaks ; the upperparts predominantly white, with dark bars and spots of varying extent ; the underparts white with scattered spotting, sometimes pure white ; the under tail-coverts always pure white. The general aspect is white.

These three " phases " do not occur haphazardly all over Greenland as was at one time considered to be the case. Doctor Salomonsen considers that " roughly speaking " the dark phase is the sub-Arctic form, the grey phase the low Arctic and the white phase the high Arctic form. He considers that the dark and grey phases, although having widely separated centres of distribution, are too much mixed in the sub-Arctic and low Arctic zones to be regarded as two subspecies. They form together, so he believes, a southern form, which he would ally with *F. r. obsoletus* Gmelin, while retaining under the name *F. r. candicans* the high Arctic form which consists exclusively of white birds. To the latter population he assigns subspecific rank. In this arrangement he comes into line with Charles and Edward Bird, who made this suggestion after their investigations in Greenland in 1935, 1936 and 1937 (cf. *Ibis*, 1941, p. 132). For those who do not like this arrangement Doctor Salomonsen points out that the Labrador birds *F. r. obsoletus* show a smaller wing-length than the Greenland birds and that if it is thought desirable to keep the southern Greenland gyr-falcons distinct on that account the name *Falco rusticolus holboelli* Sharpe, given to a Greenland bird in the dark grey plumage, is available.

Doctor Salomonsen considers that there has been much confusion as

---

[1] The principal feathers in the wing, *i.e.* the flight feathers, composed of the primaries and secondaries.

PLATE 4

WHITE GREENLAND GYR-FALCON (Adult)
Falco rusticolus candicans Gmelin

regards the correct understanding of the age variation in these falcons, but observes that the ample material in the Copenhagen Museum can be arranged without difficulty according to age. The following points must be borne in mind when attempting to assess the age of a particular specimen of a Greenland falcon :

(*a*) The young birds have slate-coloured cere, legs and feet.

(*b*) The adult birds have yellow cere, legs and feet.

(*c*) Adult examples in the dark or grey phase have at least some transverse bars on the flanks and the upperparts have a noticeable ashy-grey or silvery bloom.

(*d*) Examples in the white phase have the upperparts of the palest *adult* birds more heavily marked than in the young birds, the longitudinal streaks being black, crescentic or arrow-shaped, while in the *young* birds they are brownish, narrow and tear-shaped.

Doctor Finn Salomonsen and Doctor Lehn Schiøler had an incomparable series of these falcons, as represented in the Copenhagen Museum, from which to make their deductions. Schiøler had examined about 800 specimens, of which more than 450 came from Greenland. We have no mean series of these falcons in the British Museum collection, but nothing to compare with that of our colleagues in Denmark.

Doctor Hartert and other workers who have employed the name *candicans* for *all* Greenland gyr-falcons, irrespective of colour, were influenced by the fact that pure white birds have been taken along with the grey and the dark birds in southern Greenland but have overlooked, or were ignorant of, the fact that these white birds were migrants from the Arctic north and only exceptionally breed in the territory of the dark birds and the grey birds.

OCCURRENCES IN GREAT BRITAIN : When we come to review the occurrences in Britain of the gyr-falcons from Greenland we are faced with the difficulty of the name or names under which they should be recorded.

The all-white birds are correctly assigned to *Falco rusticolus candicans* of Gmelin, for that unique plumage is found only in the gyr-falcons inhabitating the high Arctic regions of Greenland and North America. The others, *i.e.* those which are dark or grey in colour and are probably representatives of the south Greenland bird, must now be referred to *F. r. obsoletus*.

The majority of British records come from the Outer Hebrides—to which this bird may almost be considered an annual visitor—and from the north of Scotland and islands. It is less often seen in Orkney and Shetland but it has occurred a number of times in the Inner Hebrides and on the mainland ; for the details of these occurrences I would refer the reader to records collated by Miss Baxter and Miss Rintoul in their *Birds of Scotland* (1953).

After Scotland, this gyr-falcon has been seen most often in Ireland. It has in fact been recorded on at least seventy-five occasions and about sixty specimens have been obtained,[1] the majority from Donegal, Mayo and Kerry during the months November to March.

In England and Wales the Greenland gyr-falcon is naturally a rarity. Mr. Witherby included it in *The Handbook* as " occasionally in northern England and elsewhere very rare ". Among the places listed from which it has been obtained, including four counties in Wales and seven in England, he mentions it also from Lundy Island and the Scilly Isles. Among more recent occurrences may be mentioned a bird in all-white plumage identified on 4th May 1947 flying along the Cornish cliffs west of Zennor by Mr. W. Walmesley White (*British Birds*, xl, p. 279), and a younger example captured alive at Rhoscolyn, Anglesey, on 11th January 1949 which was identified as *F. r. candicans* by Mr. Wagstaffe of the York Museum (*British Birds*, xliv, p. 134).

The birds in the white or the grey plumages present less difficulty, from the point of view of their country of origin, than the dark birds. One such dark specimen was secured in Scotland and recorded in the *Scottish Naturalist*,[2] but as Mr. Witherby observed,[3] after examination of the skin in the Royal Scottish Museum, it is like dark birds from Labrador (*obsoletus*) except that the under tail-coverts are not so strongly marked ; as, however, some Iceland specimens resemble it, notably one taken out of an eyrie and now in Mr. G. E. Lodge's collection, it is impossible to be sure of its origin.

DISTRIBUTION IN GREENLAND AND BEYOND (after Salomonsen) : The gyr-falcons in Greenland have been shown to have three phases of plumage and the distribution of these birds is worth examining more closely. Salomonsen has shown that the proportion of white birds (*candicans*) increases in areas with lower temperature. In sub-Arctic countries like Labrador the dark phase (*obsoletus*) dominates, the grey phase is fairly common, while the white phase breeds only exceptionally or not at all. The Scandinavian-Russian population, which has its centre of distribution in the sub-Arctic to low Arctic boundary region, consists of dark birds (*rusticolus*) only. In low Arctic regions like south-west Greenland the grey phase dominates and the dark phase has decreased in number, constituting less than 20 per cent. of the population, while the white phase occurs only exceptionally. The isolated low Arctic population of Iceland consists exclusively of grey birds (*islandus*).

When we approach in the north of Greenland the high Arctic region the dark phase disappears first, while the proportion of white birds rapidly

[1] *Birds of Ireland*, 1954, p. 115.
[2] E. R. Paton, *Scottish Naturalist*, 1926, p. 137.
[3] H. F. Witherby, *The Handbook of British Birds*, 1939, p. 5, footnote.

PLATE 5

WHITE GREENLAND GYR-FALCON. Immature.
Falco rusticolus candicans, Gmelin.

PLATE 5

WHITE GREENLAND GYR-FALCON (Immature)
Falco rusticolus candicans Gmelin

increases. In the boundary area between the low and high Arctic region the grey phase disappears also and in the high Arctic region only white birds are found which range from Greenland westward to Alaska, possibly also to northernmost Siberia ; in Baffin Land they range southwards almost to Hudson Strait.

In *Grønlands Fugle* the distribution in Greenland of *Falco rusticolus candicans* is given in detail, as in that land it is well known, but in North America, on the contrary, its exact range is very imperfectly defined, owing to the lack of breeding birds in collections.

As noted elsewhere, a number of Greenland falcons spend the winter months regularly in Iceland ; others, and to a much smaller extent, carry on to Europe, including the British Isles.

HABITS [1] : In Greenland the gyr-falcon frequents particularly the interior of the country. In migration time and in winter it is commonly seen in the coastal areas, where it is seldom met with in the breeding time. Its life habits resemble in many respects those of the peregrine, but the food of the peregrine and the gyr-falcon differs in many respects, though there is considerable overlap in diet, which leads to the probability of competition between the two species. It is noteworthy that the gyr-falcon is local in summer in the low Arctic region, where it shares its habitat with the peregrine, whereas it is abundant in the high Arctic region, from which the peregrine is absent. In winter the gyr-falcon is common in the low Arctic when the peregrine has left for the south.

The gyr-falcon's method of hunting differs from that of the peregrine. It frequently takes prey on the ground and feeds also on small mammals ; it has once been seen to take a grey phalarope swimming in a pond, but that is apparently abnormal. Its usual way of hunting birds is to take them by surprise, when it flies with rapid wing-beats at a high speed, quite different from its normal leisurely flight, moving only a few metres above the ground and following strictly all elevations, depressions and other changes in the terrain. In this way it surprises some flocks of birds which immediately try to escape by rising. The falcon then takes its quarry in the air or on the ground. Doctor Salomonsen has seen it make up to four attempts before it succeeded in catching its victim. It uses similar hunting methods when chasing the inhabitants of bird colonies on steep cliffs.

On one occasion during the Oxford University Expedition of 1928, while E. M. Nicholson was watching the highest occupied ledges of Kugssuk bird-cliff, one of the usual alarms and excursions of kittiwakes took place and was renewed just as the birds were coming back. Suddenly a Greenland falcon appeared from nowhere, snatched a young kittiwake from the ledges at about 600 feet, and was off along the slope of the hill in an instant, bearing the young kittiwake comfortably in his claws. The

---

[1] With full acknowledgment to Doctor Finn Salomonsen for permission to quote so generously from the account of these falcons in his *Grønlands Fugle*.

effect was terrific ; there was dead silence for the next seven minutes, except for the protests of a few Iceland gulls, almost all the members of the large colony flying silently up and down offshore. Suddenly the tension relaxed and all returned noisily to their nests. Nicholson observes that in the panic caused by the arrival of the falcon the latter could have had any of a dozen adults with ease, or struck them down in passing ; instead he swerved through them to take one of the less developed of the nestlings. On another occasion the same observer witnessed a falcon's attack on a snow bunting on the ground. The falcon used his wings vigorously to reach full speed as he headed for his quarry but the snow bunting, realizing his danger, got up and swerved two or three times, dodging with fair agility. The falcon then " threw up " almost perpendicularly to thirty or forty feet, coming down again like a stone on the spot where the snow bunting had alighted on a bare rock. The bunting dashed away just in time and the falcon, having failed in the rush, gave up the chase.

When the brothers Charles and Edward Bird were in Greenland on an ornithological expedition, a Greenland falcon was seen to swoop after a turnstone within a yard of the door of the station, and the turnstone sat within a yard of Charles Bird until the falcon disappeared !

Prey is plucked either at the place of capture or, in the case of breeding birds, at special plucking places, which are often situated on a ledge on a steep cliff which is used also as a look-out post. The manner of plucking the victim resembles that of the peregrine. The carcass is left with the breast-bone upwards ; the head and legs are torn off but generally not eaten and are left beside the carcass. This holds good even with small prey such as young Arctic terns.

Doctor Salomonsen observes that the gyr-falcon is more vulnerable to attack by other birds than is the peregrine. A pair of ravens or long-tailed skuas are capable of driving it away, and while the peregrine takes no notice of attacking Arctic terns, the gyr-falcon is obviously annoyed. When attacked by a swarm of terns while feeding on the ground in a ternery, it will continuously look up at the terns swooping down on it, and when pursued by the terns in the air it makes constant swoops and swerves to rid itself of its tormentors.

The food of the Greenland gyr-falcon is varied and consists in summer mainly of sea-birds of various kinds, mostly the smaller species of gulls, both adults and young, taken usually at the breeding colonies. In the autumn flocks of migrating Passerine birds : snow buntings, Lapland buntings and redpolls, are hunted, while in winter sea-birds and ptarmigan constitute the chief diet. Numerous other species which the falcons are known to kill are enumerated by Doctor Salomonsen but need not here be specified. Mention must, however, be made of the fact that in the distribution area of the lemming, from Scoresby Sound northwards as far as the north coast, this creature enters the diet to a considerable extent and constitutes the exclusive food in years when it is common, at least in the autumn when most birds have left. In fact, the number of gyr-falcons in north-east Greenland appears to fluctuate in accordance with the size of the lemming population. In peak lemming years the gyr-falcon is extremely common, while it is rare when lemmings are scarce. The invasions of the falcons in the Angmagssalik district are connected to some extent with peak years of the ptarmigan but it seems that there is no very close connection.

Autumn migration of the gyr-falcon in Greenland is remarkable in that the low Arctic population is resident and appears to winter as far north as the grey phase has been found breeding. On the other hand, the high Arctic white birds are all migrants which spend the winter in southern Greenland or beyond. The migration takes place to a large extent along the sea coast, where it is easily followed at the settlements. In the northern parts of the west coast, the autumn migration lasts from early September to the end of October. The migration in the northern parts of the east coast (north of Scoresby Sound) takes place from late August to the end of September. In the Scoresby Sound district a few gyr-falcons winter but many pass on. During the first days of September 1937 between 200 and 300 white gyr-falcons were observed by Christensen passing Scoresby Sound and many spend the winter in the Angmagssalik district, where they arrive from September to December. A number carry on to Iceland, where they are regular winter visitors. A few birds even reach the British Isles and more rarely others reach a number of central European countries.

The return migration in spring to the breeding grounds takes place in April and the white gyr-falcons arrive in the high Arctic in the latter part of that month or early in May. In the low Arctic, where the grey and dark phases are resident, the birds settle down at their breeding places as early as the beginning of April.

The nest is placed on a ledge or prominence on a steep cliff and is usually inaccessible. It is generally at a considerable height but occasionally is as low as ten metres above sea-level. The nest is visible from afar on account of the white droppings below it, for it is used for many years in succession. In Germania Land Manniche discovered five nests which all faced north, in order, as Salomonsen suggests, to take advantage of the heat of the sun at midnight, when the day is coldest. Usually the nests of this falcon face in any direction.

The eggs are laid on the cliff ledges without any nest being built. Egg laying takes place from mid-April to early June (in the south), usually in May. In the high Arctic region eggs are never laid until the end of May. The clutch is normally three to four, most frequently three only. The eggs are paler than those of the peregrine, often almost whitish, washed with yellowish and with some reddish-brown spots. Usually they are less richly marked than the eggs of the Norwegian gyr-falcon but closely resemble those laid by the Iceland birds. Average measurements are 58·3×45·6 mm. (Schiøler), and 58·78×45·74 (Hartert, 100 eggs measured).

According to Manniche incubation lasts for twenty-nine days. In the low Arctic region the young fledge usually in the latter half of July, but sometimes as early as the first days of that month. In the high Arctic fledging takes place in the latter half of August.

The Greenland gyr-falcon is not normally hunted by the Greenlanders, but at the settlements it is persecuted by the Danish settlers, though for no good reason, as the damage which it does to the dovecotes is negligible. In north-east Greenland, however, the trappers account for a good number. Fortunately, the bird is not considered to be in any danger of extermination. Its breeding on inaccessible cliffs in the desolate interior is its greatest safeguard and under such conditions it is likely to hold its own for many years to come.

REFERENCES : Original Descriptions. *Falco candicans* Gmelin, Syst. Nat., i, 1788, p. 275. Typical locality of white high Arctic form (by subsequent designation) Greenland. *Falco obsoletus* Gmelin, Syst. Nat., i, 1788, p. 268. " Habitat in freto Hudsonis " ; restricted type locality Labrador.

PLATE 6 (adult)   **ICELAND GYR-FALCON**
PLATE 7 (immature)
                         Falco rusticolus islandus Brünnich
                              An Irregular Visitor

IDENTIFICATION : A paler race than the Norwegian bird, more white on the head and mostly white cheeks. Barring on upperparts ashy-grey. Underparts usually less heavily spotted and barred. No moustachial streak present.

OCCURRENCES IN GREAT BRITAIN : The Iceland falcon is believed to have occurred under thirty times. In England it is recorded from Northumberland, Westmorland, Yorkshire, Shropshire and the Scilly Isles for certain, and possibly from Cumberland,[1] Lincolnshire and Suffolk.

To Scotland its visits are more frequent, too numerous to mention here, but more details will be found in *The Birds of Scotland* (1953), pp. 282-283. It is most often seen in the northern isles and in Ross, Sutherland and Caithness, but there are records from five other mainland counties, as well as from the Outer Hebrides : Lewis, North Uist, Benbecula, Barra and the Flannan Isles. From Orkney there are three records and from Shetland—where it used to be more regular in the days when Saxby chronicled the arrival of overseas migrants in that group, *circa* 1874— there have been two more recent visits. There is always the chance that some of these records may have been one or other of the other races of this falcon but that is impossible to decide now.

[1] Howard Saunders' *Manual*, 3rd ed., p. 389.

PLATE 6

ICELAND GYR-FALCON (Adult)
Falco rusticolus islandus Brünnich

In Ireland the Iceland gyr-falcon has been recorded five times, from the counties of Donegal (twice), Mayo (twice) and Galway (once). The latter bird, which was obtained at Oughterard on Lough Corrib, was reported to have been in company with another.

DISTRIBUTION ABROAD : This gyr-falcon is restricted to Iceland in the breeding season. Vagrants have appeared in Britain and the Faeroe Islands and apparently in some localities on the continent of Europe but it is difficult to be sure that all the examples which have been reported are of Icelandic origin.

HABITS : From literature which has been published about the Iceland gyr-falcon it appears that it does not differ much in its mode of life from the other two races of *Falco rusticolus* of which some description has already been given. Naturalists have shown particular interest in this bird from very early days. The first authentic egg of the Iceland falcon was figured by Hewitson [1] in 1846 in his *Eggs of British Birds* from a specimen taken by Proctor [2] during a visit to Iceland in 1837. Referring to this in his first volume Hewitson wrote :

The egg from which the figure has been now drawn was taken by Mr. Proctor, the Curator of the Durham University Museum, from the nest of the true Iceland Falcon, whilst on a visit to that country. He had gone out for the purpose of collecting birds and their eggs, but did not reach the favourite localities of the Iceland Falcon till the broods were flown. This was in the beginning of August, when he shot several full-grown young ones, and found some of the deserted nests ; the one from which he took the egg now drawn was composed of sticks and roots, lined with wool, among which the egg, a rotten one, was embedded. He supposes that the nest may have been that of a Raven, which is most probable, as it much resembled one. The remains of many birds, Whimbrels, Golden Plovers, Guillemots and Ducks, lay strewed about the nest. This nest and others which Mr. Proctor saw were all in cliffs, forming the boundary of fresh water lakes, but none of them so high in the mountainous districts as he expected to have found them.

The egg from which my former figure was taken is a much better coloured specimen than the one now given ; but as it is not known to which of the species it now belongs, I have chosen rather to draw the accompanying one, liberally sent me for that purpose from the collection of Mr. Salmon. It has probably lost some of its original colouring.

In his *British Birds*, 4th edition, vol. i, p. 50, after referring to the information supplied by Mr. Proctor to Mr. Hewitson, Yarrell wrote :

A similar account of a nest seen by him in 1821 is given by Faber. This, the only one he found, was in south-western Iceland. It was large and flat, placed on the upper part of an inaccessible wall of rock. There were three full-grown young, two of which, on the 6th of July, had already left it and sat nearby. The old birds flew around screaming, but did not attack him. Remains of various species of sea-fowl lay around.

[1] *Coloured Illustrations of the Eggs of British Birds, accompanied with Descriptions of the Eggs, Nests, etc.*, by William C. Hewitson, 1846, vol. i, p. 12.
[2] " Notes on an Ornithological Tour in Iceland ", *Naturalist*, iii, 1838, p. 410.

The above are of sufficient historical interest to be quoted again, but there are of course several much more recent accounts written by ornithologists who have visited Iceland in the last thirty years, one of the first of which was by the Japanese, Marquis Hachisuka, who visited the island in 1925, more than one hundred years after Faber. During his visit, he wrote in his book,[1] he did not find it everywhere, but for a large-sized bird of prey it was not scarce. He remarked that they were frequently seen along the coast in winter as very little food was obtainable at that season in the interior. Hachisuka tells how the bird was in danger of being exterminated prior to 1920, when a law was passed rigidly protecting it for five years. A very pale, almost white, phase also occurs in Iceland which is liable to be confused with the white Greenland birds which occur in Iceland in winter. Hachisuka declared that it was possible to distinguish the Greenland birds from the white Iceland examples by the smaller number of grey bars, which are more in the shape of drops and with hardly any markings, on the underparts.

In his book *The Birds of Iceland* (1927) Hachisuka published a good plate of the three races of gyr-falcon which gives an excellent idea of the markings of the fully adult birds of each. The field notes which he was able to give are disappointingly short, but he mentions that three or four eggs are the usual complement in the nest, although Lord Rothschild had once recorded a clutch of six.

It was left to an intrepid young Englishman, Ernest Vesey, to investigate, with marked success, the breeding habits of *Falco rusticolus islandus* in the spring of 1936. Vesey, who wrote under the name of Ernest Lewis, suffered the severe handicap of having lost both an eye and an arm, but being imbued with tremendous pluck and determination, he succeeded where others had failed, and managed to reach a number of nests of the Iceland falcon during his visit and to leave some excellent field notes. Vesey was an enthusiastic falconer, as well as a keen observer of nature, and his object, as expressed by himself, was to go to Iceland, take the eyasses himself, rush them back to England, feeding them on the very best fresh food, and then fly them at hack before taking them up to be trained. Vesey's untimely death, just nine months after he had set out on his quest, was a severe loss. In his book *In Search of the Gyr-Falcon*,[2] there are many allusions to the subject of this essay which, when pieced together, add much to what was previously known of this grand bird.

One of the most satisfactory results of his trip to the north-west coast of Iceland was his discovery that the Iceland falcon was not nearly as uncommon as had been supposed. Owing to the fact that the falcon sits very close and the tiercel hunts far afield, it became evident that many of the local inhabitants did not know of eyries which were really quite close

[1] *Birds of Iceland*, 1927, by Masa U. Hachisuka.
[2] Published under his pen-name, Ernest Lewis.

PLATE 7

ICELAND GYR-FALCON (Immature)
Falco rusticolus islandus Brünnich

to their farms. Vesey wrote on his return that we now know that the gyr-falcon is still common in suitable parts of Iceland, and proved to his satisfaction that birds can be brought over to Britain in good order and flown at hack with success. The falcons' superb powers of flying and stooping and their matchless style—to quote his description—have made them greatly esteemed by the falconer.

Of the many eyries which are described in Vesey's book, all were situated on ledges or crannies in cliffs but, surprisingly, all were fairly accessible—unlike those described by Doctor Salomonsen of its near relative in the inaccessible cliffs of Greenland. The situations of Icelandic nests are invariably given away by the white excrement on the stones beneath the eyrie which can be seen from a distance. It is known that the gyr-falcon often utilizes the old nest of a raven in which to deposit its eggs and it was the firm belief of the late F. C. R. Jourdain [1] that whenever the eggs of the gyr-falcon were found in a " substantially built nest of heather, stalks and twigs ", the nest was " almost certainly that of a raven ". He allows, however, that there is often no true nest beyond a few twigs and stalks and an accumulation of pellets, excrement, feathers and remains of prey, which presumably is all the work of the falcon. Ernest Vesey held different views. He gives various reasons for his belief that the gyr-falcon " does often build her own nest, and makes a very good job of it too ", pointing to the inaccessibility of all the occupied raven's nests which he found—and there were many—in comparison with those occupied by the gyr-falcon, and to the shallower cup of the falcon's nest, which is not always lined. Although he admits that in some cases the falcons may have been sitting on old raven's nests, he believed that in most cases they were definitely not doing so.

Be that as it may, there were occasions when the eggs were laid on the bare cliff, with no nest at all, and that is what he had expected to find.

Günter Timmermann, whose book *Die Vögel Islands* also appeared in 1938, states that the eggs of the Iceland gyr-falcon number three to five and are laid in the second half of April, less often at the beginning of May. The eggs are like those of the Norwegian gyr-falcon, but according to Jourdain are somewhat lighter on an average. The latter gives measurements of 100 eggs as averaging $59 \cdot 09 \times 46 \cdot 38$ mm. Timmermann found that sixty eggs varied from $54 \cdot 4$ to $64 \cdot 5 \times 42 \cdot 8$ to $51 \cdot 0$ mm.

Of a number of eyries examined by Vesey only one, visited on 20th May, was more than a mile from the shore. The exception was just under the lip of a crag some five miles from the sea. " The falcon slipped off very wild when we were still some way off, and after circling about for a short time, she cleared off altogether, but returned as soon as we had left. The eyrie was very easy to get down to from above. There was no nest, just a hollow scratched out in the turf of a little ledge well protected by a

[1] *The Handbook of British Birds*, 1938, iii, p. 6.

piece of rock above, and even shut in on the sides, so it was a very snug spot, an ideal peregrine site.   The two eggs [1] were laid on a carpet of old bones, so the place had evidently been used previously."   There was no sign of the tiercel at this eyrie.

Another eyrie in a less normal situation was right in a hole, the sort of place in which one might expect to find a jackdaw's nest in England.

Describing his experiences after visiting a number of nests Vesey wrote : " It was common to find the tiercels at the eyries on guard on some upthrust of rock, where they were usually silhouetted against the sky ; and when thus posed they always looked perfectly magnificent.   But I never once saw a tiercel actually brooding on the eggs or young, for that was invariably the falcon's duty, and I never on any occasion visited an eyrie at which the falcon was not present."   Vesey formed the opinion that the tiercel brings the falcon food from the time that she starts to incubate the eggs until the eyasses finally leave the eyrie, a period of well over two months.   Whether that is invariably so appears to require confirmation from other sources.

The first-year birds in immature plumage are relentlessly driven away in the spring by the breeding gyr-falcons from their own hunting ranges near the eyries.   These birds do not leave Iceland as the immature peregrines quite commonly do.

On one occasion an eagle ventured too close to an eyrie and was then hotly pursued by the gyr-falcon.   " She got up over him and stooped hard, whereupon the eagle, to avoid her, and to defend himself, made a sideways roll completely on to his back and thus presented his feet.   Then as the falcon sheered off by throwing up nearly vertically above him, the eagle righted himself, not by turning back the opposite way but by continuing his roll until the revolution was complete.   The falcon still drove him on down the fjord, repeatedly stooping at him, and she had delivered some half a dozen stoops, each as brilliant as the first, and each avoided by the eagle with the same extraordinary revolution, until both birds were lost to sight."

This was the third occasion upon which Vesey had witnessed a gyr-falcon mob an eagle and though it seemed that the falcon's desire was to frighten rather than seriously injure the eagle, yet the whole performance was highly spectacular and certainly proves that the Iceland gyr-falcon is not lacking in pluck or flying powers, whatever may be said of the Greenland gyr, which some observers have reported to be " relatively slow and not particularly agile ".[2]

[1] When reviewing Vesey's book on Iceland the late F. C. R. Jourdain observed (*Oological Record*, xix, 1939, p. 33) that the author was mistaken in believing that Iceland birds, including the gyr-falcon, lay abnormally small clutches, and pointed out that Vesey did not apparently realize that Icelanders take an egg at a time and had probably already taken eggs before he found the nests.

[2] *The Handbook of British Birds*, iii, p. 7.

During his visit to Iceland in the nesting season Vesey paid special attention to the quarry killed by the wild gyr-falcons. It was apparent that these falcons, as with other long-winged hawks, avoid unnecessarily large quarry because they dislike anything of a tussle on the ground such as the short-winged goshawk and sparrow-hawks seem rather to enjoy. Of the various kills tabulated, eider, whimbrel, kittiwake, puffin, black guillemot, mallard and ptarmigan were definitely identified, and rather doubtfully a red-breasted merganser. The species which are most plentiful within the vicinity of the eyrie naturally form the largest percentage; at one eyrie in which remains were found of eider, mallard, kittiwake, black guillemot and puffin, the kills had been mostly puffins. As Vesey observes, however, it is possible to gain a wrong impression from the kills found at an eyrie only, because those would naturally be the smallest and the easiest carried.

Ernest Vesey was successful in bringing home to England six young of the Iceland gyr-falcon which all arrived in this country in perfect feather, and his book, published posthumously, set a seal on a most successful venture. Perhaps it will not be out of place to repeat again the last paragraph from the review of it which appeared in the *Ibis*, where the Editor, Doctor C. B. Ticehurst, wrote: " The book is thoroughly well worth reading, not only for the interesting matter it contains—for the descriptions of the country, people, and bird-life all bear the stamp of veracity without embroidery—but to youth it should be an inspiration—an example of what can be done by courage and determination in the face of tremendous difficulties and handicaps."

REFERENCES : Original Description. *Falco islandus* Brünnich, Orn. Bor., 1764, p. 2. The grey-backed form in Iceland.

PEREGRINE FALCON
PLATE 8 (adult)
PLATE 9 (immature)

Falco peregrinus Tunstall

1. Peregrine Falcon

Falco peregrinus peregrinus Tunstall.　Frontispiece (Trained eyass falcon)

A Resident species in all four countries, well able to maintain its numbers in the wilder localities though much persecuted in times of war. Also a Bird of Passage from Scandinavian countries.

2. North American Peregrine or Duck Hawk

Falco peregrinus anatum Bonaparte

A rare Accidental Visitor

DISTINGUISHING CHARACTERS OF THE TWO RACES : The American race of peregrine differs from the better-known typical subspecies of Europe in having—to quote Cleveland Bent [1]—" a whiter throat and upper breast

[1] *Life Histories of North American Birds of Prey*, part 2, p. 43.

with little or no marking . . . a wider moustachial stripe and more black on the sides of the head ".

IDENTIFICATION: The upperparts from the crown to the rump are slate-grey, rather darker on the crown, which in some examples is nearly black. On the sides of the face two features arrest attention, the heavy black moustachial patch below the eye and the white cheek patch. The wings are blackish; the tail is blue-grey barred with blackish-slate. Chin and throat are white, the upper breast shading from white to pinkish-buff with dark shaft-streaks broadening to drop-shaped markings; the rest of the underparts is pinkish-buff usually heavily barred and spotted with black, but sometimes in males the barring is negligible; the flanks are very heavily barred, as are also the axillaries and under wing-coverts. About half the tarsus is feathered, the feet being quite clear of any feathering. The eye of the peregrine is dark, usually described as hazel; the bill is slate-blue, yellowish at the base, and black at the tip of the upper mandible; the legs and feet are bright yellow, the claws black.

The characteristic shape and silhouette of the peregrine are likely to be the best characters to look for when the bird is on the wing. It has been aptly described as torpedo-shaped, the wings long, pointed and narrow, the tail not very long but slightly tapering. If the bird passes within reasonable distance the black moustachial patch below the eye is easily seen, standing out conspicuously between the white throat and the white cheek patch. When engaged in hunting the flight is very rapid, and the stoop, at an almost vertical angle, incredibly swift; when the bird is returning to its eyrie at the close of the day, the flight is more leisurely, but always purposeful. The female is considerably the larger of the two if both are seen on the wing at the same time. Young birds may be distinguished by their slate-brown upperparts and brownish-buff underparts, below the white throat, heavily streaked (not barried) with sepia. The tail has interrupted buff bars. Mr. Lodge's Plate of the immature bird is characteristic.

LOCAL DISTRIBUTION OF THE TYPICAL SUBSPECIES: Although the peregrine is found fairly generally distributed in England and Wales wherever there are high sea cliffs suited to its tastes, there are naturally many wide areas where it is unknown as a breeding bird. Occasionally a pair are to be found inland but such sites are uncommon, except perhaps in the north of England and the more mountainous parts of Wales. The high sea cliffs of the Welsh coast, especially in Pembrokeshire, have always been a favourite haunt of the peregrine. In the south of England the chalk cliffs hold a number of pairs and abandoned chalk pits well inland are likewise tenanted at times, until the birds are shot or have their eggs plundered. The rugged coast of Cornwall, especially the north coast, is of all areas the most suited to the requirements of this bird and it is probably numerically stronger there than in any English county. In pre-war days there was reputed to be upwards of a score of tenanted eyries.

Its numbers were greatly thinned during the war years but they are believed to have re-established themselves with a fair amount of success.

In Scotland the authors of our latest work on the country, after giving a long account of its early history, observe that to-day the peregrine is by no means uncommon. It breeds in every mainland county except Renfrew, Lanark, Roxburgh (?), Mid- and West Lothian, Kinross and Fife. Peregrines still nest on the cliffs on both the east and the west coast, as well as on the inland cliffs, and that despite much persecution in one way and another. There are many eyries on the cliffs of the islands and Miss Baxter and Miss Rintoul in their *Birds of Scotland* (1953) go into considerable detail as to where it may still be found. Among much else of interest they remark that the Outer Hebrides have been a stronghold of the peregrines for centuries and that the birds have bred on St. Kilda since 1697. A number of pairs nest in the Orkneys on the various islands, but in 1948 their numbers were reported to have decreased generally in Shetland.[1] Both on the Bass Rock and on the Isle of May in the Firth of Forth a pair have bred from time to time.

In Ireland, where it has always been fairly common, the peregrine breeds in most maritime counties and on many marine islands, and is common in certain localities inland on high mountains with steep precipices.[2]

After the breeding season the birds spread out over the country. The first-year birds go in search of new hunting grounds and may be encountered far from where an eyrie is known to occur ; a number of our resident birds wander from their breeding haunts but British peregrines are believed to be fairly sedentary and not to migrate overseas, other than possibly to Ireland or the Isle of Man.

OCCURRENCES IN GREAT BRITAIN OF *F. peregrinus anatum* : The North American peregrine or duck hawk has twice been taken in England. One second-year bird was shot at Newbold Verdon, near Market Bosworth, Leicestershire, on 31st October 1891 ; another, also young, was netted at Humberstone, Lincolnshire, on 28th September 1910 and the fact recorded by G. H. Caton-Haig in *British Birds*, v, p. 219. In the same number of *British Birds* appears a photograph of the mounted Leicestershire example which had been shot by Mr. W. Whitaker and which had already been exhibited at the June meeting of the British Ornithologists' Club in 1911 by E. Bidwell (cf. *Bull. B.O.C.*, xxvii, p. 103), at which meeting the present writer had an opportunity of examining the specimen.

It is doubtful whether, if these examples had been obtained at the present day, they would have been given subspecific rank, for, as Doctor Hartert pointed out when the second bird was examined, it is unlikely that the second-year birds of the two North American races *F. p. anatum*

---

[1] Meinertzhagen found a pair breeding on Lunna headland in 1940 ; the young birds remained until 15th August and then disappeared.

[2] *The Birds of Ireland*, by P. G. Kennedy *et al.*, 1954, pp. 114-115.

and *F. p. pealei* can be distinguished from one another at that age. It was, however, reasonable to conclude that, as *F. p. anatum* is the representative of *F. peregrinus* in the United States and *F. p. pealei* occurs in the North Pacific islands to the Commander Islands, the examples which reached Great Britain must have had their origin in North America rather than in the Pacific.

DISTRIBUTION ABROAD : The peregrine falcon is of almost world-wide distribution, a number of races having been described from various areas. The typical subspecies, with which we are mainly concerned, is that which inhabits the greater part of Europe, ranging in Norway to 71° N. and extending eastwards through the Baltic Provinces. How far east the European race extends depends on whether we recognize a different subspecies in western Siberia. The races of *Falco peregrinus* badly need revision. The extent of the range southwards of *F. peregrinus peregrinus* is likewise difficult to define, but it is the typical subspecies which occurs in Portugal, northern Spain and probably central Spain, France, northern Italy, Albania, Jugoslavia, Bulgaria and Roumania.

Its place is taken in the Mediterranean area by *Falco peregrinus brookei* Sharpe (type locality Sardinia) and in parts of northern Africa by *Falco peregrinus pelegrinoides* Temminck, *i.e.* the true Barbary falcon of authors, which occurs in Morocco and extends to the Canary Islands. Some authorities [1] consider that this latter is the form which ranges throughout the whole of northern Africa north of the Sahara, but opinions on the respective areas inhabited by these two races do not always agree and this is no place to enter into a discussion on the subject. In winter there is a strong migration of *Falco peregrinus peregrinus* to Africa, southern Arabia, India, Ceylon and Malaya. It is more commonly seen in eastern Africa than in the west during the European non-breeding season.

H. G. K. Molineux in his *Catalogue of Birds* (1930) was able to list eight recognizable races of the peregrine in the Palæarctic Region, of which one of the better known, owing to its wandering habits, is the Siberian race, *Falco peregrinus calidus* Latham.

The North American peregrine (*F. p. anatum*) is widely distributed in North America, breeding, according to Cleveland Bent,[2] from beyond the tree limits in Arctic regions southwards to some of the more southern States ; it is very rare on the central plains and is nowhere abundant, though its range extends from the Atlantic to the Pacific.

HABITS : Prior to the First World War there was hardly a headland or cliff range of any altitude round our entire coast-line, including the big groups of islands, as well as many a steep-sided rocky islet, where a pair of these noble birds did not at least attempt to breed annually. It says much for the powers of recovery of the peregrine that it has success-fully withstood the persecution meted out to it in the years 1914-18 and

---

[1] Meinertzhagen in Nicoll's *Birds of Egypt*, ii, p. 370.
[2] A. Cleveland Bent, *Life Histories of North American Birds of Prey*, part 2, p. 43.

1939-45 when a price was put upon its head owing to the menace it remained to pigeons carrying urgent messages of war. A number of the birds shot by Home Guards and cliff-watchers by order of the Government eventually found their way to the Bird Room of the British Museum and the toll taken was considerable. Whether the British peregrine population has been reinforced by passage migrants since those days, or whether the empty cliffs were repopulated by the surviving stock of our own birds, it is not easy to say, but I incline to the latter view, for despite the numbers destroyed there were still quite a number of eyries surviving at the close of hostilities and the orders for the birds' extermination were not carried out too literally. The peregrines had more friends than enemies on many deserted coasts.

All this goes to prove that *Falco peregrinus* is, when given a chance, far from being the great rarity which some people assume. When reviewing the status of this and other birds on the British List some years ago, two well-known ornithologists, W. B. Alexander and David Lack, wrote that in the last hundred years the peregrine has undergone marked and wide-spread decrease and observed that it is now extinct in many counties due to human persecution. There has been a less marked decline in its numbers in the twentieth century and by 1939 it was probably holding its own.

It is true, as J. Walpole-Bond and others have pointed out, that a pair of peregrines may inhabit a certain area for a long time without the local inhabitants being any the wiser, for the peregrine does not advertize its presence unduly and will sit for hours on some pinnacle of rock from which it has a wide uninterrupted view, without moving more than its head. Its quick eyes take in any movement of bird or beast within its vision which may be of interest to it, but its colouring is not conspicuous and unless one knows its favourite stance it may easily be passed by unobserved.

When writing of the raven in the first volume of this work I remarked that it is associated in my mind with a wide variety of scenery, always with the lovely wild spots of the earth, including those in our own islands. That sentence applies equally to the peregrine falcon. In addition to the European bird it has been my luck to become acquainted with both the Mediterranean races *pelegrinoides* and *brookei*, whose combined range extends from the Canary Islands and Morocco to Cyprus and Asia Minor. Their habits are the same wherever they occur and their habitat equally varied and romantic; opportunity has enabled me to observe them more closely in realms beyond our shores than in these islands.

Probably no one in Britain knows the life history of the peregrine better than Desmond Nethersole-Thompson. His account of the species in *The Oologists' Record*[1] is exhaustive and with his permission I make full use of the data he accumulated. " Many of the haunts of the peregrine are very lonely," he wrote. " I have found them on the chalk headlands of the South, in the West Country, in Wales and in Ireland. I have discovered

[1] Vol. xi, No. 4, 1931, pp. 73-80.

eyries in the high cliffs that tower above rugged bleak promontories washed by the boiling sea. There from the dawn till night the raven croaks to his mate and the buzzard wheels high above, and there the chough still lingers. I know haunts in the heart of the mountains where green hills of matchless beauty rise towards the clouds with tearing waterfalls at their base. There the kite still survives and I have seen kites, peregrines, buzzards and ravens in the air together."

On the west coast of Scotland the peregrine makes its home on the great sea cliffs and in the far north, as well as on some of the Inner Hebrides, it meets with less persecution than it does in the great strongholds of the grouse where every keeper's gun is turned against it. With the great decline in keepering, the peregrine is undoubtedly increasing in places where it was formerly never permitted to exist. In the now far-off days when grouse moors were wont to become overstocked and grouse-disease made its unwelcome appearance, a peregrine on the moor was not always a bad thing, for, as Mr. Seton Gordon pointed out in a charming account [1] of the bird published around 1915, " a grouse in the early stages of disease offers a more easy mark than such a bird in the full vigour of health, and as a result will, in all probability, be captured. But where no birds of prey are present, where the eagle and the peregrine falcon are considered as vermin and are exterminated, so far as is possible, the ravages of the disease continue unchecked, and the moor is decimated in a short space of time."

The flight of the wild peregrine is indescribably fine. Seton Gordon likens it to that of an eagle, but in the same way that a fast torpedo destroyer may be compared with a battleship. " The eagle has the majesty which the peregrine can never hope to possess . . . but the peregrine is the fleeter of the two and its prey falls to it with greater ease. . . . When pursuing his prey in grim earnest a peregrine in good training has been reckoned to fly at the rate of no less than 150 miles an hour, a speed which the eagle could not attain unless aided by a following wind of great strength." Grouse, as many of us know to our cost in cartridges, fly very much faster than they appear to be moving, but a peregrine intent on killing a grouse has no difficulty in outflying it. Puffins fall easy prey to the peregrine on the west coast of Scotland but rock doves often succeed in avoiding the stoop which is of such vehemence that its prey is often decapitated.

In his study of this bird Nethersole-Thompson states that the peregrine is eternally at war with the raven and that very heavy fighting occurs between them in March when the raven is sitting and the peregrines are courting and selecting their eyrie. He was once the witness of a savage attack by a peregrine in the month of April when in two successive stoops the peregrine succeeded in knocking out a buzzard and killing a raven which had roused its displeasure. It has been said that the peregrine never attacks a raven when the latter has settled, but the author of the above

[1] *Hill Birds of Scotland.*

account has known a pair of peregrines stooping one after the other at a raven standing on a spit of rock while the big black fellow snapped his great bill at them.

In Scotland golden plover and the duck tribe are the most frequent victims of a peregrine's attack but there are records of it striking down many other birds as well, among which kestrels and cuckoos may be specially mentioned. I have watched the Mediterranean peregrines chasing rock pigeons on islets where little else but these birds, and night-flying petrels and shearwaters, was present, and have marvelled how often the pigeon by a dexterous turn eludes death as the peregrine hurls past at breakneck speed. Homing pigeons, less familiar with the peregrine's tactics, and more intent on keeping to their line of flight, fall victim to the peregrine much more easily than do their wild relatives, used as are the latter to combatting the elements and meeting the normal dangers of a rock dove's existence.

In places where the eyrie is near a rookery the rooks frequently figure largely on the peregrine's menu, and as R. J. Ussher stated in his *Birds of Ireland* (1900), rooks were by far the most usual quarry in Co. Waterford in his day. Ussher observes in his account of the peregrine that occasionally the magpie, jackdaw, corncrake, waterhen, curlew, whimbrel, dunlin or partridge forms the victim and recounts how on one occasion a Brent goose was brought down. John Walpole-Bond gives a list in his *History of Sussex Birds* of over sixty different species which the peregrine is known to have killed. On one occasion he saw a peregrine come down and carry off a young heron from a nest.

Considering what panic the sudden appearance of a peregrine can inflict on marine fowl, it is remarkable how often the bird's eyrie is to be found in the midst of a large colony of sea-birds. Ussher went so far as to state that in Ireland no great cliff-bird colony seems to be complete without its pair of falcons. It is pleasant to read in the new *Birds of Ireland* (1954) that in the opinion of the authors the peregrine is " well established and probably increasing ", after the interval of over fifty years since Ussher and Warren's *Birds of Ireland* (1900) was published.

In the various accounts of the peregrine's life history which I have read there are few references to a peregrine passing food to its mate such as commonly may be witnessed with the harriers.

In his *Bird Life in Cornwall* Colonel Ryves draws attention to this action in a striking paragraph :

The aerial " pass " of a kill is spectacular. The falcon spots her mate approaching from afar, and, as he draws near, leaps from her eggs and, with strident screams, meets him in mid-air. When almost touching both birds momentarily appear to stand on their tails and in a flash the victim is transferred from one pair of talons to another. . . . Sometimes the tiercel drops the kill for the falcon to catch but he prefers to pass it to her or to alight with it.

Nethersole-Thompson was greatly impressed by a similar performance and described what he witnessed in the *Oologists' Record* :

> I remember seeing a falcon dash out of a cliff and fly over the sea. Through my glasses I could see as a distant speck a tiercel peregrine. The two birds rapidly converged, the tiercel flying considerably higher than the falcon. They flew together for a short distance and then something dropped from the tiercel's talons. The falcon turned over on her back and caught it. Both birds then flew back to the cliff. This high speed performance had taken place hundreds of feet above the sea. It was one of the prettiest sights I have ever seen.

Mr. Nethersole-Thompson considers that the " pass " occurs usually during the early stages of incubation. Much of the peregrine's hunting is done far inland and birds which habitually nest and roost in sea cliffs will make long journeys over the adjoining moorland in search of their quarry. A peregrine which has its headquarters on cliffs overlooking the Solway not two miles from our door often flies inland to forage and passes over our farmhouse on its way to the moors. Small birds such as finches, chats, pipits and blackbirds are not disdained by the falcons on these quite normal excursions and indeed form a good proportion of the peregrine's usual fare. Of the numerous birds which these falcons attack the lapwing is probably the hardest for it to kill, but there are at least two published records of its being successful.[1] On the other hand, Humphrey Gilbert and Arthur Brook have never known a peewit taken as prey, the bird's reaction to the peregrine's stoop being amazingly quick.

MIGRATIONS : Of the migratory habits of the peregrine there is not very much to be said. It is generally conceded that our resident stock do not usually proceed overseas. The birds pair for life and though they move about considerably and cover great distances in their wanderings there is very little evidence that they entirely quit our shores. In Ireland Colonel Scroope, when preparing his article for *The Birds of Ireland*, was able to find little evidence of migration. He instances a bird killed by striking a lighthouse in Cork on 18th September 1898 (which may equally have been a Continental example on passage south) and another ringed as young in Sutherland in June 1950 which was recovered in Co. Wexford in January 1951.

We know that Scandinavian peregrines at times occur in Britain, as the following examples prove :

Ringed		*Recovered*		
Sweden . . .	5.6.35	Kent . . .	.	18.1.37
Lofoten Isles, Norway .	–.–.38	Berks . . .	.	4.11.38
(as young) Swedish Lapland .	1.7.—	Gloucestershire	.	22.2.46
Västmanland, Sweden .	20.6.46	Yalding, Kent	.	6.12.46
Sweden . . .	20.6.46	S. Molton, Devon.	.	30.1.47

[1] Nethersole-Thompson, *Ool. Rec.*, xi, 1931 p. 74.

PLATE 9

PEREGRINE FALCON (Immature)
Falco peregrinus peregrinus Tunstall

The dates when some of the above were captured point to their having remained in Britain during the winter.

There are instances of peregrines being taken at the lanterns of Scottish lighthouses, especially at Little Ross and Skerryvore, while others are recorded [1] from Sanda, off the Mull of Kintyre, and from the Bell Rock. In autumn what are quoted as " passage falcons " are seen now and then in the Solway area, " mostly fine, large, dark, beautifully-plumaged birds in the feathers of the first autumn ".[2]   Whether of Continental origin we cannot be sure, for at that season our own birds are on the move.   As George Lodge wrote in his *Memoirs of an Artist Naturalist*, the peregrine occurs often in autumn and winter in places where it is rarely seen at other times when the northern birds are making their way south.   These migrants often remain several weeks in a district when food is plentiful.

That our home-bred peregrines travel some distance from where they are born to find new hunting grounds of their own is exemplified by a bird ringed as young in Cumberland on 21st May 1946 which was recovered nearly six years later, in April 1952, in the Isle of Man.   We learn from many accounts how faithful peregrines can be to their own eyrie for year after year.   Ussher in his *Birds of Ireland* refers to an eyrie still held in his day on the west coast which was reported to have been occupied for over 200 years, and there are numerous instances in Scotland where peregrines have been known to remain in occupation of small islets and rocks, such as St. Kilda, or similar sites for over a hundred years.

In *The Birds of Scotland* (1953) Miss Baxter and Miss Rintoul give two interesting records of peregrines which are known to have been bred in England deserting their country of origin to breed in Scotland.   We cannot imagine a Scottish peregrine so forgetting itself as to behave in similar fashion.

The Isle of May in the Firth of Forth is another ancient haunt of the peregrine and there the birds take a heavy toll of passing migrants, no bird being too small for their attentions.   In contrast we read in Macgillivray of a peregrine carrying a blackcock to the Bass Rock and on another occasion a pheasant.   As an example of the peregrine's tenacity in following its quarry to the bitter end may be cited the bird which followed a lark down a lead mine in Dumfriesshire to a depth of 360 feet, where both were taken at the bottom.[3]

Although everything points to our British peregrines being fairly sedentary, yet there may be a small movement of the typical subspecies in other parts of its range, for examples of *Falco peregrinus peregrinus* have been recorded from the Delta Barrage [4] and it is conceivable that a

---

[1] Baxter and Rintoul, *Birds of Scotland*, 1953, p. 288.
[2] *Trans. Dumfries and Galloway Nat. Hist. Soc.* for 18th December 1903.
[3] Hugh S. Gladstone, *Birds of Dumfriesshire*, p. 213.
[4] Meinertzhagen in Nicoll's *Birds of Egypt*, ii, p. 368.

few may pass the winter south of the Mediterranean. It must be remembered, however, that whereas *Falco peregrinus leucogenys*, the Siberian form, is a mighty wanderer, European peregrines are not habitually migrants, a point which Doctor Ernst Hartert stressed [1] a number of years ago. Records of *Falco peregrinus peregrinus* from south of its normal breeding range should be very carefully verified. There are numerous reports of peregrines occurring in winter in Tunisia, Algeria and Morocco which do not conform to the resident Mediterranean races, but whether these can be examples of the typical European race requires much more study.

When not breeding the peregrine is said to be practically mute, but its normal scream—a wild, piercing, angry cry, as Walpole-Bond describes it—may be heard from the end of February onwards. Other cries attributed to the peregrine falcon are " a long drawn out whining *kee-ark* ; a short, sharp *kek* which is rarely heard and a low chittering or squeaking sound somewhat resembling a call of the kestrel ". All are usually uttered in flight, so Mr. Walpole-Bond has recorded.[2] Another cry, " a rasping and brisk *quat-yek* ", is used when the bird is courting, according to Nethersole-Thompson's field notes. The latter naturalist observes that the scream is pitched in different keys, but that of the tiercel [3] is always pitched much higher than that of the falcon. It is also less raucous.

No rule can be made about the behaviour of peregrines at the eyrie in Mr. Nethersole-Thompson's view : " Many falcons are very noisy, others fly right away, screaming at intervals in the far distance. A few fly away from their eggs uttering no sound at all, but when the young are hatched, most peregrines are more noisy than when they have eggs." It is exceptional for a peregrine to attack a human being who attempts to examine the eyrie but on rare occasions a bird will stoop within a few feet of the intruder's head. It is recorded by G. C. S. Ingram and H. M. Salmon that when the peregrines swoop around and chatter with rage it is a sure indication that there are young in the nest, for at other times this noisy demonstration is rarely indulged in.

FALCONRY : We have it on the authority of Seton Gordon that in the reign of James II no less than £1000 was given for a pair of peregrines. Falconry was then " the sport of kings " and though reigning monarchs of our day no longer indulge in this branch of sport, there is still an enthusiastic band of falconers in Great Britain, of whom one of the most distinguished was the late George Lodge, the artist responsible for the beautiful pictures in *The Birds of the British Isles*. In the only book which he published Lodge devoted a portion of his text to the peregrine falcon,

[1] Hartert and Jourdain, *Novitates Zoologicae*, xxx, p. 121, under *F. p. calidus* (=*leucogenys*).

[2] *Field Studies of Rarer Birds*, p. 247.

[3] The *tiercel* is the male, the *falcon* the female, in the language of falconers.

and recounts in considerable detail his experiences with trained hawks. Falconers have their own views as to whether peregrines, gyr-falcons or lanners give the finest sport, but Lodge had no two views on the subject. For " hawking " in this country the peregrine undoubtedly takes first place in his estimation, though, for actual training, he had a very soft spot for the merlin. Gyr-falcons are wasted on grouse and partridges, he used to say, and require bigger game such as wild geese, blackcock, mallard or cock pheasants, while the lanner and saker are seen to their best advantage when in pursuit of small deer. Peregrines, as Mr. Lodge emphasizes in his book, manage grouse and partridges to perfection and he had a very high opinion of their prowess. He does not stand alone in his preference for the peregrine, but observes that several must be tried before a really good one is found. For every gyr-falcon trained there must be many hundreds of peregrines. One of Mr. Lodge's characteristic paintings, that of a hooded eyass falcon named " Black Jess ", resplendent in all its trappings, which appeared in his book *Memoirs of an Artist Naturalist* is now reproduced as our frontispiece.[3] It was trained and flown by the late Kim Muir, 10th Royal Hussars.

BREEDING HABITS [1] : It is the opinion of those naturalists with the widest experience that the date of laying varies from district to district. The last week of March is an exceptionally early date for eggs to be laid, but Nethersole-Thompson has recorded finding a full clutch on 28th March and observes that he always expects to find setts by 5th April in one particular locality. In other areas 15th to 25th April is, according to his experience, the usual time for finding full clutches, while some falcons do not sit until early May. In each district an occasional pair will have a clutch either earlier or later than the majority of peregrines breeding in the same area. It has also been noted that many peregrines complete their clutch on almost exactly the same date in each year.[2]

During nearly thirty years' study of the peregrine on the cliffs of Wales, Humphrey Gilbert found 1st April to be the earliest date when he knew of a bird sitting. In his experience peregrines in Wales begin to sit earlier inland than on the sea coast, and he suggests that 9th April is the date on which most inland birds are sitting, while coast birds do not begin until 15th April. Some birds in this area do not begin to incubate before 27th April and Gilbert heard of others which did not begin until May.

In Cornwall, Colonel Ryves considers, the eggs are usually deposited

---

[1] In compiling this account full use has been made of the writings of Desmond Nethersole-Thompson and of J. Walpole-Bond, reference to whose work has already been made in this article. I have also read with great advantage the excellent accounts of the peregrine's nesting habits by my friend Humphrey Gilbert (*British Birds*, xxi, p. 26) and by Geoffrey Ingram and H. M. Salmon (*British Birds*, xxii, p. 198), as well as E. W. Hendy's *Lure of Bird Watching* and B. H. Ryves' *Bird Life in Cornwall*. To all these authorities I tender my acknowledgments.

[2] *Oological Record*, xi, 1931, p. 76.   [3] By kind permission of Miss B. Lodge.

on alternate days during the first half of April, but he had two records of clutches completed by the end of March. In Sussex the time for fresh setts is early April but there again Walpole-Bond has seen "a fair number" of new-laid clutches during the last week of March.[1] In Scotland we may expect laying to take place at a later date, from the middle of April until early in May.

Peregrines pair for life but do their hunting independently and, as Colonel Ryves has stated, they do not pass the day as close companions in the manner of ravens. Both birds roost in the region of their stretch of cliffs and the site of the eyrie is resorted to throughout the year, though it is the falcon rather than the tiercel which keeps most closely in touch with the nesting place. In Cornwall eyries are scattered along the whole of the seaboard but only thinly in the south. Three or four miles separate most of the eyries and they are never within less than two miles of one another. Most if not all peregrines, in Colonel Ryves' opinion, have one or more nesting sites which they use alternatively. He knew of one pair which had no less than six eyries, none of which has ever been occupied for two consecutive years. Some birds, however, will stick to the same site for several years in succession. Lofty nesting places with the widest possible view are preferred to those at a lower elevation, these latter being selected only if particularly favourable from some point of view.

On the wild Pembrokeshire coast-line the sites in which the peregrine nests are very diverse in kind, so Humphrey Gilbert has stated. In certain places the ledges are of bare rock with no overlay of earth and as the falcons always demand a soft material into which they can dig a scrape for their eggs, they are dependent in such places on old nests of the raven, buzzard or jackdaw for their nesting site. It is more usual, however, for the peregrine to select a ledge upon which some earth has gathered in which it can make a scrape for its eggs, sheltered occasionally by herbage or overhanging rock, though at other times the site is exposed to all the winds of heaven. Some eyries are in positions which are all too easily reached, while others may be 200 feet down a 500-foot precipice with a considerable overhang above the nest so that only the most intrepid cragsman could hope to reach the eggs. Even so, Desmond Nethersole-Thompson has stated that, given time and sufficient rope and, above all, capable assistants, the crack climber will seldom fail. And Nethersole-Thompson should know! The latter naturalist has found the peregrine's eyrie in large holes, in small caverns, on ledges and behind pinnacles, and once in a large man-made cave some thirty feet above the sea, but whether ledge, cavern or old nest is occupied, the peregrines always make a scrape in which to lay their eggs. The size of these scrapes varies considerably. In chalk they are shallow but in other kinds of cliff Nethersole-Thompson has found enormous bowls about a foot across and five inches deep.

[1] *A History of Sussex Birds*, 1938, ii, p. 253.

I have been very much interested in the manuscript field notes on this bird left me by the late Colonel R. F. Meiklejohn from observations which he made in Esthonia. From these it appears that from that country eastwards the peregrine frequently, if not normally, nests on the ground or moorland. In his notes Colonel Meiklejohn draws attention to the fact that a pair have twice attempted to breed on open heath near pine in Hampshire. While in Esthonia Meiklejohn obtained clutches taken at the end of May from nests on a rise on an extensive moor which commanded a wide view. The eggs were laid in a slight depression in heath with a few stalks and bits of fur—probably there already—as lining. He was informed by Doctor Weltz that in Siberia the local race of peregrine, *F. p. calidus* (=*F. p. leucogenys* Brehm), also nests on open moors or tundra and that a nest which he found had quite a large foundation of sticks, in which case it is probable that an old nest of the rough-legged buzzard had been utilized.

Colonel Meiklejohn's experience with the Barbary falcon (*F. p. pelegrinoides*) is the same as mine—that ledges on high cliffs are invariably preferred to any other site.

It has been pointed out by Walpole-Bond that the peregrine lays its eggs apart and they do not touch except by accident. There has been some controversy in the past as to whether, if the first eggs are taken, the peregrine will lay again. Mr. Nethersole-Thompson in his wide experience found that a second laying took place in two cases out of three if the first was interfered with, and knew of an occasion when a third laying occurred from which eyasses had flown.

It seems from the experience of the above-quoted naturalists that no rule can be made about the behaviour of peregrines at the eyrie. While some falcons will fly away and continue screaming in the distance, others will slip from the eyrie silently, uttering no sound. Some are very light sitters, others again are most difficult to dislodge and sit until almost touched.

Both falcon and tiercel incubate but the former takes by far the greater share. Incubation lasts, according to Nethersole-Thompson, twenty-eight days for each egg. He considers that the eggs are laid at two-day and more rarely three-day intervals, and he proved to his satisfaction that they are laid in the small hours of the morning. Incubation definitely commences with the penultimate egg and sometimes before it. The young remain in the eyrie for about six weeks.

Comparing the above experiences with those of Colonel Ryves, I have been interested to observe that while he agrees that incubation does not start until the last egg, or perhaps the last but one, has been laid, he considers that twenty-eight days for the incubation period is an under-estimate, and that the period is thirty days. When giants disagree it is best to be neutral.

I will conclude my notes on the peregrine's nesting by quoting from Colonel Ryves's account of the falcon and tiercel changing places at the eyrie : " It is a magnificent spectacle to watch the ' changing of the guard '. The relieving bird approaches at lightning speed close over the sea or the beach, and as it nears the eyrie shoots upwards like an arrow, emitting a fierce scream of greeting. Instantly the other, with an answering cry, leaps into space and in a few moments is a speck in the sky."

When the young are hatched the falcon remains at or by the eyrie, the tiercel doing most of the hunting for the family rations. The young, clad at first in pale creamy-white down, remain in the nest for about six weeks, by which time they are fully fledged and gradually learn to fend for themselves. According to Walpole-Bond, succulent young jackdaws take a prominent place on the young peregrine's menu, the young falcons cutting their teeth as it were on this easily-taken prey.

It stands to reason that as the tiercel does most of the foraging, it is he, and not the falcon, who so often pays the penalty at the hands of some keeper or gunner. On such occasions it is a matter of astonishment how quickly the falcon secures another mate, " sometimes, indeed, in the space of a few hours ". Mr. Walpole-Bond suggests that there are more bachelor tiercels than there are falcons, but how does it come about that a bereaved falcon knows so quickly where she may find another mate ?

Oologists do not always agree as to the clutch size of *Falco peregrinus*. In many districts, to quote again from Nethersole-Thompson's summary in the *Oologists' Record*, three is the normal clutch and mountain birds in most cases produce this number. In other localities a c/4 is not uncommon and is sometimes the rule. Genuine c/2 also occur. There are genuine clutches of five but they are very rare.

In south Wales Mr. Gilbert considers that half the nests hold four eggs while the others have three, clutches of two being rare. Sussex eyries usually have three or four eggs as the full complement and the same is true of Cornwall.

The eggs are very beautiful and it would take too much space to quote from the very full descriptions of clutches taken by the oologists [1] mentioned in this essay. Their various works, to which I have given reference, may easily be consulted. Not so the *Catalogue of Birds' Eggs in the British Museum*, and with Mr. E. W. Oates' account I will end this article :

The eggs of the Falcons vary from a broad oval to an elliptical or spheroidal shape. The shell is generally devoid of gloss. The eggs of the Peregrine Falcon vary from cream colour to pinkish buff and deep brownish red. The majority are densely marked with spots, blotches, and smears, more or less confluent, of various shades of reddish brown and, less frequently, yellowish brown, while in many specimens a very small extent of the ground-colour remains visible. Some eggs are marked with rather well-defined spots and blotches, chiefly on the larger half. On some of the richer coloured examples a few small markings of intensely deep blackish brown may be observed.

[1] *Oologists' Record*, xi, 1931, p. 73.

Supplementing the above general account of a large series it may be of interest to note that the outstanding types in Mr. Nethersole-Thompson's collection include a clutch of three with a magnificent lilac ground and purple blotches, and two clutches of the osprey type of egg. Mr. J. Walpole-Bond, after describing the normal series in his collection, mentions four extraordinary specimens : (*a*) dirty white, with faint cloudings and filmings of pink and lilac-grey ; (*b*) very pale salmon-pink with chestnut and grey spots and blotches ; (*c*) bright pinkish-purple, suffused with a bloom most delicate, as of some fruits ; and (*d*) pure white without decorations of any description. He remarks in conclusion that eggs all identical in appearance in the same sett are scarce, and, strangely enough, a repeat clutch is generally quite different from the original.

It is a matter of passing interest that Mr. Walpole-Bond observes that " south coast eggs " of the peregrine " are on the whole seldom as dark as those from other districts ; some of them, indeed, are distinctly pale ". This paragraph is interesting read in conjunction with Mr. Nethersole-Thompson's pointed suggestion [1] that south coast peregrines may belong to a distinct race. From the viewpoint of a field ornithologist of great experience he concluded that peregrines from the south coast of Britain have characteristics which set them apart from others resident elsewhere in the British Isles. He sets out these differences in the paper to which I have given a reference. He believes that the south coast birds are generally smaller, lack the snow-white chests of Welsh, Irish and Scottish birds, and lay eggs decidedly smaller and frequently of the red and dusty type. He believes that a skilled ornithologist would pick out a series immediately.

Can it be that Mr. Clancey has missed an opportunity ?

The eggs of the peregrine measure, after Jourdain : average of 100 British eggs 51·8×41 mm. Max. 58·6×43·8 and 49·8×44·2. Min. 46×38·2 mm.

As I have dealt at length with the habits of our own peregrine I have not made any reference here to the life history of the North American peregrine which has occurred only twice in our islands. A very full account of that bird can be found in Mr. Cleveland Bent's *Life Histories of North American Birds of Prey* by those who are interested.

REFERENCES : Original Descriptions. *Falco peregrinus* Tunstall, Ornithologia Britannica, 1771, p. 1. Ex Brit. Zool., p. 136 : Great Britain. *Falco anatum* Bonaparte, Geogr. and Comp. List, 1838, p. 4 : New Jersey.

[1] *Oologists' Record*, xi, 1931, p. 73.

PLATE 10 **HOBBY**

Falco subbuteo subbuteo Linnaeus

A regular Summer Visitor to England to breed locally. Elsewhere in Britain
irregular
Has bred once in Scotland but never in Ireland, to which it is a rare Vagrant

IDENTIFICATION : The adult has the whole upperparts, wings and tail
slate-grey, darker on the head, which is almost black, as are the region
around the eye and the moustachial streak. The latter contrasts strongly
with the whitish cheeks and even whiter throat. The rest of the underparts
is white, very heavily and conspicuously streaked with black. The thighs
and under tail-coverts are rust-red. The eye is dark brown, the cere and
skin around the eye bright yellow ; the bill is bluish-horn with blackish
tip to the upper mandible ; the legs and feet are bright yellow. The legs
are not feathered below the tibio-tarsal joint but the rufous feathers of the
thigh are long and extend some way down the leg.

All accounts agree that the hobby is a most graceful bird and its agility
is little short of miraculous. The wings are long, but the tail comparatively
short. The sexes are alike in plumage but the female is usually larger than
the male.

Immature birds are dark brown above with buff mottling on the crown,
and instead of the ground colour of the underparts being white, it is buffish
and even more heavily and broadly streaked with black than in the adults.
The cheeks too are buffish. Wings and tail are as in the adult but the tail
has a broad pale tip and is not so bluish-slate in colour. They lack the
rust-red thighs and under tail-coverts, which are buff or rufous-buff.

In total length the male hobby measures about twelve inches, the female
being larger by approximately two inches ; wing of ♂ 247-272, ♀ 265-280
mm. (after Witherby). As Claud Ticehurst once wrote : " In flight it looks
almost black above and white on the underparts. The sharp pointed wings,
swift straight flight and small size distinguish it from all other hawks."

LOCAL DISTRIBUTION AND STATUS : The hobby is a summer visitor
to England and as a breeding bird is more or less restricted to the south.
The counties of England in which it breeds regularly are mostly situated
south of the Thames and Severn, but it nests spasmodically as far north
as Yorkshire and Cheshire and as far west as Devonshire, and has been
known to breed occasionally in the eastern counties of Wales, notably
Glamorgan and Brecon and possibly Monmouth. Mr. Witherby listed
the actual counties in which it has bred in the 1938 edition of the *Handbook*
and not much detailed work has been done since that date. North of the
Thames it is reported to be more commonly met with in Northamptonshire
than in any other of the midland counties.

In the year 1931 Mr. Nethersole-Thompson and his friends had set
themselves to discover new haunts and breeding grounds of the hobby

which were unknown to other naturalists and by dint of combing several counties (one of which was Sussex) many new haunts of the bird were brought to light. No less than fourteen nests with eggs were discovered, an account of which appeared in the *Oologists' Record* of the year mentioned. The " new haunts " were situated in widely different kinds of country, on downland and hills, on semi-cultivated land and in wild forest regions.

Mr. Nethersole-Thompson does not say how many clutches, if any, he and his friends added to their collection, but in the following year there was an outcry in bird protection circles that owing to the depredations of egg-collectors the hobby was on the verge of extinction. The matter came up at the B.O.U. Annual Meeting and elicited a sharp reply in the *Oologists' Record*. Mr. Nethersole-Thompson was then at pains to show that egg-collectors were not entirely responsible for the diminution in numbers of the hobby and pointed out that the virtual disappearance of the carrion crow, following the use of poison, trap and gun, had reduced the possible nesting sites of the hobby to a minimum. The commercially minded egg-thief must certainly carry his share of the blame but it would be ridiculous to point to the egg-collector as the only culprit.

In the year in which I am writing (1954) it seems probable that the hobby is at least holding its own in its old haunts and may even be extending its range. The keeper ignorant of the hobby's habits is the bird's worst enemy and under the new Wild Bird Protection Act anyone shooting a hobby or taking its eggs will be subject to penalty. The hobby may for the first time have its chance of nesting in counties such as Norfolk and Suffolk where it would probably have established itself long ago had it not been ruthlessly shot at sight, and hung on the keeper's gibbet. There are many counties in England and Wales to which it comes as a rare visitor, and we may hope that with the more enlightened knowledge of birds in Britain this very beautiful hawk will be more often encountered. It is surprising how many bird-lovers are unfamiliar with its appearance.

As an occasional summer visitor the hobby has occurred in Scotland in most counties but is reported to be more frequently seen in the east than in the west. In a note to *British Birds*, xxxii, Mr. Jourdain was able to record a hobby from upper Loch Fyne in September 1920 and another shot at Ardgour in north Argyllshire on 23rd August 1938, observing that the date of the latter occurrence suggested possible breeding in the neighbourhood.

It has been recorded from Shetland, and a number of times from Fair Isle, but not as yet from the Orkneys.

North of the English Border it has bred only once : a pair at Kinnaird House, Perthshire, in 1887. There are other reports of nesting having taken place in Scotland but, to quote Miss Baxter and Miss Rintoul, " none sufficiently well authenticated to be worthy of full credence ".

In Ireland, where the hobby has been obtained on thirteen occasions only, mostly in the south-east of the country, it has never been known to breed.

DISTRIBUTION ABROAD: The hobby which visits Britain in summer to breed is to be found at that season all over Europe, ranging as far north as 67° in Sweden and extending eastwards to the Ural Mountains. Whether examples breeding east of the Urals belong to the same typical race is uncertain. Asiatic birds show very slight differences until eastern Siberia is reached, from which area *F. s. jakutensis* has long been recognized. The southern breeding range of the European bird extends to the Mediterranean countries and probably some of the larger islands, including Cyprus and Corsica. It is replaced in north-west Africa by *Falco subbuteo jugurtha*, which is slightly paler above than the European bird and breeds in Tunisia, Algeria and Morocco.

The statement in Howard Saunders' *Manual*, 3rd edition, that the European hobby has bred in Madeira is, I am convinced, founded on error. Hobbies are rare stragglers to the Canaries [1] and the Salvage Islands, so presumably to Madeira also, but they certainly do *not* remain to nest and even the race of those which have been reported from the Atlantic Islands has not been satisfactorily settled. The European hobby spends the winter months in north-west India and Africa, occasionally reaching the country south of the Zambesi. It is a mistake to write that its winter quarters are " throughout Africa ", as has been done in a recently published work. It winters almost entirely on the eastern side of the continent. In Upper Guinea it is absent and in Lower Guinea has been taken once only in southern Cameroon. Nor is it known from the forested part of the Belgian Congo, showing, as Doctor Chapin has pointed out, " a marked preference for the plains region ".

It may be that the hobby which breeds in western Europe, particularly in Spain and Portugal, where it is not uncommon between May and September, spends the winter in the French Sudan and French Niger Territory. It would then come within the area inhabited by the African hobby, *Falco cuvieri*, which frequents the savannas and forest clearings as well as the plains of tropical Africa.

Some further details of its winter range in Africa will be given in a later paragraph.

MIGRATIONS: Although the hobby rarely appears in England before the third or fourth week of April, Witherby was able to chronicle an arrival as early as February 1884 in Yorkshire, and three in March: one on the 3rd by W. Eagle Clarke in 1866 and two towards the end of the month (Norfolk in 1858 and 1863 respectively). Another early record in the *Handbook* refers to a bird on 9th April 1936 in Berkshire. No mention is made of the bird caught near Brighton in a net set for larks on 11th March

---

[1] Bannerman, *Ibis*, 1919, pp. 488-490.

1858 [1] nor of the hobby which was reported shot at Yarmouth, Norfolk, in February, as mentioned by Henry Stevenson.[2]

Mr. Nethersole-Thompson, whose past experiences with the hobby brought him considerable notoriety, states emphatically, when contradicting another writer : " Hobbies sometimes arrive in April and they are courting all through May. Although some pairs are late, most of them are on their ground by mid-May." On the other hand, a perusal of the County Faunas indicates that the hobby is seldom *expected* to arrive before May is well advanced and in Sussex arrivals at the extreme end of the month are not unusual. In East Anglia June may have arrived before a hobby puts in its appearance and we can safely state that it is almost the latest of all our summer birds to begin breeding.

It is always much easier to record with fair accuracy the approximate dates of arrival of our summer visitors, but the time of their departure from our shores is less certainly verified. The birds depart from their breeding areas quietly and without fuss and only very astute field naturalists know of their going until they have gone. The hobby is no exception to the rule and owing to its comparative scarcity its departure is seldom noted. In *The Handbook of British Birds* it is stated that there is evidence of a south-ward passage on the east coast of England in October. There are, however, very few records to go upon. Birds have been met with in Norfolk in August, September and October, and on 9th October many years ago a hobby was taken on a fishing boat off Yarmouth.[3] Occasionally a hobby will be recorded in November on the south coast, the bird mentioned from Pett in Sussex on 26th November, for which Michael Nicoll was the authority responsible, being one of the latest to have been seen in this country, but there is one other even later—a specimen shot at St. Leonards early in December—which is quoted in *A History of Sussex Birds*. The normal months of departure from that county are September and October, according to the author of that work. We have so far little help from ringed examples to indicate what direction British-bred hobbies take when they leave our shores. Only one bird has been captured ; it was ringed when young in Wiltshire on 9th August 1936 and was recovered in Landes, France, two months later, on 16th October 1936. That particular bird migrated due south.

Mediterranean records are very scanty as regards the passage *south*. Favier reported hobbies returning to Tangier from Europe in autumn and there are odd records from some of the islands. Jourdain reported a hobby in Corsica on 7th October, but Philip Munn has no mention of autumn migrants through the Balearic Islands although quite a number of spring occurrences are recorded from that group.

[1] *A History of Sussex Birds*, 1938, ii, p. 256.
[2] *Birds of Norfolk*, 1866, i, p. 18.
[3] B. B. Rivière, *A History of the Birds of Norfolk*, 1930, p. 108.

There is a small but apparently regular passage through Malta,[1] where examples have been seen between 4th September and 6th October. The late Mr. G. Despott [2] wrote of its status in Malta that it is more or less common during its migrations in spring and autumn but he agrees that it is much scarcer in some years than in others. Very rarely it has been known to breed.

From my own experience in the Mediterranean I have small doubt that the migration of European birds is much more in evidence east of Sicily than west of that island, but so far as the hobby is concerned, the main stream, if it goes that way, passes unnoticed. Curiously enough, the birds are not abundant in Egypt and are seldom recorded. They are, however, not uncommon on autumn passage from 1st October to 23rd November on the Sinai-Palestine frontier.[3] By what route the hobbies which winter south of the Equator reach their destination we can only conjecture. Sir Geoffrey Archer [4] states that records from the Sudan indicate a regular passage in both autumn and spring, and there is a well-marked spring passage though British Somaliland, though the intervening Ethiopian territory appears to be off the line of migration despite its well-wooded nature. On its way south the hobby is only an occasional straggler in September and October and even Sir Frederick Jackson with his wide experience of East African bird-life saw nothing of the autumn movement of this species. The late Herr Hermann Grote [5] believed that in addition to South Africa, in which he included Natal, Cape Colony and Benguella, the main winter quarters of the hobby lay in Nyasaland, Northern and Southern Rhodesia and Katanga, where the birds remain until the end of March, but in his valuable treatise on this subject he gave little indication of the route which he considered the hobbies followed. Sir Frederick Jackson, on the other hand, was convinced that the hobby on its way *south* to Kenya and Uganda followed the Nile Valley but returned north again by the Rift. Referring to this subject, Sir Geoffrey Archer's opinion is worth recalling. Having been Governor both of Uganda and of Somaliland he was in a good position to judge for himself the true state of affairs. Thereafter in his *Birds of Somaliland* he wrote :

Among the commoner birds of prey to be met with in British Somaliland at fixed seasons, the hobby and the so-called grasshopper buzzard-eagle (*Butastur rufipennis*) are pre-eminently the birds of quick passage. They arrive and are gone again in about three weeks. Furthermore the hobby provides a good example of the well-known occurrence that migratory birds follow different routes on their southerly and northerly course. A species may be seen in its numbers going or

[1] John Gibb, *British Birds*, xl, 1947, p. 75.
[2] G. Despott, *Ibis*, 1917, p. 476.
[3] Meinertzhagen in Nicoll's *Birds of Egypt*, ii, p. 375.
[4] *Birds of Somaliland*, i, p. 164.
[5] *Wanderungen und Winterquartiere der Paläarktischen Zugvögel in Afrika*, 1930.

PLATE 10

HOBBY
Falco subbuteo subbuteo Linnaeus

PLATE 10

HOBBY

Falco subbuteo subbuteo Linnaeus

returning, but seldom both ways. In the autumn only an occasional straggler from among the ranks of *F. s. subbuteo* will be found within our limits [Somaliland] wending its way south. . . . Between the middle of April and the middle of May these birds are passing back through British Somaliland in very considerable numbers. The peak of the northerly migration is reached about the 8th May, and by the 25th the last straggler has departed on its way.

It was Sir Geoffrey's opinion that the hobbies which passed north through Somaliland in spring travelled along the shores of the Red Sea and then crossed into Asia Minor somewhere about the Gulf of Suez, thus avoiding Egypt altogether. Their summer quarters may have been in eastern Russia or western Asia as Sir Geoffrey believed, but the only proof of this would be the recovery of ringed birds. In Kenya Sir Frederick Jackson records seeing considerable numbers at Machakos on 30th March and for several days following. They were flying overhead in a leisurely manner, going north. This seems a very early date for hobbies to be on the move in mid-Africa, as it is not before mid-April that they appear in the Mediterranean countries. Philip Munn had notes of their arrival in Majorca on 19th and 27th April in consecutive years, and John Gibb of their passage through Malta on 11th, 28th and 29th April of three consecutive years. At Gibraltar Colonel Irby in three other years noticed them first on 8th, 13th and 20th April respectively and by early May they were to be seen around Seville. By the 10th they have reached the latitude of Oporto and, as already indicated earlier in this account, we expect them to have reached their breeding areas on the south coast of England about the middle of May, when they quickly settle down to family duties.

That the migration north is a protracted one is, I think, shown by Admiral Lynes' experiences in Spain, for those who are familiar with his early writings will recollect that he found hobbies migrating through the Coto Doñana in some numbers during the second and third weeks of May.[1]

The dates quoted give a very rough idea of the hobby's passage from its winter quarters to its breeding places in central and northern Europe.

HABITS : Before dealing with the behaviour of the hobby after it has reached our shores, some account of its habits in its winter quarters may be of interest. The hobby, though a woodland bird in Great Britain, shuns closely timbered country and the same is true of it in Africa. It avoids the forest, preferring what is usually termed open savanna. It seems too, from Doctor Chapin's and the late George Bates' experiences in the Congo and Cameroon respectively, to avoid passing over the Great Equatorial Forest. Those birds which reach Benguella in their migrations do so by passing round the vast forest area rather than over it. We learn from Doctor Austin Roberts that those of the species which reach South Africa often do so in company with lesser kestrels (*F. naumanni*) and red-footed falcons (*F. vespertinus*), but the birds which have been observed passing

[1] *Ibis*, 1912, p. 485, footnote.

through Kenya have usually been unaccompanied and Sir Frederick Jackson particularly observed that on their way through East Africa the birds are unhurried.

It is of interest to note that in British Somaliland Eleonora's falcons appear with the hobbies when on their northerly passage and with them depart again within two or three weeks of their arrival.

During their comparatively brief stay in the Protectorate Sir Geoffrey Archer, who was at one time Governor and Commander-in-Chief, had ample opportunity of observing their habits and has left us the following account of his experiences :

During the passage through Somaliland—and particularly any evening at Sheikh after rain when the termites have emerged from their cones—flights of ten to twenty of these beautiful little falcons may be seen high in the heavens hawking. Now to watch the hobby for a while on the wing is to be rewarded with an arresting study of grace and speed. As the bird poises in the air, the wings move rapidly for a few moments " winnowing ", then are held steady in a bow as it glides forward, and now and again a leg may be dropped and shaken during flight. Presently with a swift swoop, a juicy termite in the winged stage is scooped up in the talons, the head depressed, the foot raised, and the insect is transferred to the mouth and swallowed —all in the course of a perfect aerial evolution. And it is only the oncoming of the night, when the flights disperse, that puts an end to the quest. . . . In tropical Africa the hobby is essentially a crepuscular feeder, preying for the most part on white ants, beetles and locusts, and probably on bats.

When on passage the hobby, like many other of the smaller Raptores, will help itself to Passerine migrants, especially to the *Hirundinidae*. Captain Munn observed in Majorca on 27th April 1925 a hobby accompanying a great migration of swifts, swallows and martins, one of which it had seized and was carrying about in its claws, mobbed by a crowd of the migrants.

Harry Witherby when in central Spain was much struck by the aggressive habits of hobbies which he encountered about the middle of June when the falcons would be nesting. One of these birds he saw many times and often put it off the same tree-top. It was very much engaged, in partnership with a cock kestrel, in chasing a buzzard which had a nest in the vicinity. There were a great many black and red kites all round the spot, but it was only very rarely that the hobby and kestrel attacked any of them. Yet they never let the buzzard pass without screaming at it and diving down upon it. Later in the month yet another partnership of male hobby and cock kestrel came to his notice in a pine wood of the Sierra de Gredos at about 4500 feet. Together they were frequently engaged in stooping at a booted eagle and twice they were seen to chase it right through the wood.

In Britain Mr. Walpole-Bond states that there may be " sparring " with any big bird which comes too close to its nest—such as heron, rook, crow or kestrel—and on one occasion he witnessed an attack on a marauding cat, but there appear to be few instances in this country of the ferocity displayed by the bird in Spain which Mr. Witherby had the good fortune to witness. Most naturalists who know the bird well agree that hobbies are noisy and bold in the vicinity of their eyrie, though, as Nethersole-Thompson has pointed out, they are temperamental creatures and often behave differently from day to day. He has had them stooping within three feet of his head and in contrast has seen them settle on a branch a few yards away and watch while their nest is examined.

The call notes, from the many accounts of close observers, seem to be varied in the extreme and are well set out by B. W. Tucker in the *Handbook*. Some of the notes there given are taken from Nethersole-Thompson's account in the *Oologists' Record*, where he wrote, " The scream of the hobby is a thin, querulous *tew tew tew*, and its courting and hunting note a brisk *cir-ic* ". The late Captain C. S. Meares [1] considered the hobby's scream to be expressed by the words *keek-keek-keek*, a sharper note considerably than that of the kestrel.

Prior to nesting the behaviour of the hobby shows marked individual variation, as Mr. Nethersole-Thompson emphasizes in the following account :

It may be that one pair has a hunting beat close to the nesting site, and is consequently seen in the neighbourhood, while another pair hunts mainly at a considerable distance and is never seen near the site of their nest by the casual observer. Again a pair of hobbies may spend much of their time in the air together, chasing one another playfully and calling querulously, while another pair apparently disdain such " skylarking " and the two birds are rarely seen together. It must be emphasized that the observer who suggests that hobbies hunt *only* in the dusk of evening and at dawn cannot have studied the species. There are certain periods when it is customary to find the male hobby perched in the vicinity of the eyrie, but it hunts periodically at all times of the day. [2]

When discussing the habits of the hobby on migration in tropical and sub-tropical countries mention was made of its fondness for termites. In Britain, where termites are non-existent, the hobby has to be content with grasshoppers, beetles of several groups, and moths, and from examination of stomach contents it is obvious that insects in one form or another play a large part in the diet. Small birds are of course taken in considerable numbers. Finches, sparrows, buntings, larks, warblers, tits, starlings, thrushes and blackbirds are listed among the species habitually captured and there are a number of records of the swift being captured, and even of a woodpecker. On one occasion Mr. D. J. May [3] watched a hobby take a

[1] " Field Notes on the Hobby ", *British Birds*, xi, pp. 50-54.
[2] *Ool. Rec.*, xii, 1932, p. 58.
[3] *British Birds*, xliv, 1951, p. 205.

house martin in the air and eat it leisurely, bending its head down to its talons as it flew and glided overhead. A starling has also been captured and eaten in mid-air and no doubt when opportunity occurs other species are devoured in the same manner.[1]

In his contributions to the *Oologists' Record* Mr. Nethersole-Thompson has emphasized that hobbies like a varied diet of insects and birds and he has observed that they have wide but regular hunting beats and often feed a long way from the eyrie. Of the smaller birds upon which they prey he found that in his experience meadow pipits, tree pipits, wood larks and skylarks were often captured but the variety of the menu is no doubt influenced to a large extent by the environment.

When chasing a dragonfly the hobby's evolutions are extraordinarily skilful as the insect twists and turns as only a dragonfly can do when thoroughly alarmed. Still more impressive is its flight after a mounting lark. With swifts and swallows it has more difficulty. Its capture of a swallow is thus described : " Dipping and rising the swallow attempted to outpace its rival but the hobby overhauled it rapidly and rising above it darted down, missed, but flew up. Then, passing below, the hobby turned over on its back and cut the swallow down." [2]

Although the point is usually neglected in written accounts of the bird's flight, the hobby loves to soar in the sky and Mr. Nethersole-Thompson has watched it ring its way upwards beyond the range of his binoculars. Referring to the disputed question as to whether the hobby will hover, he is of opinion that while it does not do so regularly like a kestrel, it will often hover momentarily over gorse on a common or over a reed-bed when searching for dragonflies. Moreover, it will occasionally hover head to wind when high up and on the look-out for prey.

Before leaving the question of the bird's feeding habits, mention must be made of the pair of hobbies which Mr. W. B. Alexander observed flying low over the water-meadows of the River Isis a few miles above Oxford. They were busy catching mayflies (ephemeroptera). Their movements could be closely seen and it was noticed that they caught each insect in one foot and immediately conveyed it forward to the beak without checking their flight. Sometimes they flew low over the water, over which and over the waterside herbage great numbers of insects were dancing. Specimens of the insects collected by Mr. Alexander were found to be all adults or subimagos of the mayfly *Ephemera vulgata*, with the exception of a single alderfly which may or may not have been one of the insects seized by the hobbies.

BREEDING [3] : It has been stated that in southern England those

[1] *British Birds*, xxxviii, 1945, p. 334.

[2] *British Birds*, xxv, 1931, p. 143.

[3] This account is based on Desmond Nethersole-Thompson's excellent field notes which he published in *British Birds*, xxv, pp. 142-150.

hobbies which have reached their summer quarters by the end of April or early May continue their courting all through the latter months and most of them are on their breeding ground by the middle of May. The 29th April is stated by Nethersole-Thompson to be the earliest date on which he actually saw them on their ground and a pair together were once seen on 2nd May. The pairs remain much together at that time, playing and soaring in the clouds and calling to one another.

Mr. W. H. Thompson has studied with great care various displays of the hobby during the three or four weeks before the eggs are laid and his notes have been extensively used in *The Handbook of British Birds*. He describes the long soaring flights in which the birds indulge, in the course of which the male frequently stoops at the female. He emphasizes, as do other writers, that at all times the hobby is a playful species and is to be seen performing in most spectacular manner, singly or in pairs or several together. He finally describes the remarkable exhibition which follows the capture of a small bird by the male hobby, which with the prey in its talons ascends to a great height, then suddenly dives down upon the female in headlong flight to throw himself up and pass to her at full speed.

By early June most hobbies have chosen the nest in which they intend to lay and at this date are prone to be very noisy, screaming excitedly over the tree-tops and nesting site. I quote now from Mr. Nethersole-Thompson's experiences in the hobby's " headquarters ", situated mainly in Dorset, Wiltshire and Hampshire, and to a lesser extent in Sussex. Great diversity is shown as regards its haunts. Three distinct types may be instanced : (*a*) squat, heather-covered hills, with clumps and belts of Scots pines ; (*b*) the outskirts of true forest land where mile upon mile of beeches mingle with old oaks and an occasional clump of pines ; (*c*) a region of green hills and stony pastures in which the hobby nests in the clumps of beech and pine that spring up on the hillsides and in the folds of the valleys.

For preference a clump, line or plantation of thinly planted trees is chosen, but failing that hobbies readily go to a big wood, provided the trees are not too close together. Sometimes, as Jourdain observed, a hedgerow tree will be selected but the other sites mentioned are preferred when these are available. Of twenty-five eyries examined between 1928 and 1931 seventeen were in clumps or lines, seven in big woods and one in an isolated tree on a hilltop.

The selected trees differ greatly. Some pairs breed in tall straight pine clumps, others in scrubby downland plantations, while others haunt little groves of oak trees. When a big wood is chosen the nest may be on the outskirts of a big beech or oak forest or it may be in a vast pine wood with birches growing thick beneath them ; it is not by any means always in an outside tree. In a well-thinned pine wood the eyrie may be anywhere, but a commanding position and good " take off " have always been preferred, so Mr. Nethersole-Thompson discovered.

The hobby never builds a nest for itself but appropriates that of another bird. Almost invariably in this country the nest of a carrion crow is chosen but it has been known to occupy a " decrepit nest of a magpie, occasionally of a rook or sparrow-hawk and very rarely a squirrel's drey. In some districts the hobby prefers a new crow's nest, in others it is not so particular." Mr. J. Walpole-Bond adds to this list the use of an old heron's nest but only on rare occasions, and in Russia Colonel R. F. Meiklejohn found a clutch in an old nest of a jay.

In Mr. Nethersole-Thompson's experience the female hobby will often, for a week before an egg has been laid, brood the empty nest. The new occupant usually occupies the nest as she finds it but if a new crow's nest is taken the hobbies often remove the wool-hair lining and lay their eggs on a scrape in the dried grass and twigs beneath. Some authorities do not agree with this latter statement but it is confirmed to some extent by Mr. Walpole-Bond's experience that in the case of a magpie's nest being chosen the fibrous root lining is removed and a shallow scrape made in the bottom. Should old fir cones be lodged in an old nest these are allowed to remain when the hobby takes possession. One would imagine fir cones being uncomfortable objects in a nest but the hobby does not trouble to remove them.

It is during the early stages of incubation that the food " pass " of the hobbies may occasionally be witnessed. The hobby begins to sit very late in the year, and as Mr. Nethersole-Thompson points out it is an exception rather than the rule to find the hen brooding before 10th June. In his view the best date for a full fresh clutch lies between the 14th and 20th of that month but some pairs are habitually later. It is interesting to realize that some hobbies lay their first egg almost to a day annually. The eggs are laid every second day, but there is sometimes a longer interval of three days between the second and third. Brooding begins with the second egg.

The *Handbook* gives the incubation period as twenty-eight to thirty-two days. Mr. Nethersole-Thompson gives twenty-eight as his experience. Mr. Walpole-Bond gives the period as " a lunar month ". The clutch is usually of three eggs, though nests with two and four are on record. The eggs are very similar to those of the peregrine falcon in colour, and are thus described officially by E. W. Oates in the *Catalogue of Birds' Eggs in the British Museum* : " The majority are densely mottled and spotted with rufous of various shades, chocolate-brown or deep blackish-brown. Some are deep rufous, mottled with a darker shade of the same, and marked with a few black dots. On the whole the eggs are free from smears and large confluent blotches, the markings being small and more or less well defined, and it is seldom that they form a cap at either end."

That is a very accurate description of the series in the British Museum but it is instructive to compare Mr. Nethersole-Thompson's own description of the many clutches which he has taken or examined. He states :

The eggs are objects of great beauty and, contrary to conventional opinion, they vary considerably. By some it is wrongly held that the main characteristic of the hobbies' eggs is the yellowish-brown wash. In the *Practical Handbook of British Birds* Mr. Jourdain says that yellowness appears as incubation advances, and that is quite true. There is a yellow type of hobbies' eggs, others become yellow after incubation, but the most characteristic thing to note about most eggs is the peppery nature of the markings. One type has a pure salmon-red ground peppered with very light brown, another has a blood-red ground, in others the markings approach those of the wood-warbler's in type. One lovely variety has a rose-pink ground with a chocolate cap. Some eggs are capped with deep chocolate-brown, others are blotched at the smaller end. Often a few spots of deep sienna-brown are scattered haphazard over the surface. In rare varieties blotches replace spots, in others the ground colour is almost white.

Mr. Nethersole-Thompson adds that on the whole the eggs of the hobby are larger than kestrels' and though some eggs do approximate to those of *Falco tinnunculus*, he has yet to see a clutch of hobbies' eggs about which there could be a reasonable doubt.

Measured by Jourdain the average of 100 British-taken eggs is $41 \cdot 57 \times 32 \cdot 73$ mm. Max. $45 \cdot 5 \times 31 \cdot 8$ and $44 \cdot 1 \times 35 \cdot 7$. Min. $38 \times 31 \cdot 4$ and $41 \cdot 4 \times 31$ mm.

The hen does most of the incubation but the partners have been seen to exchange duties and the male has been flushed from a nest. The young when first hatched are " beautiful little balls of down with dark eyes ". Only one brood is reared in the year.

REFERENCES : Original Description. *Falco subbuteo* Linnaeus, Syst. Nat., 10th ed., 1758, p. 89 : Europe, restricted type locality Sweden.

MERLIN

Falco columbarius Linnaeus

PLATE II　　　　　　　**1. British Merlin**

Falco columbarius aesalon Tunstall

A Resident, breeding locally in England, more generally in Wales, Scotland and Ireland.
Also a Winter Visitor and Passage Migrant in small numbers

2. Iceland Merlin

Falco columbarius subaesalon Brehm

A regular Autumn Migrant to Fair Isle in small numbers and other parts of
Britain including Ireland ; probably some remain to winter

3. American Merlin or Pigeon Hawk

Falco columbarius columbarius Linnaeus

A rare Accidental Visitor which has been obtained once in South Uist,
Outer Hebrides (see p. 55)

DISTINGUISHING CHARACTERS OF THE THREE RACES : From the resident race of the British Isles, *F. c. aesalon*, the Iceland subspecies, *F. c. sub-aesalon*, with which the merlins from the Faeroe Islands are united, can be separated on the greater length of the wing.[1] It has been suggested also [2] that Iceland birds are darker than those from Britain and Scandinavia but some writers consider there is too much variation and it seems that the relative size of wing in these two geographical races is a more reliable distinction.[3]

The American merlin, *F. c. columbarius*, is darker on the mantle than *F. c. aesalon* in both sexes and the bars on the tail feathers are broader and blacker.

IDENTIFICATION : This is the smallest of our British falcons, the male being no larger than a mistle thrush, some $10\frac{1}{2}$ inches in total length ; the female is about $2\frac{1}{2}$ inches longer. Its low dashing flight as it follows the twists and turns of its intended victim has gained for it a very high reputation, especially among falconers. The male has a blue-slate back which is characteristic, with fine black shaft-streaks on each feather, and fine narrow wings, the wing-coverts coloured like the mantle and the flight-feathers greyish-brown, the secondaries with bluish outer webs. The

---

[1] Salomonsen has shown (" Aves ", in *Zoology of the Faeroes*, lxiv, 1935, p. 123) that *F. c. subaesalon* is separable from the Continental bird on its longer wing, with practically no overlap sex for sex. Measurements are given. See footnote 3 below.

[2] Kleinschmidt, when describing *Falco alfred-edmundi* from Iceland (*Falco*, 1917, p. 9), shown by Hartert to be a synonym of *Falco c. subaesalon*, considered Iceland merlins to be darker than Continental birds.

[3] K. Williamson (*Scottish Naturalist*, lxv, 1953, pp. 76-77) records that birds trapped on Fair Isle measured ♂♂ 205-210 mm., ♀♀ 228-232 mm., all beyond the upper limit of over 100 Scandinavian specimens measured by Salomonsen, *i.e.* ♂♂ 193-202 mm., ♀♀ 199-222 mm.

PLATE 11

BRITISH MERLIN

Falco columbarius aesalon Tunstall

Upper Figure	. .	Adult Male
Lower Figure	. .	Adult Female

PLATE 11

BRITISH MERLIN

Falco columbarius aesalon Tunstall

Upper Figure   Adult Male

Lower Figure   Adult Female

nuchal collar is broad and rufous-buff in colour ; the breast and flanks
are rufous-buff, broadly and heavily streaked with blackish-brown. The
ground colour of the underparts shows some individual variation, some
examples being more creamy-buff than rufous. The tail is bluish-slate,
broadly banded and tipped with blackish. The bill is bluish-horn,
yellow at the base of the lower mandible ; the legs and feet are yellow. The
eye is dark brown.

The female merlin differs from the male in being larger in size and with
the upperparts—mantle, scapulars and coverts—brown with pale edges to the
feathers instead of being slate-blue. It might perhaps be confused with
the female kestrel, but is not nearly so red. The tail is brown crossed with
five narrower bands of buffish-white. The underparts are creamy-white
with broad rufous-brown streaks. The soft parts are as described in the
male.

As Mr. Lodge has emphasized in his book, merlins in their
first plumage, and females when adult, are very similar in colour and
markings to peregrines in first plumage, much more so than are hobbies.

LOCAL DISTRIBUTION OF THE BRITISH RESIDENT MERLIN : In
England, as opposed to the rest of Britain, this, the smallest of our
indigenous falcons, is not by any means universally spread as a breeding
species. It is, however, to be found on Dartmoor and especially Exmoor
in rather more numbers than the reference to it in *The Handbook of British
Birds* indicates, at any rate as regards the latter locality. The merlin,
though not common, is fairly well distributed all over Exmoor. During
the breeding season it is to be found only at the higher altitudes, roughly
at or above 1000 feet. At other times of the year, from September until
March, it may be seen hunting at lower levels : over Porlock Marsh and
the adjoining fields and shingle bank which lie only a little above high
water mark.[1]

To the rest of southern England [2] and the Midlands, south of Notts
and Derby, the merlin when it occurs is only a visitor. In the Pennine
Chain, in the Cheviots and on the Yorkshire moors, and especially in
Lakeland, it is well established. In Lancashire it retains a number of
breeding haunts and we read with pleasure that in the hill districts of
Rochdale and Oldham it is fairly numerous [3] ; in addition there are quite
a number of other localities where it still holds its own.

It will be remembered that in 1874 John Hancock took a very pessimistic view of the survival of the merlin when he wrote : " This beautiful
little falcon is rapidly disappearing by the hands of the gamekeeper, from

[1] My informant is the late E. W. Hendy, writing to me in 1944 from Porlock.
[2] In Monmouthshire, Herefordshire and Shropshire there have been records of the
merlin breeding.
[3] In Mr. Clifford Oakes' *Birds of Lancashire* (1953) a thoroughly up-to-date review of
the merlin's status in that county will be found.

the north of England, and will, I fear, soon cease to give interest to our moorland rambles." Happily the merlin lingered on in many estates until a more enlightened generation of keepers came to walk the moors, and an enquiry as to the present-day [1] status of the merlin in the country of which Hancock wrote has elicited the following reply from Doctor Hugh Blair of County Durham :

Here and there, where old prejudices yet dictate policy, it even to-day meets with a hostile reception. On the majority of estates, however, it is freely granted that the little hawks do no harm, and on some they receive not only welcome but protection. Game-preserving certainly cannot be held responsible for a recent diminution in the breeding stock over the whole district. From some breeding stations the birds have withdrawn as the trees of the new state forests have grown around them. Others have remained untenanted since that prolonged and widespread frost of 1947 which proved so disastrous to our wild life. There are, on the other hand, many which continue to be occupied every season along the line of the Cheviots, and a few on the adjacent lower-lying moors. Merlins also breed regularly, and locally in some numbers, on the fells around the dales of South Tynedale, Wear and Tees, including Crossfell itself.

Wales can boast of many more breeding pairs and there, as the *Handbook* asserts, " it breeds in many parts ".

Scotland is equally fortunate in having this attractive little hawk widespread. In fact it is reported to nest in every mainland county except possibly Kinross and Nairn, from which there are no records to date. It is, unfortunately, not common anywhere, as being a member of the hawk family every keeper's gun is against it—thereby showing complete ignorance of the bird's habits, for the damage which it does to game is absolutely nil. It has everywhere decreased in the last hundred years, owing to persecution. Fortunately it is to be found on many of the Inner Hebrides. Thus Miss Baxter and Miss Rintoul are able to record it from Bute, Arran, Islay (commonly), Jura, Colonsay, Coll, Tiree, possibly on Rhum, Mull, Skye, Tanera and once on Eilean a' Chleirich. The Outer Hebrides are likewise a fairly safe stronghold and there, according to Doctor Bruce Campbell, it is widely distributed and a common resident. In Shetland the protection now afforded it has come none too soon. In Saxby's account he wrote that of all the Shetland *Falconidae* this is by far the most abundant, being met with at all seasons and occasionally in considerable numbers. To-day Mr. and Mrs. Venables (*Birds and Mammals of Shetland*, 1955) report that merlins breed regularly and fairly commonly on Mainland, Unst, Yell and Bressay, and single pairs on several of the other islands. During nesting time they are confined to the hills. In these authors' estimation merlins are quite as numerous in winter as in summer. The suggestion put forward by Mr. Williamson that the Shetland merlins are

---

[1] This essay is being written in 1954.

stationary and do not migrate in normal years has been reinforced by the recovery of one of a brood ringed in Shetland on 31st July which was recovered at the end of December close to where it was ringed.

When in 1943 Doctor David Lack made his report on the breeding birds of Orkney he was able to state that a number of pairs bred on Mainland and Hoy, and at least one pair was found on South Ronaldsay and on Flotta. G. T. Arthur found it breeding on Rousay also. Though formerly much more abundant there is no further decrease, and perhaps an increase in the near future will become apparent.

In Ireland the merlin appears to be steadily decreasing in numbers despite acres of suitable wild country. In *The Birds of Ireland* (1954) the authors have a depressing tale to tell, for it is considered by them to be rare in Ulster, though nesting sparsely in most counties. In Leinster and Munster it is decreasing and they had no news of it from the midlands or Co. Clare where it was once established. It is believed to be more numerous in Wicklow than in any other county. The other bright spot appears to be Connaught, where the merlin is also well established, breeding on the Mullet and Achill as well as in Connemara. In south Mayo it is much less plentiful than formerly.

Two other races must figure on the British List : the American merlin and the Iceland merlin.

The American merlin, *Falco c. columbarius*, was obtained on South Uist by Colonel R. Meinertzhagen on 11th November 1920. That being the only record (cf. *Ibis*, 1934, p. 58, and especially 1953, p. 365), the American merlin is included here on the authority of the authors of the statement in the 1953 *Ibis* quoted above. This example has not yet been submitted to the List Committee for final acceptance to the British List. As the specimen agrees absolutely with the typical North American race there is no valid reason for not recognizing it, especially in view of the increased number of North American birds which are now reaching our shores.

The Iceland merlin *Falco c. subaesalon*, which also occurs on the Faeroe Islands, has been proved to come to the British Isles in autumn and winter. Doctor Salomonsen believes that the Faeroe stock is resident and that may be the case, but the Iceland merlins are certainly not so. Mr. Kenneth Williamson [1] has proved that there is a regular stream of merlins referable to the Icelandic race which pass through Fair Isle in the autumn and in some years at any rate (such as happened in mid-August 1952) synchronize with the peak period of migration of the white wagtail. These merlins presumably winter in Britain, on the evidence of recoveries of Iceland-ringed birds. Examples have been recovered in the northern counties of Scotland, in the Highlands and in Ireland which will be discussed in a later paragraph.

[1] *Scottish Naturalist*, lxv, 1953, pp. 76-77.

DISTRIBUTION ABROAD : In one race or another the range of the merlin extends from Alaska right across northern Europe and Asia to Kamchatka. The race which is resident in the British Isles, *F. c. aesalon*, is that which ranges over the greater part of northern Europe to north-west Russia, east of which other races have been described. *F. c. aesalon* occurs in Norway to 71° N. and breeds also in Sweden, Lapland, Finland and the Baltic States. Its range in Russia extends to the River Mezen and the Minsk Government and it is this race (according to Doctor Salomonsen) which is recorded as a casual visitor to Greenland. Some of the northern breeding birds pass through the countries of central Europe to winter in the Mediterranean Basin. A few are reported to occur in North Africa in winter in Tunisia, Algeria and Morocco and to be found in certain of the Mediterranean islands, but only very small numbers appear to cross the sea. The merlin was said by Shelley to remain in Egypt in winter and to pass north again in considerable numbers, but this is the Asiatic merlin *F. c. insignis* and the European bird is unlikely to occur in North Africa east of Tunisia or Cyrenaica. The Asiatic race is reported to reach the Sudan in its winter wanderings. Sinai is probably the most easterly locality reached by the European bird. Examples from Cyprus are said to be the Asiatic form, but specimens should be collected. To the other Mediterranean islands, Sicily, Malta, Sardinia, Corsica and the Balearic Islands, *F. c. aesalon* is a passage migrant in winter ; in all these islands it is very scarce, with the possible exception of Sicily. In western Europe the merlin is a well-known visitor to central Spain,[1] though scarce. In Andalusia it is more often to be seen. Sixty years ago it was numerous in the vicinity of Casas Viejas and at the present day may be seen in the neighbourhood of Gibraltar.

To Portugal it is a winter visitor which is not uncommon in the Oporto area.[2] Probably it occurs more numerously in the south of that country, which is little known by ornithologists. Portuguese records extend from November to May. All the merlins which winter in the Iberian Peninsula go north to breed.

Of the two other merlins which have occurred in Britain the typical race *Falco columbarius columbarius* of Linnaeus is confined to America. It nests from eastern Canada to Maine and Manitoba, migrating in winter to the Gulf States and to northern South America (Wetmore).

We in Europe consider our merlins to be subspecies of *F. columbarius*, but Mr. Cleveland Bent in his *Life Histories of North American Birds of Prey* restricts the name *columbarius* of Linné to the four American races of which the typical subspecies is the eastern form. He believes the European birds to be best kept distinct, raising our British resident race to specific rank, *Falco aesalon aesalon*, and treating the other western hemisphere

[1] H. F. Witherby, *Ibis*, 1928, p. 634.
[2] W. Tait, *Birds of Portugal*, p. 142.

merlins as subspecies.   That fact is mentioned here to save any confusion arising in the mind of the reader who may share Mr. Bent's views.

The Iceland race *Falco columbarius subaesalon* is also resident on the Faeroe Islands.   The Iceland birds have been proved, as noted elsewhere, to migrate to Britain in autumn, a number of ringed birds having been recovered.   Whether the Faeroe Islands merlins also migrate has not been proved.   (See under " Migrations " p. 59.)

Habits :   The charm of this diminutive falcon has been felt by all who have had an opportunity to watch it ;   it is a favourite on account of its fearless disposition, boldly attacking birds much larger than itself, and of its amazing powers of flight.   Moreover, it is a bird which is easily tamed and thus has gained for itself a high reputation among falconers, for, as Mr. Lodge has written in his *Memoirs of an Artist Naturalist*, the merlin is the easiest of all hawks to train.

To watch a merlin hunting its quarry is a most inspiring sight, for of all the *Falconidae* it is perhaps the most persevering and dashing.   Its flight is even more rapid and direct than that of the sparrow-hawk, resembling more the flight of the peregrine, as Charles St. John [1] wrote many years ago.   That naturalist himself kept and trained merlins and he reminds us that in the days of falconry the merlin was in great request.   It was the favourite hawk of ladies, because of its fine temper and also because its size prevented it from being too great a weight for a lady's wrist.   " So courageous is this beautiful little bird," wrote St. John, " that if trained to do so it will fly at and strike either grouse or black game, though without much effect."   He adds that in a wild state it preys on small birds, snipe and even partridges.   Robert Gray [2] also mentions the merlin's prowess at capturing snipe very cleverly at the seashore on the Berwickshire coast near Dunbar.

It was St. John too who witnessed the capture of a swallow by a pair of merlins.   The hawks helped each other, one keeping above and the other below their prey, till at last, after a long chase, by some unlucky turn the swallow came into a favourable position for one of the merlins, and was immediately seized in the air and carried off.   That St. John was not alone in his admiration of the merlin can be seen by Robert Gray's eulogy of this falcon in his *Birds of the West of Scotland* :

When in pursuit of prey, this spirited little bird will rush headlong anywhere, after getting fairly excited, and is rarely baffled in its hunting expeditions, however large the object of chase.   It will ascend beyond the range of ordinary vision in its endeavours to surmount the flight of a snipe, or come down like a falling star on a hurrying plover striving to reach some friendly marsh.   At other times the chase is persevered with a courage and determination quite extraordinary in a bird so small, its feats reminding one more of the theftuous acts of a sparrow-hawk than the stoop

[1] *Natural History and Sport in Moray*, 1882, p. 120.
[2] *Birds of the West of Scotland*, 1871, p. 33.

of the nobler falcon. With the rapidity of an arrow, it will fly along some enclosure, by the hedgerows, seize an object, and glide out of sight, leaving the spectator to marvel at the transaction as at a deed of magic.

My collaborator in this work, the late George Lodge, had a knowledge of falconry second to none and when writing of the subject of this essay in his own book observed that the difference in tactics between a wild and a trained merlin is very noticeable : " The former is so much quicker, especially in turning, that it is always close on to its quarry which it seems able to prevent going to ground or getting away high, until at last it is taken in the air. A trained merlin in pursuit of a ringing lark takes such wide rings as it mounts that much time is taken to close up to the quarry, get above it and put in a stoop. The lark is almost always forced down and taken either on the ground or just before it alights, and rarely taken in the sky." From a falconer's point of view that is certainly the best thing to happen. There is always a danger of a hawk getting lost.

Pipits and larks form a very great part of the merlin's food supply and no doubt linties in season when they are present in any numbers. The list of species which the merlin is known to have captured is a long one. Mr. E. W. Hendy told me that on Exmoor the commonest victims are meadow pipit, skylark and whinchat (often fledglings) but he has also found feathers of blue tit, chaffinch, goldfinch, greenfinch, redstart, blackbird (juvenile) and wheatear. He added that grouse and blackgame breed on Exmoor but he had never found any feathers of these species at the plucking places, nor had he ever seen any evidence of merlins attacking game birds or their chicks—and yet, as he points out, the number of ringed merlins shot is 19·9 per cent. against 14·0 per cent. for the black-listed sparrow-hawk ! It is of interest to note that in that particular area—Exmoor—plucking places exist, usually in large numbers in the vicinity of the nest, ant-hills of the yellow ant being the commonest site, though stumps of dead thorns and also rocks are likewise utilized.

Among larger prey than the Passerine birds mentioned, the smaller waders come in for considerable attention, especially in winter time when the merlins are fond of frequenting the low ground in the vicinity of the shore.

It is extraordinary what heavy quarry a merlin can carry. It has been seen to kill a lapwing, then lift it from the ground and carry it over a quarter of a mile.[1]

My friend Collingwood Ingram recounts how when he was in Iceland a male merlin attacked a phalarope which was hovering anxiously round his head but on that occasion the latter escaped unharmed. That phalaropes are not always successful in eluding the stoop is mentioned by Doctor Hugh Blair, who identified redwing, dunlin, meadow pipit and red-necked phalarope among the birds successfully captured in East Finmark in the month of May. Doctor Blair remarked that as Passerine birds and small

[1] D. Stubbert, *British Birds*, xxxvii, pp. 17-18.

waders were at that time present only in small numbers, it is difficult to understand how the merlins managed to find sufficient food, unless voles were amongst their victims. The little falcons were there common and generally distributed.

Small mammals are captured at times and there is a reference in Charles St. John's *Natural History and Sport in Moray* to the author watching his tame merlins eating worms and insects, and that when not pressed by hunger, from which he deduced that the smaller hawks will resort to that sort of food when larger game is difficult to procure.

There are many instances of merlins fearlessly attacking birds many times larger than themselves. Hendy watched a merlin take on two buzzards at once, while those who are in possession of Coward's book on British birds will recollect his account of a pair of merlins harrying a passing heron until it squawked in terror. He had witnessed fearless assaults by this little falcon on the crow and short-eared owl, and even on a peregrine, when the merlin's eyrie was approached too closely. Only when the breeding season is over do the merlins take life less seriously. An instance of that was witnessed in Fair Isle by Kenneth Williamson [1] during the latter days of August when a pair of merlins were observed to be having what appeared to be a game with two, and sometimes three, hooded crows, the performance lasting about twenty minutes. Between the aerial " bouts " in which they were indulging, the birds rested on telephone poles and wires spanning the moorland, and after a brief rest first the hoodies, and then the merlins, would stoop at their opponents and drive them from their perch. The merlins kept up an intermittent " keening " and the hoodies croaked protestingly at intervals but it was quite obvious from their movements and the way in which first one species, sometimes the other, initiated the " attacks " that the enjoyment was mutual.

MIGRATIONS : The passage movements of the merlin are not easily studied in countries like our own where there is a breeding stock, many individuals of which remain in Britain the year round. It is difficult to distinguish the genuine birds of passage and winter visitors from overseas from the resident birds which often move about locally. Merlins are often to be seen in coastal areas in winter where in summer they are absent and there is no means of telling the origin of the newcomers. That some of our British-bred birds go overseas in winter, probably to return in spring, is proved by the recovery of a few ringed birds.

A merlin ringed at Dent, Yorkshire, on 2nd July 1938 was recovered at Dax, Landes, on 20th October 1938 ; just 110 days after it was ringed in Britain it was in the south-west of France. Another merlin, ringed at Hebden Bridge, Yorkshire, on 25th June 1944, was recovered at Rochefort, Charente Inférieure, on 30th March 1950, *i.e.* nearly six years after being ringed and probably on its way north again to breed.

[1] *Scottish Naturalist*, 1949 (1), p. 28.

Foreign-bred merlins come to Britain from more countries than one, as is shown by a merlin ringed in Sweden on 10th July 1929 recovered in Jersey, Channel Islands, on 21st January 1931. Professor Lönnberg [1] has shown from the recapture of ringed Swedish merlins that this little hawk migrates towards the south-west and many must pass by the British Isles which do not tarry on their way. Swedish-bred merlins have been found during the winter as far south as Spain.

A more regular source from which merlins reach these islands in the autumn is Iceland. That bird, *F. c. subaesalon*, can fortunately, when trapped and handled, be recognized by its wing measurements, but in addition some have been captured at Fair Isle bearing rings from Iceland. In Miss Baxter's and Miss Rintoul's *Birds of Scotland* two such records are quoted of merlins recovered which were ringed as nestlings in Iceland : one in Stirlingshire in October of the year when it was ringed, the other at Dumbarton in April three years after being ringed.

Iceland birds have also turned up in Ireland. One merlin ringed as young in Iceland in June 1932 was recovered in King's Co. (now Offaly) in the following December. Colonel Scroope in the recent *Birds of Ireland* (1954) assures us that there is very good evidence from the occurrence of long-winged birds at isolated islands and light-stations that the Iceland merlin enters Ireland in autumn. He states that a number of specimens in the National Museum, Dublin, can, without hesitation, be assigned to that race. Many of these Iceland merlins when they come south with the migrating Passerine birds are likely to pass near or through Fair Isle and it has been suggested by Mr. Kenneth Williamson that some of the merlins which harry the migrants may emanate from the Faëroe Islands although the very small breeding population in those islands is said by Doctor Salomonsen to be sedentary.

The authors of *The Birds of Scotland* have rightly drawn our attention to the definite passage of merlins which takes place on the east coast of Scotland in autumn as well as in the northern and western isles, the main movement taking place in September and October, occasionally as early as August, and to the return movement, chiefly in April and May, which is not so well marked. Some of these birds may be passage migrants which only touch the British Isles on their way to northern latitudes ; others may come to breed with us, having wintered further south.

As regards the local migrations of our own breeding merlins it has been suggested [2] that their movements are governed a good deal by those of the meadow pipit and that when the pipits leave the moors in autumn the merlins tend to go too. In all the big rushes of migratory birds in autumn merlins take part, visiting the places in considerable numbers where the small migrants are known to pass through. On occasion they

[1] *Proceedings of the VIIIth Internat. Orn. Congress* (1934), p. 610.
[2] *The Birds of Scotland*, by Evelyn Baxter and Leonora Rintoul.

work havoc among the migrants on the Isle of May in the Firth of Forth, just as they do further north on Fair Isle. When winter has set in merlins are visitors to many parts of Scotland where they do not breed and the same may be said of them elsewhere in the British Isles. If weather conditions remain favourable some adults keep to the moors throughout the cold months but in a hard season all leave the high ground. Doctor Blair, writing from County Durham, tells me that once autumn has set in in north-east England large numbers of merlins appear in the coastal districts. Some of these no doubt have been bred locally but many are evidently immigrants from Scandinavia and beyond. While the majority pass on after a brief visit, a few settle for the winter. One particularly hardy bird managed to survive the almost Arctic weather of early 1947 along the narrow stretch of beach between high water mark and the fringes of the snowdrifts, where it maintained itself in good condition by capturing the benumbed and starving redwings that had wandered from the nearby farms. In autumn and winter alike, merlins commonly take up their quarters on the outskirts of the coastal towns, and it is by no means exceptional to see them flying along the busiest streets in pursuit of sparrows and other finches.

BREEDING HABITS: Our resident merlins return to their nesting places earlier than those which may have gone overseas and even quite early in the year pairs may be seen in the act of courting. It is seldom, however, that matters have advanced to the extent witnessed by Mr. Stubbert [1] in the early days of March, for the merlin does not usually lay its eggs until the month of May. On this occasion a male and female merlin flew past the observer, keeping close and calling as if at the nest:

They landed on the branch of an oak tree and chased one another up and down the branch for about ten minutes, moving sideways with tails fanned and depressed. Sometimes they would jump up from the branch, fluttering together with wings partly raised like cocks fighting, then settle on the branch again and begin the hopping chase, first one chasing, then the other. After coition both birds sprang into the air and gave a magnificent aerial display lasting nearly an hour. They kept very close together, appearing almost touching, and flew straight up 500 to 600 feet, then, making a rapid turn simultaneously, swooped down at tremendous speed, one above the other, the male usually, but not always, on top. At the tree top level they turned again and repeated the performance.

Aerial displays on the part of merlins such as that described must be uncommon, for in the several seasons during which Professor Rowan studied the species so meticulously in Yorkshire and elsewhere he saw nothing of it. He went so far as to say that if there *are* any aerial courtship displays on the part of the male he failed to interpret them as such. Courtship feeding—or such it appeared—was witnessed in the middle of April and it was noted that from that time on the male will feed his mate, who

[1] *British Birds*, xxxvii, p. 17.

appears to do very little hunting for herself until the young are flying, though allowance must be made for the behaviour of different individuals. The feeding operation takes place at the nest, or what is ultimately to be the nest, and is frequently followed by sexual union.

The late E. W. Hendy wrote to me that only once had he seen any part of the courtship of the merlins. In early May he watched a pair flying around a patch of heather near an old nesting site. The jack uttered a note resembling *tchok* and the hen, besides a *kee-kee-kee* call, sometimes keened a curlew-like whistle. On one occasion coition was seen to take place on the top of a bare thorn tree, the jack swooping upon the hen after a chase when the latter had settled.

More than any of our birds of prey, except for the golden eagle in Scotland, the merlin is associated with our high fells, where it was once so much more numerous than it is at the present day. In almost any sort of wild country the little falcon may be encountered, but in spring the birds which have sought lower elevations in the winter return once again to the higher ground and there in the solitude of the moorlands they can breed undisturbed unless some mishap unhappily befalls them.

As a rule, with the possible exception of the birds on Exmoor, the merlin's nest is on the ground and is barely worthy of the name, for the eggs are laid on the earth in a scrape in the heather, or perhaps with a few heather stalks and some particles of moss doing duty for a nest. That is the normal situation for the eggs when the birds are nesting on the moorlands. More rarely a nest may be amongst bracken, the cup in the ground lined with any bracken debris that may chance to be there, in the same way as bits of heather may occur when the nest is in the more usual situation. Professor Rowan observed that during the early stages of incubation the birds amuse themselves by breaking off twigs from the heather within reach and adding them to the nest. In several cases he noticed small bits of bracken in a heather nest, but this only happened if a bracken patch chanced to be within a few feet. At other times again the nest of a hooded crow may be used, particularly one which has been built on the ground. Such a nest was found by the late W. E. Glegg in Shetland and photographs of the site and the very substantial nest appeared in the *Oologists' Record*.[1]

There are numerous records of merlins using the nests of other birds which have built in trees. Published instances are given by T. H. Nelson,[2] George Bolam,[3] Hugh Gladstone[4] and J. Walpole-Bond[5] in the standard works of which they are the authors, but it is to my friend, the late E. W. Hendy, that I am indebted for the following note of the habits of the merlin

---

[1] *Oologists' Record*, vii, 1927, pp. 6-11.
[2] *The Birds of Yorkshire.*
[3] *The Birds of Northumberland and the Eastern Borders.*
[4] *The Birds of Dumfriesshire.*
[5] *A History of Sussex Birds.*

on Exmoor which he wrote specially for this book from his long intimate association with birds in that locality :

Exmoor merlins, though they sometimes nest on the ground, more usually prefer to bring up their families in disused tree nests of other species. In twenty years I have found only four nests on the ground and at least double that number in old tree nests. These include those of magpie, carrion crow, raven and buzzard. All the tree nests which I have seen have been situated in trees growing in deep, secluded coombes where they are quite invisible against the surrounding moorland. These nests have been in mountain ash, thorn and beech.

This tree-nesting habit may have originated on Exmoor in order to obtain security from ground-haunting enemies or from the danger of eggs being destroyed by wandering deer or ponies. . . . On the other hand a tree nest, at any rate up to the end of May, would be more visible to human enemies, for until about that date moorland trees are usually leafless. But when the leaves are out the concealment afforded by beech or mountain ash is admirable ; in fact, the nest is often invisible even when one is standing immediately below it. The tree-nesting habit would in time produce a strain of birds with a preference for such a situation, and the custom—even though an " acquired character ", would become almost universal with their descendants.

Most authorities state that the merlin makes no real nest. The *Handbook of British Birds*, vol. iii, p. 32, says : " Generally eggs are laid on ground in a scratching among heather or with apology for a nest in shape of a few heather stalks, bits of moss and lining of bents." In my experience this is not strictly accurate, at any rate as to Exmoor merlins. The wool lining of an old ravens' tree nest which merlins used in 1938 had entirely disintegrated, and there was a distinct subsidiary nest of twigs, inside the ravens' structure, in which the merlin's eggs were laid. The same year another merlin's nest on the ground was not a mere scratching or a fortuitous collection of twigs, but a definite nest composed of fine heather bents. On at least two other occasions I have found merlins breeding in old nests of carrion crow or raven from which the wool lining had not disappeared. In both cases the eggs were laid on the original wool lining and no fresh subsidiary nest had been constructed.[1]

The truth probably is that the merlin selects the most convenient situation in which to deposit its eggs, wherever it may be, regardless of other considerations. Usually the nesting place is situated in picturesque surroundings, while most of the moorland nests are hidden away in lonely places which can be reached only after a scramble. Cliff nests are not entirely unknown and one such site in Iceland is described by the late Ernest Vesey in his book *In Search of the Gyr-Falcon*. He had followed a little burn for a short way up into the fells, when after about a mile the narrow glen opened out into the most charming miniature amphitheatre, only some three or four hundred yards across and entirely enclosed by low crags or steep hills, for the burn and a tributary came in through deep clefts, almost gorges, and left by an abrupt turn about the shoulder of the hill. The floor and sides of the hollow were well clothed with the usual

[1] *The Field*, clxxxiv, 1944, p. 482.

hill grasses and plants and an abundance of dwarf birch just springing into leaf. A pair of merlins had adopted this sanctuary for their own. The nest was eventually located on the edge of a sheltered ledge in a small crag —a typical gyr-falcon site—and in fact was more difficult to reach than some of the gyr-falcons' eyries to which he had climbed. Five eggs had already been laid.

One more unusual nesting site of the merlin remains to be described. It was found in south Glamorganshire in Wales by Geoffrey Ingram.[1] The birds had chosen to nest on the summit of a sand-hill which was closely covered with the usual coarse grass. " The nest was a well-constructed one, quite different from the rough scratch which is usually thought good enough when the birds breed among typical surroundings." It was made of dead grass and contained five eggs on 21st May. Two other nests were found in this area on other occasions ; both were similarly constructed and similarly placed, screened from view by long grass but well made. The site, sand-hills bordering the seashore and rising to well over fifty feet in height, is surely peculiar to Wales, for a similar nest has been reported from the sand-dunes near Tenby in Pembrokeshire.

No account of the merlin's nesting habits would be complete without reference to the detailed work of Professor W. Rowan, who for several seasons made the merlin his special study.[2] Rowan chose a locality in Yorkshire—the Barden and Embsay moors near Skipton—upon which to make his observations. These moors form a single stretch of moorland nearly twenty miles square in area. The vegetation is typical of such moorland, the predominating plant being ling, relieved in the damper parts by patches of bog-moss and various coarse grasses. Bell heather occurs in limited quantities, while extensive stretches of bracken and less frequent ones of bilberry are also found. The area comprises a number of well-marked elevations and a number of streams with a north to south flow.

Very old heather was preferred by the Yorkshire merlins to any other nesting site and the distribution of the birds is to a great extent bound up with the heather-burning. If this is left until the ling has passed its prime (eight to ten years' growth) the chance of bracken encroaching on the cleared ground is very great and this in turn affects the distribution of the merlin.

Professor Rowan examined a large number of eyries and was struck by certain similarities which never seemed to be wanting : the most characteristic is the view obtained from the nest. There is the almost invariable valley to one side, looking down which one gets an expansive view of rolling moorland and distant fells. On looking upstream one generally finds one is near the head of the valley, with the view limited by a

[1] *British Birds*, xiii, pp. 202-206.
[2] *British Birds*, xv, 1921-1922, pp. 122-129, 194-202, 222-231 and 246-253.

hilltop close at hand. The proximity of a path, or more occasionally a fence or stone wall, appears to be an essential. Above the nest (not below it) there will be as a rule a well-" chalked " boulder or two, sometimes a very large number of them, while on the opposite side of the valley, frequently below the level of the eyrie, will be some more whitewashed boulders used as perches [1] by the merlins. The eggs themselves will in most cases be found in very old heather, but very exceptionally the eggs may be laid among bracken, bracken which has replaced ling after the latter has been burnt off and where a merlin's eyrie had been situated before the spread of the bracken. The above are the conditions which Professor Rowan found to constitute the site of a merlin's typical eyrie. The rule that the eyrie should be within a few feet of the edge of the heather holding it, he has never known to be broken, nor has the expansive view ever been absent from the scene. Most remarkable of all perhaps is his statement that a valley devoid of a path, stone wall or fence, however desirable in other respects, is not used. The area described had almost countless sites which provided all the necessary conditions but only four pairs of merlins were ever known in a single season, the law of territory probably limiting the numbers. A fact of some significance was that the merlins showed an extraordinary preference for a small minority of sites.

Professor Rowan was himself convinced that some localities, apart from actual nesting sites, must hold a special attraction for the merlin, else how does it come about that on a moor where scarcely a single young bird was successfully reared and not one of the old birds survived to go south in winter, the stock of merlins continued, despite almost complete annual extermination ? He asks, where does the unfailing supply of merlins come from ? and suggests that this—and other favoured areas—is drawing from others in which the species is disappearing.

Although it is now almost twenty-five years since Professor Rowan published the results of his observations there is no reason to believe that conditions have changed very much since he wrote. Moors are less strictly keepered than formerly and the Yorkshire moors are no exception. Much of what he wrote about the Yorkshire merlins is true of other districts in Wales and Scotland, and though we must allow for local variation in habits, as for instance on Exmoor, there are certain rules for the behaviour of the merlin which are characteristic of the species wherever it may be found.

The average time of arrival of the merlins on the Yorkshire moors is the middle of April, though in some years it is considerably earlier. To Professor Rowan it appeared that they spent some time in the selection of a site, but they will frequent the spot they finally choose off and on from their arrival until egg laying, although during this period they may be away for days together. On the moors of Exmoor E. W. Hendy

[1] Probably plucking stations as we should now consider them, of which Professor Rowan makes no mention.

has known the merlins to frequent the area in which they subsequently breed as early as February and March. The first egg is sometimes laid in the first week of May, though a more usual date is 11th or 12th May. Laying may even be postponed until as late as 21st May. In comparison with dates of laying in Wales and in Scotland the dates quoted by Mr. Hendy are all early. In south Glamorgan Geoffrey Ingram found a full clutch of five on 21st May and in another year a nest with four eggs on 1st June. In Ayrshire Richard Paton found that the merlins arrived back on the moor on 29th April and eggs were not laid until the fourth week of May. In Shetland clutches were found by Venables between 15th May and 20th June, those later in June being on point of hatching (*Birds and Mammals of Shetland*, p. 196). It was the opinion of F. C. R. Jourdain, who had a great many records to assist him, that most merlins on the mainland of Britain have laid by the last week of May, exceptionally early in June.

In the *Catalogue of Birds' Eggs in the British Museum* the merlin's eggs are said to be of the same character as those of the peregrine and hobby, descriptions of which are given in this work. Jourdain, however, describes them as being in most cases thickly and uniformly marked with fine stippling of dark brown, sometimes quite purplish; occasionally rich red-brown or tawny showing the white ground, and in rare cases almost unmarked. He gives the average of 100 British-taken eggs as $39 \cdot 95 \times 31 \cdot 28$ mm. Max. $42 \cdot 4 \times 32$ and $41 \cdot 4 \times 33 \cdot 8$. Min. $37 \times 29 \cdot 1$ and $40 \cdot 3 \times 29$ mm.

The eggs are laid every second day and incubation lasts from twenty-eight to thirty-two days. E. W. Hendy found the period on Exmoor to be about thirty days. Professor Rowan's view that incubation does not begin until the clutch is completed is not invariable. Sometimes incubation begins before the clutch is complete, as Mr. Hendy proved by finding a laying of two warm eggs which were later increased to four. The eggs are incubated by both sexes but principally by the hen. The male when brooding is much more shy than his mate, who often does not quit the nest until almost touched. The female takes by far the greater share of bringing up the family and Rowan believed that she alone fed the young, but as E. R. Paton discovered a male merlin in the act and supported his statement [1] with photographic evidence, we must allow that on rare occasions both sexes take part. Should the female be killed, then the male takes the full responsibility until the young have flown.

When the young are hatched the male merlin does most of the hunting. *The Handbook of British Birds* states that the female leaves the nest to take the food from the plucking place and *occasionally* by the pass, but in Mr. Hendy's experience the pass to the hen in the air is quite as commonly employed as the other method; in fact, with one breeding pair he had under

[1] *British Birds*, xv, p. 276.

PLATE 12

KESTREL (Adult Male)

Falco tinnunculus tinnunculus Linnaeus

PLATE 12

KESTREL (Adult Male)

Falco tinnunculus tinnunculus Linnaeus

observation, this was the usual method adopted. Mr. Hendy adds that it does not appear to be generally known that the male also passes prey in the air to the eyasses when they are on the wing, but he has witnessed the performance himself.

The fledging period was found by Hendy to last roughly twenty-five days, but, as he emphasizes, almost invariably one of the eyasses is a weakling and does not attempt flight until after the rest of the brood have been on the wing for a day or two.

Readers who desire a detailed account of the rearing of the young merlins should consult Professor Rowan's article in *British Birds* magazine, xv, pp. 222-231 and 246-253.

REFERENCES: Original Descriptions. *Falco aesalon* Tunstall, Orn. Brit., 1771, p. 1: type locality France. *Falco subaesalon* Brehm, Ornis, iii, 1827, p. 9: " Patria Islandia, hieme in Germaniam migrant ". Restricted type locality Iceland. *Falco columbarius* Linnaeus, Syst. Nat., 10th ed., 1758, p. 90: Carolina, U.S.A.

KESTREL PLATE 12

Falco tinnunculus tinnunculus Linnaeus

A Resident, also Bird of Passage and Winter Visitor

IDENTIFICATION: The adult male and female kestrel differ very much in appearance. The former is the smaller of the two and much more handsome, the crown, nape and sides of the neck being bluish-grey and the cere and rim round the eye lemon-yellow; there is a black moustachial streak on each side of the throat. The scapulars, mantle and back are bright reddish-chestnut spotted with black; the rump and tail are blue-grey like the head but even bluer; the tail has a terminal broad black band and narrow white tip. The flight feathers are mainly blackish. A white chin merges into buff underparts, boldly streaked and spotted with black. Very noticeable is the bright eye, brown in colour; the bill is bluish-horn and the legs and feet are yellow.

The female kestrel is altogether duller and lacks the blue-grey head and tail of her consort. Crown and nape are pale chestnut streaked with dark brown. The moustachial streak is only faintly indicated. Mantle and scapulars are reddish chestnut barred with blackish brown, the back similar but the barring less pronounced. The tail is pale chestnut, rather closely barred with brownish black and broadly banded subterminally; usually a greyish tinge of varying intensity is visible on the tail feathers. The underparts are buff, varying in intensity individually, the whole fairly closely streaked with brownish-black. Soft parts are coloured as in the male.

The wings are fairly long and pointed in the kestrel and a characteristic of the species is its habit of hovering, and its power to remain poised in the air in a high wind.   On the ground it has been seen to run with a fast loping gait with the body held in a crouching attitude.[1]

Juvenile examples of both sexes are very like the female when adult. First-winter examples show a mixture of plumage and not until after the third moult is the fully adult plumage acquired, when the kestrel is between two and three years old, the moult being very gradual.   Young birds may usually be distinguished by their darker appearance on the upperparts and their more heavily streaked underparts, and in the male by the absence of the clear blue-grey crown.

For distinctions between this and the lesser kestrel see under that bird.

LOCAL DISTRIBUTION :   This is by far the most numerous and most widely spread of the *Falconidae* in Britain.   Indeed there are few who do not know the bird by sight for it is to be found in every county from the northern isles to the English Channel and is as common in Scotland and its many islands as it is in England, where it is found throughout the country.   It is resident everywhere in Ireland and while described as Ireland's " commonest bird of prey ", it cannot be termed numerous anywhere, which is very surprising.   Its status in Scotland needs defining more carefully, for while in summer it is widespread, there is a considerable movement southwards in winter.   In the recently issued *Birds of Scotland*, the authors state that the kestrel is resident in southern Scotland up to the line of the Grampians, north of which it is more of a summer visitor, the higher parts of its range being deserted and many birds leaving for the winter.

To Shetland the kestrel is *only* a passage migrant, the islands being devoid of kestrels during the winter months.   If kestrels are seen in the Shetland Isles after autumn we may be fairly certain that they have come in from further north and are not our breeding stock.   According to L. S. V. and U. M. Venables (1955) evidence points to the kestrel being extinct as a breeding species in that group of islands.   In Saxby's time, 1859-1871, they bred regularly.

It is interesting to find that the kestrel population of southern Scotland is larger in winter than in summer and the same must apply to England to an even greater extent, for we then have our resident population augmented by visitors from the Continent.

In the Orkney Islands a number of pairs were found on several islands —South Ronaldsay, Hoy, Mainland, Shapinsay, Rousay, Sanday and Eday—by Doctor David Lack when he made his survey of the breeding birds of the Orkneys in 1941, and it doubtless breeds on most of the islands. To what extent, if any, the kestrel remains in Orkney over the winter Doctor Lack does not specify, but Harvie-Brown and Buckley (1891) considered that it remained there the whole year round.

[1] Colonel Scroope in *The Birds of Ireland*, 1953, p. 120.

DISTRIBUTION ABROAD : We find the kestrel throughout the whole of Europe and also in North Africa north of the Sahara as far east as Tripoli. It ranges north to 70° in Scandinavia and to 63° in Russia, and eastward to western Siberia, the Altai range of mountains and Mongolia. It inhabits most of the Mediterranean islands and in the eastern Mediterranean area it occurs in Palestine, Syria, Iraq, Persia and Transcaspia. A survey of the status of the kestrel in the Mediterranean islands made by Admiral Lynes when serving in his younger days in that station convinced him that the birds were resident in most of the islands which he visited from Sicily and Malta to Cyprus, and we know from other sources that kestrels are permanent inhabitants of Corsica, Sardinia and the Balearic Islands.

In the non-breeding season the European kestrel is to be found in tropical Africa, reaching Tanganyika Territory on the east coast and Nigeria on the west. It also occurs then in Arabia and India.

Considering how sedentary the kestrel is over much of its wide range, it is rather astonishing to find that it reaches tropical Africa so regularly and in such numbers. Presumably these are mainly birds which are annually forced to leave the higher latitudes when the rigour of winter sets in, and it is quite possible that the birds which have their breeding range farthest north are those which proceed farthest south. Over much of central Europe, and almost entirely in Mediterranean countries, the kestrel is believed to be on the whole non-migratory.

The species has not been split into races in Europe but oddly enough two races occur in the Canary Islands : *canariensis* in the western islands of the group, *dacotiae* in the eastern islands. Still another race, *neglectus*, inhabits the Cape Verde Archipelago. In tropical Africa we have several resident subspecies ; *F. t. rufuscens* restricted in the breeding season to the higher ground of the west coast is the darkest of these, and there are other representative forms in East and South Africa. Only by collecting is it possible to distinguish the winter visitors from the residents in Africa where both occur, unless seen on passage through a given area. There is a well-known race inhabiting Egypt, *F. t. rupicolaeformis* ; in that country the European bird is of uncertain status, very few having been obtained. On the other hand, *F. t. tinnunculus* is a plentiful bird of passage through Cyprus, where I saw many during the spring migration of 1954. A number of Asiatic races of the kestrel have been described. One particularly interesting subspecies occurring in the south-west corner of Arabia, named *F. t. buryi*, is a small and dark race, the female of which has a dark slate tail. It will be apparent from this brief survey of the better-known subspecies how widely in the Old World the kestrel is spread.

That more races have not been recognized in Europe is due no doubt to the great individual variation in the tone of plumage in specimens from within a single geographical area. I am still puzzling as to the identity of two kestrels which we met with this year (1954) in Cyprus on 22nd March.

Compared with the European kestrels actually perched on the same tele-graph wire, this pair were distinctly smaller in size and more mealy sand-colour in plumage, leading one to suppose that they were of desert origin. But no description of any known kestrel could possibly apply to them. The pair remained together and did not join the common kestrels when the latter went on their way. Their spotted backs and wing-coverts pre-cluded their being *Falco naumanni*.

HABITS : Because the kestrel is to be encountered so frequently, not only in our own islands but also abroad, it is better known than most hawks by the general public. Moreover, it has an attractive way of hanging motionless in mid-air over a particular spot for quite an appreciable time, and thus attracts the notice of passers-by who marvel that any bird can remain almost stationary when half a gale is blowing, as frequently is the case. When thus hovering with tail widely expanded and head inclined downwards on the look-out for any moving prey below, the wings are beaten fast for a few seconds and then held rigid, when perhaps the bird will glide a few paces before poising once again. Now and then it will partly close its wings and dive into the grass but it does not often appear with a mouse in its talons. More often than not it has seen a beetle or some other insect which on capture is quickly transferred to the bill and as rapidly devoured.

It is the opinion of many who chance to see it so engaged that it is pouncing on some small bird, but that is very rarely the case in Britain, where to a very great extent our local kestrels live upon insects and mice. From the agricultural point of view it is not only harmless but distinctly beneficial. Seton Gordon when writing of the hill birds of Scotland, on which there is no greater authority, quoted a statement, evidently based on reliable evidence, that a single kestrel remaining in a district for 210 days would be the means of destroying no less than 10,395 mice. If that has not earned for it the gratitude of the farming community it is high time that it did so.

Unfortunately, in game-rearing areas any bird inimical to the rearing of game chicks is ruthlessly destroyed, without taking into con-sideration the good that the bird may do in other directions. That kestrels are a danger to grouse or partridge chicks must be acknowledged but in no case is it such a menace to game preserves as the sparrow-hawk, whose prowess in that respect cannot bear investigating. Even Mr. Seton Gordon admits that there is a good deal to be said on the keeper's side, and much as we delight in most of its ways it is no use whitewashing the kestrel's character entirely. That excellent naturalist, the late T. A. Coward, wrote in his book with a similar title to mine that it is mere sentimentalism to say that the kestrel never takes larger game than mice and beetles. He was able to add, however, that he had examined many pellets of the kestrel without finding a single bird bone, and while admitting that it may snatch up an occasional pheasant chick, he rightly points out that the real attraction to the rearing-field is the host of mice which glean the scattered grain.

I have remarked above that small Passerine birds afford only a small part of a kestrel's diet in Britain, where mice and other more easily captured prey exist in abundance. Grasshoppers, beetles and the caterpillars of lepidoptera are devoured in vast numbers and it is not unusual to see a kestrel hawking for insects, especially cockchafers, when these objectionable creatures are on the wing. Reliable instances of its capturing birds in this country are not as common as one might think, but that it does so when hungry or a good opportunity offers there can be no doubt. On three separate occasions T. A. Coward knew of a kestrel killing a full grown starling. Another interesting case is reported by Mr. Clifford Oakes [1] of a kestrel attacking and catching a tree creeper on the bole of a tree, while a correspondent writing to the *Naturalist* [2] records a kestrel capturing and devouring bats. It cannot be often that a kestrel is seen following a plough, but such an instance is recorded in *British Birds*,[3] where a plough was closely attended by a kestrel during the greater part of the day near a village in Nottinghamshire. From time to time the plough turned up spherical nests of field mice and the bird, being only a few feet behind, was on many occasions successful in capturing the displaced rodent, which was promptly carried to a nearby post and devoured, after which the kestrel resumed its methodical following of the plough.

My own experience in Europe and North Africa is that kestrels are much more daring, not to say pugnacious, in foreign lands than they are with us and that their feeding habits are much less conservative. Birds and reptiles form a much larger part in the diet sheet, and these observations are reinforced by those of other naturalists who have studied the kestrel abroad. Thus Captain Munn noted that in the Balearic Islands it was a much bolder and more aggressive bird than in some other countries and preyed largely on small birds. He observed one capture a whitethroat and saw another caught in a trap with a goldfinch as a decoy. He has seen them in those islands worrying kites and vultures and stooping repeatedly at peregrines, one of which was actually struck as it passed too close to the kestrel's nest. The late Harry Witherby has described how in the Sierra de Gredos, central Spain, he watched a golden eagle on 8th June being " mobbed " by a cock kestrel. The kestrel swooped at the eagle's head repeatedly and the eagle kept flinching ; once when the kestrel touched it the eagle half turned over in the air and dropped a little. Hobbies and kestrels sometimes join forces to attack buzzards and booted eagles, to both of which the kestrel has a rooted objection. Ravens too arouse its ire, as I noted with interest this spring (1954) in Cyprus when witnessing a

[1] *Bird Notes and News*, 1943, p. 88.
[2] R. J. Flintoff, *Naturalist*, London, 1931, p. 286.
[3] J. Staton, *British Birds*, xxxvi, p. 245.

battle royal between a raven and a kestrel which took place far over the sea. The kestrel dived again and again at the raven, stooping with closed wings from a considerable height but never seeming to do much harm to its more clumsy adversary.

That kestrels will make life a misery and danger for migrating Passerine birds my wife and I had an opportunity of witnessing this year when returning home on a cargo boat in the Mediterranean. On 9th May migration was in full swing in the Ionian Sea and some twenty different species were identified, many taking refuge on the ship, though the sea was calm and the weather glorious. Our position was between Greece and the Straits of Messina when two female kestrels took up their stance high up on a mast from which they had a clear view of what was happening below. Both kestrels were very much alert, and when a tired garden warbler fluttered out from its hiding place one of the kestrels stooped upon it like lightning but just missed it, returning at once to its look-out post fifty feet above the deck with all its feathers awry with anger. Again the warbler ventured on to the deck, this time much nearer where we were standing. Suddenly there was a whir of wings and the kestrel pounced again, this time missing by inches and actually touching the deck. My wife and I were at the time talking to two sailors and the kestrel made its pounce as the terrified garden warbler was within a yard or two of our feet. Turtle doves which were on the ship all day were not molested by the kestrels, which kept their murderous attentions for the smaller and more exhausted of the Passeres.

In Grand Canary, where mice are scarce, I used to watch the kestrels dropping on lizards, which abound in all the Canary Islands, and G. L. Bates had a similar experience in Arabia. I have been interested to note that skulls of lizards and chameleons were found amongst other remnants in kestrels' nests in Palestine when Mr. P. H. T. Hartley [1] was analysing the remnants of prey and pellets below a kestrel's nest near Gaza some years ago. The examination of the debris from two nests showed that the diet of kestrels in southern Palestine differed markedly from that of birds in north-west Europe in the great bulk of reptilian and insect foods eaten ; there were relatively few birds and mammals were of scant importance, the only mammalian remains being the hind foot of a gerbil ! When we compare this with the analysis made by W. E. Collinge of food eaten in Britain the difference is striking. The result of eighty stomachs examined showed 64·5 per cent. mice and voles, 8·5 per cent. small birds, 6 per cent. nestlings, 16·5 per cent. injurious insects, 2·5 per cent. earthworms and 1 per cent. frogs to have been consumed. Clearly in the British Isles mammals are the principal food.

That on rare occasions a kestrel will attack a snake is recorded by Colonel Meinertzhagen, a male kestrel having been found dead in Egypt

[1] " The Food of the Kestrel in Palestine ", *Ibis*, 1946, pp. 241-242.

with a dead snake coiled round its neck.   The snake's coils were still taut round the kestrel's neck, causing strangulation, and the talons of the kestrel were firmly embedded in the snake's neck.   An Egyptian kestrel has also been seen to take a frog.

Not only abroad but also in the British Isles the kestrel has an astonishingly varied habitat.   It will appear as much at home in the vicinity of a town, attracted no doubt by an abundance of mice and sparrows, as it is hovering over our bramble-covered cliffs by the sea or poised over the heather-clad moors in some Highland glen.   The local name " windhover " is applied to the bird in many parts of Britain and under that title, given to it with good reason, it figures in several of the older bird books.   Kestrels are commonly met with in very desolate regions as well as in fertile country. In Morocco, Algeria and Tunisia I have met with the common kestrel in great numbers wherever my travels have taken me.   It is no uncommon sight to see half a dozen or more in sight at once hovering over the vast cultivated plains, or maybe perched on the telegraph poles which are so often a feature of the landscape.   When crossing the arid desert south of the Great Atlas range, then capped with snow in early March, we constantly saw wintering kestrels all the way from Ouarzazate to Tinerhir. Later, when journeying south from Colomb Béchar, we were to meet with them as far as Taghit on the edge of the Grand Erg Occidentale, but not in the oasis itself, which was curious, as in my experience kestrels are particularly fond of palm trees and further north will regularly nest in the palm fronds which afford them welcome shade and shelter from dust storms.

Kestrels occur at all elevations and we were not surprised to see them high up in the Great Atlas near where the pass of Tizi N'Test crosses that great mountain chain at 6400 feet.   We wondered what the birds could find to eat in these desolate mountains, for even small birds seemed scarce at the time of year we happened to be there.   These kestrels in the Great Atlas were as likely as not residents in the mountains, as there are many sheltered valleys and ideal breeding places where food would be abundant later in the year.   South of the Sahara and Libyan Deserts the kestrel is a migrant only, and there it may be encountered at all altitudes during its winter sojourn in the tropics.   R. E. Moreau has recorded [1] that in Tanganyika the European kestrel winters throughout the country at all elevations up to at least 6000 feet, while in the highlands of Abyssinia R. E. Cheesman collected specimens at 9000 feet, at Dabat, on 21st October. [2]

MIGRATIONS :   Towards the end of July and during August the kestrels which have remained in the northern isles during the early summer begin to take their departure and the movement southwards is continued by those birds which have bred on the higher ground in the northern half of Scotland.

[1] *Tanganyika Notes and Records*, 1937, reprint, p. 23.
[2] *Ibis*, 1935, p. 181.

This has already been indicated in the paragraph in which I have discussed the kestrel's distribution in the British Isles. Even in the southern counties of Scotland this urge to wander south is exhibited, and though the kestrel population in the south of Scotland is larger in winter than it is in summer, yet all the birds which have been bred there do not remain. Young kestrels bred in southern Scotland have been recovered in England as far south as Sussex, and movements in the reverse direction are also recorded, as for instance the kestrel (mentioned in *The Birds of Scotland*) which was ringed in Northumberland on 27th May 1945 and recovered at Fort William, Inverness-shire, in January 1946. Sir Landsborough Thomson has drawn attention to this record, adding the information (omitted by Miss Baxter and Miss Rintoul) that another member *of the same brood* was recovered in Surrey !

In the recently published *Birds of Ireland* Colonel Scroope writes of the kestrel in that country that some migration movement in winter has been noted, as numbers are then reduced in parts of Ulster and Leinster. On two occasions both in spring and autumn specimens have been obtained at lighthouses. A kestrel ringed in northern England as a nestling was recovered in Wexford, south-east Ireland, in the following April.

In addition to considerable movement within the confines of the British Isles, Continental migrants arrive in the northern isles in the autumn and, as Miss Baxter and Miss Rintoul have shown, this movement is to be witnessed all down the east coast of Scotland and to a lesser extent in the Western Isles. The main passage takes place in September and October but early passage migrants have been observed in August and late ones in November. At that season it is a regular migrant to the Isle of May, where it no doubt harries the smaller birds which daily cross the Firth of Forth on their journey south.

The passage of birds down the east coast of England can now be studied at the bird observatories at Spurn Head and at Gibraltar Point, Lincolnshire, and a well-marked passage of kestrels to the south-west has been noted during the early days of October, with others later in the month. Claud Ticehurst wrote in his history of the birds of Suffolk that in that county the kestrel is a very marked migrant on the coast and considerable numbers arrive in the autumn from overseas. On a certain 4th of September he had no less than eight kestrels brought to him alive which had been captured on fishing boats at sea off Lowestoft, and another bird was taken in August forty miles out to sea. Every September Ticehurst noticed increased numbers on the coast, which was suggestive of immigrants, and occasionally saw birds coasting south. That these birds had come from across the sea seems more than probable. It is unfortunate that so few kestrels which have been ringed abroad have been captured in Britain, but two records available are of interest as showing the probable country of origin of some of these overseas visitors :

A kestrel ringed in Norway on 30.9.46 was recovered at Bedford on 19.12.46.

A kestrel ringed in Siberia on 5.7.36 was recovered in Yorkshire on 14.11.37.

These may of course have been genuine *winter* visitors to Britain and not passage migrants.

The list of kestrels which have been ringed in Great Britain or the Channel Islands and have been recovered overseas is more satisfactory. From the dates it seems that all were ringed as young with one exception, and that was a fully grown bird. The recoveries are as follows :

Ringed		*Recovered*	
Eton, Bucks	. . . 22.6.28	Calvados, France . .	—.3.29
Thursby, Surrey	. . . 15.6.40	Cortes, Navarra, Spain	.14.12.40
Clapham, Beds	. . . 19.7.47	Hay, Liège, Belgium .	. —.5.48
Peel, Isle of Man	. . 22.6.49	St. Jean de Luz, France	. 25.9.49
Woburn, Beds	. . . 21.6.50 (immature)	Neuvy-Pailloux, Indre, France	27.12.50
Fair Isle, Shetland	. . 26.8.50 (full grown)	Jouy en Pitniverais, Loiret	29.12.50
Burnley, Lancs	. . . 2.7.49	Västergotland, Sweden	. 24.1.51
Sunninghill, Berks	. . 9.7.50	Condé sur l'Escaut Nord, France . . .	. 19.2.51
Lancashire	. . . 2.7.52	Ostend, Belgium . .	.13.10.52
Goxhill, Lincs	. . . 22.6.47	Breteuil, Eure, France	. 8.1.53
Jersey, Channel Islands	. 13.7.52	Maine et Loire, France .	. 4.7.52

This short list contains one remarkable record, the recovery from a more northern country (Sweden) of a bird ringed in Lancashire some eighteen months earlier. It is useless to speculate what that bird was doing in Scandinavia at the end of January. According to the rules it should not have been there ; perhaps the same remark applies to the immigrant from Siberia which arrived in Yorkshire. The number of recoveries in France and Spain does, however, point to these countries being the principal winter quarters of British-bred kestrels which have elected to go south. So far there have been no returns from south of the Mediterranean. As already indicated, there is a large population of kestrels which breeds in North Africa and some of these kestrels—by no means all—appear to remain in their breeding area all the winter. Having spent several winters and the early spring months in Tunisia, Algeria and Morocco for the express purpose of studying the bird-life, I can write from personal experience of the kestrels in these countries. In Tunisia the kestrel is very abundant and, as my old friend Joseph Whitaker wrote in his delightful book,[1] the species is also migratory to a certain extent there, its numbers being considerably augmented during the periods of passage. When

[1] *Birds of Tunisia*, vol. ii, p. 17.

collecting in that country in 1925 for the British Museum we found them far from common early in the year on the plains, though a number had congregated in the ruins of the Roman amphitheatre at El Djem which we visited on 6th February. It was not until April had come in that we noticed any real influx of the birds and on 14th April we encountered migrants from the south. They were passing through Feriana, sometimes in little bands of a dozen together, and must have crossed a tremendous stretch of desert on their way north. In Morocco, where the kestrel is relatively more numerous than I have ever seen it elsewhere, it breeds in great numbers and many must winter in this latitude, for they were common around Marrakech and the surrounding plains on 21st February and we were to see them south of the Great Atlas range every day between Ouarzazate and Skoura during the first week of March. It was not until the great migration north set in on 23rd to 26th March that we saw kestrels actually on passage and then a number were identified at Tangier heading over the Straits towards Spain in company with black kites and snake eagles.

On the Spanish side of the Straits Colonel A. J. S. Tuke [1] has noted how considerably the resident kestrel population is augmented by migrants from North Africa, and thus we are able together to substantiate Favier's statement,[2] upon which Doctor Hartert threw some doubt at the time, that there is a regular trans-Mediterranean passage. I have had no opportunity to verify the autumn migration across the Straits of Gibraltar but we have no reason to doubt that it takes place. From many reports which I received at the British Museum when preparing my *Birds of Tropical West Africa* it was apparent that kestrels from Europe, and perhaps from North Africa also, arrived in Gambia and on the Guinea Coast early in October and soon spread all over the country. I believe that many must spend the winter months in the French Sudan and French Niger and it is interesting to recall that when the late C. G. Bird was exploring in the Rio de Oro he encountered common kestrels on their way north on 21st April and 1st May.

Fairly numerous as they are in winter in western tropical Africa, they are very much more so in the east of the continent and this I think can be explained by the fact that the whole kestrel population from north-east Europe and western Siberia must congregate in East Africa for the winter. I doubt very much if it will be the birds from central and southern Europe which cross the eastern Mediterranean, Arabia and the Red Sea in such numbers to winter in tropical Africa but, as Meinertzhagen suggested many years ago, the kestrels from the far north. It was H. E. Dresser who observed that the great gathering of European kestrels in the southern

---

[1] *An Introduction to the Birds of Southern Spain and Gibraltar* by Lieut.-Colonel A. J. S. Tuke, 1953, p. 74.

[2] *Ornithology of the Straits of Gibraltar*, by Lieut.-Colonel Howard Irby, 1895, p. 195.

deserts of Siberia and central Asia seemed to point to that area as the starting place for the vast autumnal migration into India and north-east Africa.

Writing of the species in British Somaliland Sir Geoffrey Archer, one-time Governor of the Protectorate and a keen observer of bird-life, states : " In British Somaliland the European kestrels begin to arrive in the first half of October, stay throughout the cold weather and depart again in March. Though practically all my specimens were shot on the high plateau about Sheikh and elsewhere in the interior, it is probable that the majority of the kestrels seen in the winter months at the coast—hovering over the dunes or perched on some mound or hummock rising out of the hardpan close to the foreshore—belong to this race. . . . These gay winter visitors from the Palæarctic regions are just as common in the highlands of Abyssinia and on the Asmara Plateau of Eritrea as in northern Somaliland." It has been recorded by Count Zedlitz that the Asmara Plateau was crowded with kestrels in the months of January and February when he passed through that country nearly fifty years ago. Geoffrey Archer defined the winter range of the European kestrel on the eastern side of Africa as " the southern border of Tanganyika Territory, the north end of Lake Nyasa and the eastern shores of Lake Tanganyika, that is, to about 10° S. latitude ", and correctly observes that they never remain behind to breed in Africa south of the Sahara. " Their movement is purely migratory, coming and going with the seasons—and when they go they leave behind them the resident breeding forms."

Some idea of the numbers which pass through or remain in Abyssinia in the autumn and winter may be gathered from Major R. E. Cheesman's statement that while they are not seen in that country during the rains (June to September) they are very plentiful during the rest of the year and are met with *in thousands* following a swarm of locusts. He notes that they are often seen crossing the Red Sea, when they roost in the rigging of passing ships and catch the tired swallows and other migrants that seek shelter on the decks.

To Uganda and Kenya the kestrel comes in September and many stay until March but in some years an unusually large influx appears, sometimes in November, and then the majority pass on southwards or disperse over the country. Sir Frederick Jackson, whose name is still a household word in East Africa, noted that a large proportion of the birds which arrived early in November were immature, and this is of special interest when taken in conjunction with Admiral Lynes' experiences of the kestrel in Darfur, where he found that in the western basin kestrels of sorts [1] began to arrive early in October ; by mid-October they had become very

---

[1] Admiral Lynes was unable to be sure that many of these birds of passage were not lesser kestrels (*Falco naumanni*), but ten specimens collected were indistinguishable from *Falco tinnunculus tinnunculus*.

common, considerably in excess of winter proportions, which were not assumed until early November. By daily fluctuation of numbers during the foregoing period it was evident that many of the birds were passing on to winter further south. For the first three weeks of the immigration there were scarcely any adults. Not a single adult male appeared until 30th October.

In Kenya Doctor V. G. van Someren saw evidence of flocking before the spring move northwards at the end of March and beginning of April. Often several hundred birds together were observed. Colonel Meinertz-hagen noted many in winter quarters round Nanyuki and Naivasha in February and March, but before April is out all these visitors from Europe and Asia would be on their way north once more. March is the month when they depart from Somaliland.

There is evidently a passage of these kestrels through Arabia, for G. L. Bates collected a number around Jidda in spring and autumn, but whether their route is across the waterless desert, or, which is more likely, follows the shores of the Red Sea, I have no definite proof. In the year in which I am writing, 1954, my wife and I spent from February to May in Cyprus studying the migration through the island and on several occasions saw a strong passage of kestrels taking place. Cyprus lies a little far to the west of the route taken by a very large number of migrating birds, for the rush of birds through Cyprus, large as it is under favourable weather conditions, is as nothing compared with the numbers which from all accounts pass through Syria and Asia Minor. We formed the opinion that Cyprus lay just on the fringe of one of the principal migration routes to Europe. Kestrels are very common in the island but it was possible to distinguish those which were definitely on passage. On one day in particular, 16th April, when a terrific southerly gale was blowing, bringing with it a thick dust haze, we encountered a number of female kestrels laboriously battling with the wind, flying close to the ground and obviously migrating into the teeth of the gale. We were then on the coastal plain between Yialia and Polis and noticed that the kestrel was one of the few birds able to stand up to the conditions though many migrants were congregated on the plains that day. Blue-headed wagtails were picked up by the wind and scattered in all directions and a purple heron which had been standing near the shore was blown far inland over a pine forest, so helpless was it in the gale. Only the kestrels seemed to make progress.

We finally left for England on 6th May but again fell in with two kestrels on the 9th, when we were crossing the Ionian Sea. We thought the date late for migrating kestrels but I recollect that Professor Omer-Cooper obtained one on 8th May at Siwa Oasis just north of the Great Sand Sea which was assigned to the typical form and was believed to be on its way to Europe, and that Admiral Lynes encountered another in the Sierra Nevada at 7000 feet on 1st May which he believed to be on passage.

There is also the statement of van Someren that occasionally European kestrels have been known to remain in Kenya as late as 10th May.

We may hazard the guess that these late-staying kestrels in the tropics are those which will go furthest north to rear their young, for in southern and central Europe most kestrels are already breeding long before the date mentioned.

BREEDING HABITS : As B. W. Tucker has stated in the *Handbook*, the display of the kestrel is not especially marked and though several writers have described various aerial acrobatics and noted attempts at coition in the early days of April, nothing very spectacular has been witnessed unless it be by Professor Julian Huxley, who observed a male bird repeatedly beating up wind and then bearing down at headlong speed on the female while the latter sat on a bush, only to shoot up vertically just as he appeared to be about to strike her—repeating the display more than once.[1]

Kestrels make use of a variety of nesting sites, laying their eggs in scrapes on ledges or in cavities in cliffs, in holes in buildings, in ruins and church steeples, in the hollows of trees, in disused lime kilns or in the abandoned nests of certain birds, among which old nests of the raven, rook, carrion or hooded crow, magpie, buzzard, sparrow-hawk, heron and wood pigeon have been reported. Usually a flattened nest of magpie or crow is selected in preference to those of the other species cited. In none of these situations is any material used which is not already there. When earth is the foundation of the nest the scrape prepared for the eggs is an extremely neat affair some seven or eight inches across by about one and a half inches in depth, to quote Walpole-Bond's description. When a magpie's nest is selected the kestrel is said to remove the root finish. On very rare occasions a nest is found on the ground.

In the southern counties of England, judging by what takes place in Sussex and Cornwall, kestrels have laid full clutches by the middle of April and though some birds in the north of England lay later in the month it is not uncommon to find mid-April clutches also. In the Border counties the first week of May is a likely date on which to find eggs in normal seasons but that on occasion a bird will lay very much earlier is certain. Doctor Blair has drawn my attention to one remarkable instance when on 14th May 1953 a kestrel's nest in Northumberland held three young with feathers already showing. This, as he states, is a remarkably early date and the eggs must have been laid in March. Other nests examined on the same date contained almost fresh eggs. The preceding March had been exceptionally warm and mild. It is of interest that on that very same date some Spanish kestrels had not completed their clutches in Andalusia.

In the north of Scotland, especially on the high ground, the middle of May has arrived before full clutches can be expected.

[1] Quoted in *The Handbook of British Birds*, vol. iii, pp. 26-27.

We learn from Colonel Scroope that in Ireland eggs are sometimes laid in April but more often in early May in the south, usually in the first half of May in the north.

When building in sea cliffs, which is perhaps the most favoured situation, the bird has to compete for a cleft or hole with the ubiquitous jackdaw, and often a nest of kestrel and daw will be within a few feet of one another ; but ledges, with perhaps some sheltering ivy or other protection from the weather, are preferred to holes and it is not unusual to find several pairs of kestrels nesting in close proximity to one another. George Bolam in his *Birds of Northumberland and the Eastern Borders* drew attention to this when he wrote : " Birds of prey can seldom be said to nest in colonies, in this country at any rate, but such a description would scarcely be an exaggeration of the numbers of kestrels which nest in some of the low ranges of rock on the south Northumberland moors. At Crag Lough, on the line of the Roman Wall, a few miles east of Haltwhistle, I have seen nests within ten yards of one another, in one case seven nests within a lineal distance of about forty yards, and have had a little ' flock ' of thirteen of the birds hovering in the air above me, all calling at the same time."

That their fondness for nesting together is not restricted to kestrels in these islands will be apparent to anyone who has travelled much in North Africa, where in some of the old Roman ruins—of which there is no lack in Tunisia and Algeria—common kestrels literally swarm. In central Tunisia Whitaker found this hawk particularly numerous in the neighbourhood of Kasrin, where, he states, the rocky ground and precipitous cliffs bordering the oued of that name are admirably adapted to the nesting requirements of this and other rock-haunting species of birds. Later in the same account he observes that in its habits the kestrel is gregarious to a great extent and in Tunisia *is usually to be found nesting in colonies*. On the great plains of that country there stands alone the vast Roman amphitheatre to which I have already alluded, known as El Djem, and there, on the highest tiers of this well-preserved ruin, the kestrels, lesser kestrels and rock doves nest on the crumbling ledges, all in the closest proximity.

Kestrels will sometimes breed close alongside other birds of prey, such as the peregrine and the hobby, and then the two species appear to exist on tolerable terms with each other. I have already cited instances in this account when kestrel and hobby will join forces to drive away another adversary from the jointly owned territory in which they may have their respective eyries.

I have known kestrels in the Canary Islands nesting in the same date palm as several pairs of Spanish sparrows, and there again the noisy sparrows seemed to have come to an amicable arrangement, for they show no fear of the kestrels and the kestrels completely ignore the sparrows.

In Britain the eggs of the kestrel are usually four or five in number, occasionally six. There are records of abnormal clutches of seven, eight and nine having been found. We may expect exceptional clutches only at a time when food is in superabundance, as during the great vole plague on the Borders, when the birds are reported to have produced more than the normal single brood in the season, as well as laying large setts of eggs.

Incubation of the eggs is mainly by the hen but the cock bird will occasionally take a turn. Normally he is engaged in bringing food to the female while she broods the eggs. Incubation lasts from twenty-seven to thirty-two days (Jourdain). Both sexes bring food to the young once the eggs are hatched.

In the *Catalogue of Birds' Eggs in the British Museum* Oates observes that the eggs of the common kestrel resemble and are subject to the same variations in colour as the eggs of the peregrine and the hobby, exhibiting all the variations in the eggs of these falcons from a pale brownish-yellow example speckled with brown to one in which the markings are confluent masses of the richest reddish-brown.

Jourdain gives the ground colour as white, blotched, spotted and smeared with various shades of red-brown.

In a great many eggs of the kestrel which I have examined the white ground colour is completely obliterated by the rufous and sepia markings, the ground appearing to be a paler shade of rufous-chestnut. In shape the eggs are blunt ovals, sometimes nearly round. I have seen kestrel's eggs very like some eggs laid by the sparrow-hawk and others resembling those of the merlin but, as noted by Jourdain, kestrel's eggs are on the average much darker than those of the lesser kestrel or hobby and in this respect resemble normal eggs of the merlin more closely. Readers who possess Kirkman and Jourdain's *British Birds* will find on Plate 196 good pictures by the late H. Grönvold of all these eggs, which are very typical of the species.

It is very rare that species of the *Falconidae* lay unmarked eggs and it seems worth while therefore to draw attention to a completely white clutch of kestrel's eggs taken in Berkshire on 27th June 1923 by F. C. R. Jourdain, whose account of his find appears in *British Birds*, xvii, on p. 62. In the course of his remarks on this abnormal clutch Mr. Jourdain observes that he had several times met with instances in which one egg of a clutch of the various species of falcon was white or nearly so, but he was not aware that a full clutch of white eggs of any species had ever been met with previously. These eggs proved to be infertile, which may account for the late date when they were taken.

100 eggs of the kestrel average in measurement 39·73 × 31·77 mm. Max. 43·7 × 33·5 and 41·5 × 34·2. Min. 35·4 × 29·7 mm. (after Jourdain).

REFERENCES : Original Description. *Falco tinnunculus* Linnaeus, Syst. Nat., 10th ed., 1758, p. 90 : Europe, restricted type locality Sweden.

PLATE 13

LESSER KESTREL

Falco naumanni naumanni Fleischer

An Accidental Visitor

IDENTIFICATION : Such careful naturalists as Colonel Howard Irby and Admiral Lynes both maintained that certain identification of the common and lesser kestrel is only possible in the field at a very short range. There is, however, considerable difference in the character of each bird and those who are thoroughly familiar with the subject of this essay will be able to make a good guess at identification by something almost indefinable in the bird's flight which distinguishes it from *Falco tinnunculus*, quite apart from its unspotted mantle and scapulars, so much brighter in colour than in the common kestrel. It is when a bird is seen hovering over a plain that very great care is necessary to distinguish the two, for although the common kestrel unquestionably hovers much more than the lesser kestrel, the trait is common to both, and it is never safe to rely on that characteristic as peculiar to *Falco tinnunculus*.

When both birds are seen together, which may often be the case, it will be seen that the male lesser kestrel is slightly the smaller of the two. In build it is more delicate, as Bernard Tucker observed, and the females too can generally be distinguished by their proportions, though only when both species are in view at once. A male lesser kestrel measures about 12½ inches in total length.

As a general rule the lesser kestrel is more often seen in company with others of its kind, whereas the common kestrel is more solitary, but that trait cannot always be relied upon. I have constantly seen lesser kestrels which appeared to be alone and this year, 1954, in Cyprus was particularly struck by the number of solitary birds encountered—so different from my experiences in Morocco and southern Spain. In the latter countries it was more usual to encounter little parties of a dozen or more.

At the nesting places the lesser kestrels are nearly always more gregarious. Sometimes they simply swarm around old ruins or crumbling walls, breeding in the closest proximity, and then a colony of lesser kestrels can be recognized from afar. They are, moreover, usually the noisier of the two kestrels in their behaviour. Doctor Blair, who has recently been studying these falcons in Andalusia, considers that at the nest the identity of the bird should hardly remain long in question, since there it can be recognized by ear alone, its shrill chattering rising to a higher pitch than the note of the less vociferous common kestrel. It is, moreover, the most confiding of the European Raptores in the breeding season. A pair will flutter together upon the creviced wall which is later to hold their eggs, regardless of the interest they arouse among passers-by no more than ten yards away.

Some writers stress the lesser kestrel's habit of nesting in communities

PLATE 13

LESSER KESTREL

Falco naumanni naumanni Fleischer

Upper Figure	. .	Adult Male
Lower Figure	. .	Adult Female

PLATE 13

LESSER KESTREL

Falco naumanni naumanni Fleischer

Upper Figure . . . Adult Male
Lower Figure . . . Adult Female

as an aid to its recognition, and it is undoubtedly far more gregarious than any of the other European hawks, the red-footed falcon excepted. Still it must never be assumed that a colony of kestrels is necessarily of this species. One of many exceptions comes to mind with the recollection of an old watch-tower visited by Doctor Blair commanding the last frontier between Christian and Moorish rule in Spain. This ruin harbours a strong colony of common kestrels only, the birds nesting amongst the crumbling masonry like their smaller relatives, and as closely together.

When we come to describe in more detail the lesser kestrel's plumage it becomes obvious that the male is infinitely brighter in colour than the common kestrel. The crown is clear blue-grey, purer and clearer in colour than the crown of the larger bird, which is often washed with rufous and has darker feather-shafts. The lesser wing-coverts, mantle and scapulars are uniform bright chestnut-red, more of a brick-red in tone than in the kestrel and entirely unspotted, but the ground colour is not constant and various degrees of red can be found in members of the same colony. The primaries are dark brown, the inner secondaries mainly blue-grey. The throat is cream and the rest of the underparts pinkish-buff with dark drop-shaped spots on the sides of the breast and flanks. These spots are variable in number and may be entirely absent. The rump and upper tail-coverts are blue-grey. The tail is pure blue-grey with a broad black subterminal band and white tip ; the white tip is *also* present in the tail of *F. tinnunculus*, though perhaps it is more obvious in the fanned tail of *F. naumanni*. At very close quarters when at rest the lesser kestrel will be seen to have whitish claws ; the common kestrel has black ones.

The female is like the common kestrel and has the upperparts closely barred as in that bird ; moreover, the moustachial stripe is barely noticeable. The tail of the lesser kestrel is barred with blackish until near the tip, the subterminal band of black intervening between the barred area and the narrow white tip.

The immature is scarcely distinguishable from the adult female.

Although adult males can always be distinguished by their colour pattern alone, it is important to remember that *Falco naumanni* can invariably be distinguished in either sex or at any age from members of the *Falco tinnunculus* group by the wing-formula, for in the lesser kestrel the first primary equals the third in length or nearly so, whereas in the common kestrel the first primary equals the fourth or nearly so.

The cry of the lesser kestrel is a high-pitched, rattling *kik-kik-kik*, shriller than, and quite different from, the *klee-klee-klee* of our bird.

LOCAL DISTRIBUTION : The first lesser kestrel to be obtained in Britain was obtained in November 1867 near York and is preserved in the York Museum. Including that specimen, fifteen examples have been recorded, in the following sequence : Dover, Kent, May 1877 ; near Shankill, Dublin, Ireland, February 1891 ; Scilly Isles, 3rd March 1891 ; Thirsk,

Yorkshire, 12th April 1892 ; Carisbrooke, Isle of Wight, 25th November 1895 ; St. Leonards, Sussex, 8th May 1896 ; Parish of Crimond, Aberdeenshire, Scotland, October 1897 ; Chat Moss, Lancashire, about 1901 ; [1] near Shorewell, Isle of Wight, 11th April 1903 ; Spurn Head, Yorkshire, 14th October 1909 ; Steeplecross, Sussex, April 1914 ; Scilly Isles, May 1925 (sight record) ; Scilly Isles, February 1926 ; Bembridge, Isle of Wight, 1934.[2]

The majority of the above records refer to adult males and it is reasonable to conclude that a certain number of females have escaped detection through confusion with the resident kestrel of our islands. It will be noticed that there is only one established record from Scotland, and one from Ireland, and with the exception of the three Yorkshire records, all have been from southern counties, the Scillies or the Isle of Wight.

DISTRIBUTION ABROAD : The lesser kestrel breeds commonly over the whole of southern Europe, extending as far north as southern Portugal and central Spain in the west and in the east to the Russian Governments of Volhynia, Kief, Don Cossacks and south Samara. It is a breeding bird in Italy, Austria, Hungary, south Czecho-Slovakia, southern Poland and Roumania, Greece and Asia Minor. South of the Mediterranean it nests in large numbers from Morocco to Tunisia. East of that its nesting has not been confirmed in Tripoli, Cyrenaica or Egypt [3] but it will be surprising if it does not do so in any of these countries through which it passes on migration in considerable numbers. At the eastern end of the Mediterranean it nests in Syria, Palestine and Cyprus and ranges east to Persia and Russian Turkestan. East of the Caspian its place is taken by an eastern subspecies, *Falco naumanni pekinensis*, in which the blue-grey of the wings extends up to the scapulars, the secondaries being broadly tipped with white and the terminal portion of the primaries blacker.

In the Mediterranean islands the western race is recorded only from Sicily, Sardinia, Crete and, as already noted, the island of Cyprus. It seems to be unaccountably absent from the Balearic Islands [4] as a breeding species, which, considering how common it is in much of Spain, is difficult to explain.

The winter quarters of the lesser kestrel lie in tropical and sub-tropical Africa south of the Sahara.

At that season it ranges over a wide area. Birds from south-western Europe and north-west Africa appear to migrate due south and to range

---

[1] Mr. Witherby accepted this record in the Supplementary Additions and Corrections to *The Handbook of British Birds*, 2nd ed., as a valid record but for further details see Mr. Clifford Oakes' account in *The Birds of Lancashire*, 1953, p. 186, where the author places the species in square brackets.

[2] For details of this record see C. Morey, *Proc. I. of Wight N. H. Soc. Newport* (ii), 1934, p. 327.

[3] Von Heuglin reported a few nesting in walls in Alexandria many years ago but no recent confirmation. None winter in Egypt.

[4] Philip Munn, *Novitates Zoologicae*, xxxvii, 1931, p. 102.

over the drier parts of West Africa : Senegal, Gambia, French Sudan, French Niger Territory, the northern territories of the Gold Coast and northern Nigeria. It may be expected to occur also in the Chad Territory of French Equatorial Africa, though as yet it is unrecorded from there.

In eastern Africa there is a very large passage of lesser kestrels from eastern Europe and western Asia, of which more will be told later. These birds winter from Kenya and Uganda southwards, but avoid the Equatorial Forest region ; great numbers are reported to reach the high veld in South Africa.[1] There, as on the eastern seaboard, they mingle with the eastern race, *pekinensis*, which also spends the non-breeding season to some extent south of the Equator. Unless handled these two forms would be practically impossible to distinguish in the field. It is significant that in Somaliland only the eastern race has been recorded, with *one* exception, a single bird shot at Sheikh [2] by Sir Geoffrey Archer which was assigned to the typical race. In the spring migration, when lesser kestrels return to their breeding area, individual birds on rare occasions wander beyond their normal range and thus have been recorded from Normandy, Switzerland, Germany and Heligoland (several times), as well as from Great Britain.

HABITS : Of the numerous accidental visitors to Britain which I have had the opportunity to see in their homeland, there are few which give greater pleasure to observe than the lesser kestrel. In the first place it recalls periods of prolonged sunshine, for it does not arrive in its breeding strongholds until the weather in the Mediterranean countries has become reasonably warm and settled, and when it does arrive it comes in force, transforming in the space of twenty-four hours what has probably been until that moment a deserted crumbling ruin into a thriving and lively colony. I have witnessed its arrival at both ends of the Mediterranean— in Cyprus and in Morocco—and have always been thrilled with my first encounter after a lapse of months.

The 18th of February 1951 will remain in my memory as a red-letter day for lesser kestrels. We were then exploring the Forêt de la Marmora in western Morocco and on entering a glade of the forest we saw no less than ten lesser kestrels in a single tree and others close at hand which had obviously just arrived, as we had been walking in that forest for a week without sign of a bird. Then, all of a sudden, the glades were alive with them, gliding in turn from the branches to the ground, where they were feverishly engaged in devouring grasshoppers. In the bright sunlight the heads of the males looked wonderfully blue, and as they descended to the ground they spread their blue-grey tails and exhibited the broad white tips to all the rectrices. A few hours later our way took us to the mouth of the Mehdia River and there we had the delight of finding the lesser kestrels in solitary possession of an old ruined castle which overlooks

[1] Austin Roberts, *Birds of South Africa* (7th impression), 1949, p. 49.
[2] Geoffrey Archer, *Birds of Somaliland*, i, p. 182.

the estuary.   Many of the birds were sitting quietly on the ancient battlements, making occasional flights over the water, while others soared above the ruin.   Against the clear blue sky these birds looked very lovely, so gracefully did they fly and so clean and fresh was their plumage.   We were soon to find them preparing to nest in a high wall overlooking the shore, flanking a single-track railway.   This wall was honeycombed with holes, while circling in the air above, or flying out over the estuary, were literally dozens of lesser kestrels, all obviously watching for our departure, as we were the only disturbing feature in an otherwise deserted landscape. We made as if to depart then sat down to watch, and all at once the birds came pouring in.   Each swooped into its hole ; sometimes several entered the same aperture but within two minutes the air was empty of birds and from every hole protruded a lesser kestrel's tail.   A little owl, perched on a wall close to where we were sitting, seemed as interested a spectator as we were ourselves of this truly astonishing sight.   The kestrels shot into the holes as quickly and as adroitly as the white-bellied swifts we were to see doing the same thing in the walls of Fez.   Only now and again would a bird cling for a moment to the entrance with outspread tail and half-folded wing, occasionally to take another flight over the sea before finally entering its resting place.   At such moments a glimpse of the white claws might be obtained as a bird fluttered against the wall.   There must have been quite a hundred birds in the vicinity.

The colony described was situated in a fairly deserted area of the coast, but lesser kestrels are amazingly fearless birds and may often be found in close proximity to human dwellings.   On one occasion I had my attention drawn by their gliding flight to two obviously breeding pairs which were hawking for flies over a narrow and noisy Arab street in the dirty little township of Oezzane, enchantingly situated in the hills of northern Morocco close to the Riff boundary.   Between flights the kestrels sat on the roofs of buildings overlooking the narrow street, apparently unconcerned by the incredible noise below and the constantly moving Berber life.   Travellers in Morocco who have taken the coast road to the south may recollect the picturesque entrance across the Oued Oum to the town of Azemmour, part of which crowns the high cliffs flanking the river ; those cliffs were swarming with lesser kestrels on 23rd February when we passed that way and there again the birds showed by the selection of their home how oblivious they are to the bustle and noise which is daily the lot of an Arab township. On the date mentioned the birds could not long have arrived from tropical Africa, but already they appeared to have settled down in their breeding quarters and by their graceful evolutions added much to the charm of this ancient Moorish town.

Although I have chosen to describe some personal experiences with lesser kestrels in Morocco, it must not be imagined that this is their only stronghold.   The numbers which cross the Straits of Gibraltar and have their home in Spain have excited the imagination of ornithologists from earliest days. Lord Lilford in his " Notes on the Ornithology of Spain "[1] summed up his experiences nearly ninety years ago in the following words : " The two species of kestrel are, I think, in April and May, the commonest birds in Andalusia, with perhaps the exception of the bee-eater. Every church-steeple, belfry and tower, every town and village, every ruin, swarms with them ; I believe I am not at all beyond the mark in saying that I have seen three or four hundred on wing at the same moment on more than one occasion, notably at Castro del Rio in April 1864."

A few years later, 1868-1872, Colonel Howard Irby of the 74th High-landers was stationed at the Rock, and during those years, with another brief spell in 1874, he gathered the information which resulted in *The Ornithology of the Straits of Gibraltar*. Writing of *Falco cenchris*, as the species was named in those days, Irby observes :

The Lesser Kestrel is almost entirely migratory, though a few remain at Gibraltar during winter. Vast numbers nest there, chiefly on the steep face of rock on the North Front. These birds arrive about the 15th February, but I saw a great flight passing as late as the 4th of April. Probably these were birds which would breed much further north. They nest on rock and ruins, particularly on the old Moorish buildings and towers, of which there are so many in Andalusia. In some, as for instance at Las Alcantarillas, near Seville, they swarm like bees at a hive, as also at Seville ; while curiously enough at Cadiz they were absent.

It is getting on for a hundred years since the two famous ornithologists whose words I have quoted were writing of the birds of Andalusia, and to learn that the lesser kestrel is to-day almost as abundant as it was in those distant days will bring pleasure to all who have visited that most attractive province.

My informant is Doctor H. M. S. Blair, who has now happily turned his attention to Spanish ornithology. Having just returned from an expedition to Andalusia, he has had ample opportunity to assess the present-day status of *Falco naumanni* and writes as follows :

In one of the papers which enrich the earlier volumes of the *Ibis*, we read of the lesser kestrel : " The cry of these pretty birds is as certain to strike the ear in the towns of Andalusia as the twang of the guitar and click of the castanets." Save that the guitar seems, unhappily, less in fashion, Lord Lilford's words are as true to-day as when he penned them ninety years ago. From March until September, no bird is more characteristic of southern Spain than the lesser kestrel. It makes its home, as Lord Lilford remarked, about the old churches of the larger towns ; around villages ; on the buildings of isolated farms ; in old ruins ; as well as in such natural sites as cliffs and rocks. Only in the woodlands and on the higher sierras does one look in vain for these, the least of the European falcons. Everywhere they are rather less in evidence after September, when many fly south, to return in February or March. A few remain during the winter and do not depart with the main body.

[1] *Ibis*, 1865.

W. H. Riddell [1] esteemed the lesser kestrel one of the two birds most useful to Spanish agriculture, the other being the buff-backed heron. It certainly destroys large quantities of locusts, grasshoppers and such beetles as the various cock-chafers and the large rhinocerus beetle. Abel Chapman gives a vivid account of the capture of a carpenter bee. Many of the aerial victims are not large enough to be distinguished, and they may well be creatures as small as diptera. Insects apart, the food of these useful little hawks includes spiders, scorpions and those large millipedes and centipedes which are such unpleasant features of rural Spain. Examples of all these—some dead, others partly disabled—can soon be found beneath the nests of a colony, together with lizards and even small snakes. Much of the prey of the lesser kestrel is not only caught on the wing, but dissected while the bird is still in flight. Large insects are stripped of legs and wing-cases before being consumed, and Seebohm could hear such rejecta strike the ground as the bird fed overhead.

The extent to which lesser kestrels feed on insects can be appreciated from a study of their pellets. These are small black masses, chiefly of beetles' elytra and the like, which soon disintegrate for the lack of any material such as the fur or feathers which give cohesion to the castings of other falcons.

MIGRATIONS AND BEHAVIOUR IN WINTER QUARTERS : One has only to read of the experiences of naturalists in tropical Africa to realize what huge numbers of lesser kestrels visit that continent every winter. By what route the birds which congregate in East Africa and southern Africa reach their destination in autumn still seems to be something of a mystery. In Kenya the lesser kestrel was reported by Sir Frederick Jackson to be a scarce bird until January, and in his opinion it did not apparently follow either the Nile or the Rift Valley when moving south as Sir Geoffrey Archer tentatively suggests in his *Birds of Somaliland*. Archer was at a loss to account for the paucity of lesser kestrels of the typical European race passing through Somaliland and assumed that Abyssinia and the horn of Africa generally lay outside the line of their migration. All those which he collected, bar one specimen, were examples of the Asiatic lesser kestrel *pekinensis*. His observations apply, so far as Somaliland is concerned, to both migrations. In Egypt and Sinai Colonel Meinertzhagen has recorded that the lesser kestrel is much more noticeable in spring than in autumn ; in fact he had only four records for the latter season between late August and early October, whereas in spring the birds abound. Much the same tale comes from Arabia. Is it possible that such vast numbers as occur in Kenya and South Africa later in the year pass south from Europe *west* of the Nile ? That route would enable them to reach Kenya via Darfur and it is significant that when the late Admiral Lynes and

[1] The late W. H. Riddell, whose paintings of birds and wild game in Africa enrich the pages of Abel Chapman's *Retrospect*. Riddell was an excellent observer of wild life, as well as a delightful artist-naturalist, and from his home, El Castillo, at Arcos de la Frontera near Seville, had excellent opportunities of becoming acquainted with the birds of Spain, as his glowing letters to the author of this book bear testimony. He was also a great personal friend of Hugh Blair's.

Willoughby Lowe made their prolonged—three years—survey of the birds of that area Lynes considered that the majority of the October immigrants in the Western Basin were *Falco naumanni*.

After their arrival in Kenya, which takes place between the end of September and mid-October, van Someren reports that the flocks disperse and then only scattered individuals are seen from time to time. After the dispersal birds may even be encountered in clearings of the Congo forest, as well as in savannas, as Doctor Chapin has noted in his great work.[1] We hear of it in Tanganyika [2] both as a winter visitor, up to at least 6000 feet, and as a passage migrant through the country, for it seems to be well established that the great majority of lesser kestrels proceed as far as the high veld of South Africa. There, to quote Doctor Austin Roberts,[3] it is found commonly in the South African summer in great numbers. He continues : " During the day it disperses over the veldt searching for insects, perching on any conspicuous post, telegraph wires, etc., and at night roosts in great hosts in large trees. Owing to its usefulness in the destruction of noxious forms of insects it is protected [in South Africa] by sentiment and law, and consequently in the towns, where very often the only large trees are to be found, it becomes quite a nuisance and spoils the gardens below the trees with the chalky droppings." Doctor Roberts does not give any specific dates when the first birds arrive in their winter quarters, nor does he say when they prepare to leave, for, as they are not known to breed anywhere in southern or indeed central Africa, these birds of the high veld have a very long way to travel ere they reach the country in which they may rear their young and their departure cannot be unduly delayed. For all that, Mr. A. Loveridge observed lesser kestrels flocking over Rungwe, Tanganyika, as late as 15th April, by which time many are already nesting north of the Sahara.

Kenya seems to be one of the chief spring gathering centres for the lesser kestrels before they set out to cross the great wastes which lie between that country and their final destination. Sir Frederick Jackson [4] has left us, from his personal experience when Governor and Commander-in-Chief of that Colony, an account of what then takes place.

On its return northwards it [the lesser kestrel] congregates in immense numbers in the vicinity of Nairobi, between mid-January and March. Many opportunities were afforded of witnessing large flights of this industrious and useful little Kestrel returning about 5.30 to roost in the croton and other trees fringing the forest, after spending the day quartering and scouring the Athi plains for locusts, grasshoppers, beetles and other crawling animals. Such a vast area, yielding an unlimited food

[1] *Birds of the Belgian Congo*, 1932, i, p. 640.
[2] R. E. Moreau, " Migrant Birds in Tanganyika ", *Tanganyika Notes and Records*, iv, 1937, reprint, p. 23.
[3] *Birds of South Africa*, 1949 edition, p. 49.
[4] *Birds of Kenya Colony and the Uganda Protectorate*, i, p. 159.

supply, is eminently suited for large concentrations before leaving for the north. An actual migration was witnessed in Nandi on 24th March, while we were on the march between Doinyo Lesos and the old Kapturi Station on the Sclater road. It was a dull grey morning with drizzling rain and a cold, searching north wind that kept the birds low. During the whole of that march, a distance of about eight miles, at least a couple of thousand must have passed in front of me, not in various sized flocks like Swallows or Sand Martins, but singly and at a little distance apart and continuously. Not one of them was more than forty feet up, the majority being less than ten feet when topping a rise or fold in the ground.

Many years after the above words were penned Colonel Meinertzhagen noted a small migration on the east shore of Lake Naivasha on 12th March, and again in the northern Aberdares on 27th March, in both cases birds passing due north. Of their habits in East Africa Sir Geoffrey Archer, one-time Governor of Uganda, observes :

There are to be seen on the plains, seasonally, great aggregations of kestrels, principally no doubt the lesser species—which number many hundreds and are attracted to the scenes of grass-fires where they prey on the beetles and locusts driven out by the flames. Also on the blackened ground left by a recent grass-fire they are often numerous and are then no doubt engaged in feeding on the charred remains of the Orthoptera. Always they follow the swarms of locusts and flying white ants, and it is believed that this species is entirely insectivorous.[1] It is an attractive sight to watch twenty or thirty of these brightly coloured, decorative little falcons working systematically over the open plains—hovering and gliding, and hovering again, but always with eyes intently fixed on the ground below. They will hover over and stoop to locusts and beetles in the same way that common kestrels will stoop when hunting for mice. But like the hobbies, they catch their prey more often on the wing, striking at them with their feet and conveying them to their mouth with their claws, whereafter the clipped and discarded elytra may be seen falling to the ground. They are confiding birds which will freely pass within gunshot.

Admiral Lynes did not remark any migration of lesser kestrels through Darfur in the spring and the inference is that the birds travel north further to the east than they do when moving south in autumn. The main passage probably follows the Nile Valley and the Red Sea coast but it must be on a very wide front for there are many reports of its passage all the way from Tripolitania to Arabia, quite apart from the crossing of the Mediterranean west of Malta.

It appears to me most probable that rather than cross the Libyan Desert on a broad front the very great numbers which are reported to pass

[1] That statement is not strictly correct. L. N. G. Ramsay noted that in Anatolia the *young* were fed chiefly on mice, and other observers have recorded the adult taking lizards, frogs and small birds. On one occasion, when at sea between the Straits of Bonifacio and Naples, I personally watched a lesser kestrel kill a wheatear which had taken refuge on board the ship upon which I was travelling (cf. *Bull. B.O.C.*, lix, 1939, p. 124) but I concede that such an action on the part of a lesser kestrel is most unusual and insects of various kinds are without doubt their staple diet.

through Egypt[1] between 1st March and 3rd May must follow the Nile Valley and then split into two main streams, the one going west along what used to be termed the Libyan Desert plateau, where the crossing to Europe may take place anywhere between the Delta and Benghazi, the other branching east to pass through Sinai, Palestine and Syria or to make the crossing of the sea in a due northerly direction, which would enable them to break their journey—as in fact they do—in Cyprus, before continuing across the narrow sea which separates that island from Turkey.

In the spring of the year (1954) in which I am writing, my wife and I had many opportunities of watching the arrival of the lesser kestrels in the island of Cyprus. We ourselves arrived in mid-February but it was not until 1st March that the first *Falco naumanni* was seen. Thereafter, during a bird-survey of the whole island in which we drove 3000 miles until mid-May, we were to see them at various places, two marked immigrations taking place on 11th March and 26th and 29th April respectively. We formed the opinion, admittedly after not more than three months' constant observation, that Cyprus lies too far west from the main line of flight for the birds to pass through in anything like the numbers which invade Sinai, as for instance when Meinertzhagen saw flocks of many hundreds passing north over El Arish on 2nd March. From Cyprus the coast of Turkey can be easily seen on a clear day, the Grand Taurus Mountains towering in the sky with their mantle of snow clearly visible. Viewed from the summit of the northern range of mountains, Anatolia seems but a short distance away and Cyprus but a convenient stepping stone for the many migrants that pass that way in spring and autumn.

Much further to the west Colonel J. K. Stanford[2] saw numbers passing through Cyrenaica in April and had already encountered " an enormous gathering " on 21st March at Sirte, Tripolitania, and nearby saw seventy to a hundred flying out in scattered formation over the plain towards the sea.

I have already made mention of the passage across the Straits of Gibraltar of birds which winter in West Africa and it may well be that the numbers seen by Stanford in western Libya may have been lesser kestrels which had wintered in northern Nigeria and French Niger. A passage due north would have brought them to Tripolitania and there are many convenient oases in which they could rest and feed on their way across the desert. We now know that birds—especially powerful fliers such as the kestrels—can pass through desert country without thinking twice about it.

One statement I should here like to refute emphatically is a note quoted in Archer's *Birds of Somaliland* on the authority of Professor Neumann to the effect that " the population of *F. n. naumanni* in Tunis, Algeria and Morocco does not migrate at all ". That is sheer nonsense and, as Geoffrey Archer fortunately observes in the same paragraph, " does

[1] Meinertzhagen in Nicoll's *Birds of Egypt*, ii, p. 383.
[2] " Ornithology of Northern Libya ", *Ibis*, 1954, p. 455.

not accord with the views expressed by David Bannerman "! I have to date spent several winters—at least five—in the three countries specified and have never seen a lesser kestrel in any one of them before February, either south or north of the Atlas ranges. I know that occasionally odd birds are reported to remain in southern Tunisia, on the strength of a small flock being seen south of Gabès on 8th February by O. V. Aplin, but those were much more likely to have been exceptionally early *arrivals* from the south ; still less do I believe in the few birds said to winter in south Spain, Sicily and Sardinia [1] unless they be ailing specimens unable to make the journey to the south. The whole lesser kestrel population in my opinion clears out of Europe, the Mediterranean Basin and its breeding places both north and south of the Atlas chain in northern Africa.

One other spring migration record must be mentioned—that which takes the birds through Arabia. We have it on the excellent authority of St. John Philby [2] that he met with a small number near Taif between 17th May and 2nd June ; on 31st May seven or eight were seen at once and their habits suggested that, even at this late date, they were migrating in company. 2nd June is the latest date I have found for a lesser kestrel to be still on the move so far south as 21°. Four males were shot and their identity established as the western race at the British Museum.

Before leaving the migrations of *Falco naumanni* something must be said about the manner in which they migrate. Most naturalists who have observed them in Africa write of them being seen in flocks. Archer writes : " Not only does it constantly associate in flocks of considerable size but it migrates in enormous numbers." Sir Frederick Jackson told his nephew, Sir Geoffrey Archer, that they appeared in Kenya in *thousands* on migration, and other writers, Colonel Meinertzhagen included, refer to flocks passing given points where they have been observed. Sir Frederick qualifies his statement in his own book,[3] an extract from which I have already quoted, to the effect that those he observed passing flew not in flocks of various size like swallows or sand martins but singly and at a little distance apart, and continuously. In Morocco in 1950 the first arrivals were definitely in flocks, as I have described earlier in this account, though when we saw them beating up the coast in face of a fierce levanter they were more dispersed and flew, as did the Montagu's harriers, singly and spaced out. Indeed so strong was the wind that no bird could keep its position for long without being blown out of it. For all that, in the two consecutive springs which we spent investigating the bird-life of Morocco, the lesser kestrels were usually seen in little companies, and in little companies I imagine they arrived at their pre-arranged breeding places in the old walls of towns and in ancient ruins and towers.

[1] Whitaker's *Birds of Tunisia*, ii, p. 149.
[2] G. L. Bates on " The Birds of Jidda and Central Arabia ", *Ibis*, 1937, p. 57.
[3] *Birds of Kenya Colony and the Uganda Protectorate*, i, p. 159.

In Cyprus in 1954 we were surprised to see the lesser kestrels one or two at a time; only once did we see as many as six together, with the exception of a day in April, the 26th to be exact, when the plain near Patriki was alive with red-footed kestrels obviously freshly arrived, among which were quite a few lesser kestrels as well, which we presumed had come in with their red-footed cousins on the same migration. It may be that Cyprus lies a bit off the regular route of lesser kestrels flying to Europe and consequently only scattered individuals made the island which were either blown out of their way or were on the fringe of the main body, but it struck us as peculiar that we never saw an arrival of a compact flock, as was undoubtedly the rule in Morocco. When encountered at sea lesser kestrels are usually alone or perhaps with a single companion, but if one comes to think of it, so are most birds which take refuge on ships, with the exception of turtle doves, which so often come aboard in little flocks.

BREEDING HABITS IN SPAIN [1] : Many of the lesser kestrels that have emigrated return to their breeding stations in Andalusia as early as February,[2] and a colony generally reaches full strength in the following month. The late W. H. Riddell found males preponderating amongst the earlier arrivals, from which he naturally inferred that they preceded their mates. Spring is well advanced before these small hawks set about nesting, and in a backward season some may still be engaged in courtship in May. Their aerial displays, if inconspicuous, yet afford a charming spectacle. There will be anything from a dozen to a hundred birds wheeling and screaming in the sunshine about some old building. Presently amidst the familiar chattering the onlooker distinguishes a more sustained, plaintive —almost mournful—note. The caller proves to be a male encumbered by what, at first glance, might almost be mistaken for a miniature jess. More careful scrutiny reveals the dangling burden as the limp body of a small lizard. After circling for a while, the fox-red little bird picks out his mate from the wheeling throng and glides towards her. For a time she may ignore the offering, but sooner or later the two dart swiftly towards their nesting hole to the accompaniment of much chattering. Later they will be seen pairing on a ledge of the cliff, or, if the site be a building, about its eaves or parapet. Abel Chapman watched " a pair fall, interlocked, for quite 100 feet " when toying together in mid-air.

A breeding site of the lesser kestrel commonly holds two or three dozen nests, and at some the birds may be reckoned in hundreds. One of the most populous strongholds is a sandstone precipice, fully 300 feet high, which overlooks an Andalusian river. This cliff flanks the waterside for a good half mile, and every suitable niche and cranny, both there and in the

---

[1] Contributed by Doctor H. M. S. Blair.

[2] Recorded dates : Gibraltar, 15.2 (Irby) ; Forêt de Marmora, Morocco, 18.2.51 (D.A.B.); Azemmour, Morocco, 20.2.52 (D.A.B.) ; Fez, 19.2 (W. A. Payn) ; Cyprus, 27.2 (W. A. Payn) ; Cyprus, 1.3.54 (D.A.B.) ; Marrakech, 21.2.51 (D.A.B.).

old town above, is occupied by a pair of lesser kestrels. The late W. H. Riddell, of Arcos de la Frontera, put the strength of the colony at about 500 pairs, which, if anything, seems an underestimate. Besides the kestrels, the cliff houses a pair of ravens, and one of Egyptian vultures, barn, tawny and scops owls, a small but growing community of jackdaws, and a host of spotless starlings. A varying number of griffon vultures resorts to certain higher ledges, but only to roost. Another great cliff some miles away the kestrels share with choughs, rock sparrows, crag martins and Alpine swifts.

Lesser kestrels soon bestir themselves, and their shrill voices can be heard while the morning mists still cling to the riverside pastures. As the sun mounts, more and more leave their roosts to disperse over the country-side. Delightful little birds they are to watch as they hawk to and fro, almost like so many swallows. To the artist's eye of W. H. Riddell they appeared so unsubstantial as to recall " little bits of tinted paper blowing about . . . so unlike a peregrine falcon, which looks as if carved out of steel ".

A colony of lesser kestrels has many enemies. Snakes—both whip-snakes (*Zamenis hippocrepis*) and black colubers up to six feet in length—kill some of the sitting birds and later destroy whole broods of nestlings. Or the marauder may be a yard-long green-eyed lizard (*Lacerta ocellata*). While still unable to do more than flutter, young kestrels often tumble out of their nest, to afford easy prey to genets, ichneumons and village cats.

A far from welcome visitor to a kestrel community is the handsome little peregrine of the Mediterranean (*Falco peregrinus brookei*). At one colony a tiercel suddenly dropped headlong through the busy swarm, his stoop carrying him out of view beyond the cliff-head, whence a little cloud of kestrel feathers presently eddied. Returning a few days later, he fairly hunted every kestrel that chanced to be abroad into the zenith. This or another peregrine encountered a very different reception one day in July when several male kestrels joined forces in mobbing him as soon as he skirted the cliff. Some of the nesting holes still held broods at the time, and it may well have been the parents of these which hustled the falcon. Or the latter was perhaps full-fed, and for the time being innocuous. The kestrels' reactions towards other birds of prey showed them to be well aware which were, and which were not, likely to prove dangerous. A lanner falcon created as much panic as the peregrine, the little hawks forthwith seeking refuge in their nests, or if cut off, disappearing in the upper sky. They went in equal fear of a booted eagle, but kites and buzzards they ignored. The griffon vultures that roosted in the cliff left and returned without any demonstration by their little neighbours other than an occasional seemingly playful stoop. An Egyptian vulture too went unmolested for the most part, though one day a party of kestrels persisted in their teasing of the big white bird until it turned on its back the better to face its tormentors. It need hardly be said that the ravens which nested in a sheltered recess of the cliff received their due of attention if they trespassed overlong on the kestrels' territory.

Lesser kestrels draw in to their nesting places as the afternoon wears on, and it is during the last hour of daylight that the stir and bustle of a colony reach their height. As the little hawks are as noisy as swifts, the din of a large colony becomes almost incessant. At one great stronghold the evening chorus of the thronging birds recalled the clamour of young kitti-wakes on a Yorkshire cliff in July. On still nights, the kestrels continue their hawking until long past sundown, and some are still a-wing when the big noctule bats emerge from their dormitories.

Lesser kestrels have yet to be found nesting in open sites, the eggs always being laid in holes, and often so far in as to be out of reach. An occupied nest can always be recognized by the droppings immediately beneath the entrance, as well as by the remains of prey on the ground below. For some time before the female lays, one of the pair can often be found crouched on the empty nest, and so reluctant to leave as to suggest that it is covering eggs. Like that of a cliff-breeding common kestrel, the nest is no more than a slight depression scratched out in the floor of the recess. About it, as incubation progresses, there accumulate the discarded remains of the insects the sitting bird has devoured.

In very early seasons, a few lesser kestrels finish laying in the last week of April, but mid-May is usually soon enough to look for full clutches, and some birds are even later. It will be remembered by those who have studied Irby's *Ornithology of the Straits of Gibraltar* that the author records having obtained on 12th May no less than sixty eggs of the lesser kestrel from an old tower near Manchena, Andalusia, and might have taken as many more. Some of these eggs were already hard set. The same naturalist mentions taking four eggs out of a hole in a wall at Coto del Rey on 26th April.

The eggs are laid, like those of other small falcons, at intervals of two days, to the number of four or five. Occasionally a full clutch will consist of three or six eggs, and Seebohm had one of seven. Lesser kestrels' eggs measure, on an average, $34 \cdot 78 \times 28 \cdot 66$ mm., according to Jourdain, with minima of $31 \cdot 6 \times 27 \cdot 7$ and $35 \cdot 56 \times 26$, and a maximum of $37 \cdot 5 \times 31$ mm. They are therefore noticeably smaller than common kestrels'. While the eggs in a large colony can include every variety of form recorded for the larger bird, the majority will be almost globular, with little difference between their poles. In colour, and in the character of their markings too, they show a great range of variation. The most distinctive type, and also the commonest, is blotched with orange or brick-red on a cream or buff ground, the individual markings being small and less dense than with the common kestrel. Some are more deeply tinted, while others show much of the white ground between bold markings of sienna. Very sparingly marked clutches are far from uncommon, one fine type being pure white with a few spots of sepia, and immaculate specimens, while rare, occur more frequently than with any other falcon. Colonel R. F. Meiklejohn had a clutch in his collection in which one egg was pure white, while the rest were all normally coloured. If a series of eggs of this bird is compared with a similar number of those of the common kestrel, the former will immediately be seen to be much the paler. This difference seems the more significant when it is remembered that the lesser kestrel's eggs are normally laid well under cover, while those of the common kestrel are as frequently found in open nests.

As lesser kestrels allow themselves to be handled on the nest, the sex of a sitting bird can readily be determined. While this generally proves to be the female, at one out of twenty nests in a large colony it will be the male that is incubating. Harry Witherby was able to prove this himself when he discovered a male bird sitting on four eggs in central Spain on 21st May. One or other is often found in the nest when only one or two eggs have been laid, but incubation does not appear to commence until the clutch is complete. The eggs hatch after being brooded for four weeks, and the young fly a month later. While it is uncertain how soon the female takes to hunting for her brood, she certainly does so when they are half-grown.

Although this account is already long I am persuaded to include a description of a very different nesting colony in Macedonia which was described [1] by the late F. N. Chasen, who, at the time of his early death, through enemy action at sea, was Director of the Raffles Museum at Singapore. His observations were made during the First World War at a village in the valley of the Struma, and Chasen contended that the conditions under which the birds were met with on that occasion differed in some interesting points from those usually associated with the species.

The kestrels had selected for their breeding place a corner of the village of Ormanli in which was situated a dilapidated mosque and priest's house with numerous dwellings of the ordinary native type in close proximity. By 8th March (which Chasen considered an early date) a pair of lesser kestrels were paying attention to the mosque and contending with the jackdaws which were already in possession of the suitable nesting places, but within two days of their arrival the kestrels had established a firm claim to a suitable hole under the low roof of a long mud-built hut which was at the time being used by troops as a stable for mules. The entrance to this nesting place was but six feet from the ground and very conspicuous by reason of the white splashes of excrement that marked it. Every time the birds entered the hole they had to swoop within a few inches of the mules' tails. Transport drivers were constantly at work grooming and saddle-cleaning and usually singing and shouting about their work and, as Chasen remarks, mules are not the quietest creatures to live with or near.

[1] *British Birds*, 1921, p. 170.

Another pair of kestrels which arrived on the scene settled down under the low roof of another native hovel and soon several other pairs appeared in the village and took up their nesting quarters, all of which were under the tiled roofs of native houses and entered by a hole in the eaves.

The birds in Ormanli spent many hours circling or swooping about in the air, above or near their nests, uttering incessantly a harsh *kee-chee-chee*. Most of the summer hours of the day were spent in this manner, while at dusk all the birds in the neighbourhood would form into one large band and repeat the performance. Each pair of birds also had their own favourite perch, usually a particular twig on the tree nearest to their nest, and there they would huddle most affectionately together.

Chasen's observations bear out Doctor Blair's in Spain that lizards form a large part of the food supply of the lesser kestrel, for he notes that it was a common sight to see a kestrel flying about with a lizard grasped in its feet. Sometimes a hen bird could be seen sitting complacently on a twig while the male was foraging for food. This obtained, he would feed his mate with great solicitude, she greeting him on each arrival with a prolonged call.

Mating was first noticed at the beginning of April and was very frequent about the 19th of the month. It usually took place on the topmost slender twig of a tree and in such a precarious position that both sexes had to extend their wings to maintain their balance. A low chattering, which Chasen describes as a peculiarly penetrating noise, was made the whole time, but this note is not peculiar to the mating time as it was heard from two birds on a different occasion sitting quietly together in a pomegranate bush. A nest in Ormanli contained two eggs on 22nd April. On the other hand a nest of young at least a week old was seen at another village on 8th June. A number of nestlings examined in June were very uniform in their appearance. The beak and fleshy angle of the gape were flesh-coloured. All the bare skin on the head was of the palest green ; the legs, toes and claws were yellow and quite as bright as in the adults.

Sometimes at noon, when it was very hot and sultry and myriads of midges and other pests were humming about in the air, sixty or more lesser kestrels would flock together and hunt the insects with many downward swoops and pursuing flutters but when not indulging in such evolutions the normal flight, so Chasen considered, was very like that of the common kestrel : " With quivering wings and tail bent down to its fullest extent, feet drawn up and head and neck inclined forward, eagerly scanning the earth, the lesser kestrel will remain poised practically stationary." Small grass-fires are extremely common in the summer in Macedonia, and columns of smoke can often be seen curling upwards. As soon as the tiniest wisp of smoke wreaths up from the hillside, the kestrels begin to arrive and the aggregate of the small flocks that unite on these occasions often totals more than a hundred birds, all showing great activity in pouncing upon the scattering grasshoppers and other victims of the fire.

In case it be supposed from Chasen's account that breeding and egg laying takes place in the Near East at an earlier date than it does in Spain, I will end this article with a note from the late Colonel R. F. Meiklejohn, whose diary remains in my possession. Meiklejohn states therein that he found *Falco naumanni* nesting in numbers in the steep banks of the Corinth Canal and took eggs at Larissa, Lamia and Thebes amongst other places. The nests were, as described elsewhere, in crannies in steep banks, under eaves and tiles of buildings and in holes in walls, the eggs being laid in a single hollow or scrape with no nesting material beyond a few stalks or an occasional feather. The normal clutch in Greece he found to be five and the clutches were complete in mid-May. Thus, at both ends of the Mediterranean, the nesting time, or rather the date when completed clutches are normally found, shows no apparent variation.

REFERENCES : Original Description. *Falco naumanni* Fleischer, Sylvan Jahrbuch auf 1817 und 1818, 1818, p. 174. Visitor to South Germany and Switzerland. Restricted type locality South Germany.

PLATE 14   **RED-FOOTED FALCON**

Falco vespertinus vespertinus Linnaeus

An Occasional Visitor which has occurred about seventy times in this country

IDENTIFICATION : This falcon is in size and in some of its habits rather like a lesser kestrel but may easily be distinguished at a distance by its colour. The sexes are very unlike one another and a glimpse of the male's plumage should enable it to be recognized, for it is almost entirely leaden blue-grey (nearly blackish-slate on the head and the rump), with the exception of the centre of the lower abdomen, the thighs, vent and under tail-coverts, which are reddish-chestnut. The under tail-coverts are sometimes marked with slate-grey. The tail is black, and the wings are grey like the upperparts, as are also the axillaries and under wing-coverts. The colour of the soft parts is noticeable, the bill being bright reddish-orange, except for the horn-blue tip, and the bare patch round the eye. The cere and the legs are all likewise bright orange-red in colour. The iris is dark brown.

The female is much more easily confused with a kestrel but should be recognized by its bright uniform chestnut crown and nape, without any dark streaks present. I have seen these parts described as chestnut-buff by a leading authority but if buff is the term it is a very reddish-buff which easily attracts attention by its brightness. The mantle and back are slate, the former often tinged rufous, and like the scapulars are closely barred with blackish. The wings are blackish ; the tail (which is a very distinctive feature) is pale blue-grey to slate, narrowly barred with brownish-black, and has a broad subterminal band of the same colour, the tip being pale rufous.

The face, chin and throat are pale buff; a dark patch is noticeable on the lores and the moustachial streak is chestnut. The creamy-buff throat merges gradually into the dull chestnut of the rest of the underparts. The soft parts are the same as in the male, the bright orange-red legs being an additional distinction should there be any danger of confusing it with a kestrel of any species or age.

Usually males and females are present at the same time, for the red-footed falcon is the most sociable of all the falcons. Remember too that it may be seen hovering exactly like a kestrel. When handled it will be seen that the long wings of this species reach almost to the tip of the tail.

Care must be taken when young birds are abroad not to confuse them, as Favier did in Tangier, with young hobbies. A good distinction lies in the tail, which in the immature red-footed falcon is closely barred above, while in the young hobby it is uniform slate-colour above though barred on the underside.

Ticehurst and Whistler made some interesting observations on the structure and plumages of these falcons from fifteen specimens which they had collected in Jugoslavia. The first point they noted was the considerable variation in wing-length among adults and the fact that contrary to the usual rules amongst Accipitrine birds the wings of the females are not the longest. The adult female may be deep rust-coloured underneath or quite pale, but the slate-blue barred tail is then characteristic. The one-year-old male has the tail and wings barred and the body plumage particoloured slate-blue and red-brown; the one-year-old female has also the old juvenile wings and tail, black and buff barred, and the head and underparts paler rusty streaked with black.[1]

OCCURRENCES IN GREAT BRITAIN : Considering that this falcon is usually referred to in British bird literature as a very rare vagrant, it may come as a surprise to learn that it has occurred about seventy times in our islands, though only very rarely outside the English counties. In England it was first noted near Doncaster, Yorkshire, in April 1830, while the last record of which I have note is of a bird seen on Hickling Broad, Norfolk,[2] by Mr. Roland Green, the well-known bird artist, in 1946. Between these dates over sixty have been recorded in England alone, chiefly, as Mr. Witherby has stated, in the eastern and southern counties ; it is rare in the north-west and south-west of the country. Among some of special interest the records from Cornwall and the inland counties of Wales, Westmorland and Cumberland may be specified.

To Scotland the red-footed falcon has wandered on seven occasions, as follows : Foveran, Aberdeenshire, 29th May 1866 ; near Kinghorn,

[1] *Ibis*, 1929, p. 684.
[2] *The Field*, 1946, p. 414.

Fife, 20th September 1880 ; near Jedburgh, Roxburghshire, June 1888 ; Crimonmogate, Aberdeenshire, 7th May 1897 ; Aboyne, Aberdeenshire, 17th October 1913 ; Moss of Cree, Wigtownshire (a sight record), November 1944 ; Kinlochrannoch, 6th May 1947.

The single record from Ireland refers to a bird reported to have been shot in Wicklow in the summer of 1832. The specimen is preserved in the National Museum, Dublin.

Most of the occurrences have, as Doctor Eagle Clarke put on record prior to the appearance of *The Handbook*, taken place in spring, between 15th April and 18th June, but the majority in May with a few autumn records (September and October), and exceptionally in winter.

DISTRIBUTION ABROAD : The red-footed falcon is a summer breeding bird in eastern Europe and in Asia Minor, western Siberia and the Aral-Caspian region, ranging east to the Altai and Tarbagatai, east of which, from Lake Baikal to Manchuria, it is replaced by another race, *Falco vespertinus amurensis.*

Through the kindness of Madame E. Kozlova I am able to give a more detailed account of the range in Russia of the red-footed falcon than has previously been published in Europe.

Madame Kozlova writes that *Falco vespertinus* breeds irregularly in the Baltic States and near Pskow. The northern limit of its range extends from the Onega Lake and Archangel to the middle course of the Petchora River (about latitude 62° N.) ; on the Ob River north to latitude 61°-62° N. ; in western and central Siberia, north to Tiumen, Tara, Tobolsk, Tomsk and Krasnoiarsk.

East of the Yenisei River the northern boundary acquires a northern trend, extending to the upper Lena and the upper reaches of the Lower Tunguska. The eastern limit of the range passes near the western shores of Baikal Lake.

It is found breeding near Irkutsk, in the Sayan and Altai Mountains, and also on the Urungu River in Dzungaria and is common in the forest-steppe zone near Kansk and Minussinsk, but it is absent from north-western Mongolia and the Zaissan Depression.

The southern limit of the range in western Siberia runs west of Semipalatinsk (on the Irtysh River) approximately along 51°-51° 30', extending down to the mouths of the Ural and Volga Rivers. In eastern Europe the range of the red-footed falcon extends south to the steppe regions of the northern Caucasus, to the Crimea and to the mouth of the Danube. There are also single winter records from the Crimea.

Its range in Poland is not clear but it is found commonly in the western portions of the Ukraine.

The above range has been compiled by Madame Kozlova from Russian sources, in particular from the researches of Doctor Dementiev (1951).

PLATE 14

RED-FOOTED FALCON

Falco vespertinus vespertinus (Linnaeus)

Upper Figure	. .	Adult Male
Lower Figure	. .	Adult Female

There seems to be very little evidence as to its breeding in western Europe even spasmodically.

The winter range of the typical subspecies is in Africa and extends over a wide area from the Sudan to South Africa. Examples have been taken occasionally in the Belgian Congo [1] and on one occasion from Uam in French Equatorial Africa.[2] In West Africa there are records from the Province of Adamawa and from the Bauchi Province of Nigeria. South of the Equator the red-footed falcon is known to reach eastern Cape Province, Damaraland and Namaqualand.[3]

It is remarkable, considering its breeding range, how far west in the Mediterranean Basin this little falcon can be seen during the period of migration, which lends some support to the rather vague statement by F. C. R. Jourdain in *The Handbook of British Birds* that *Falco vespertinus* possibly breeds in Bulgaria and Roumania, and probably *has* bred in Germany, Denmark, Finland and eastern Sweden.[4]

In South Africa and south-east Africa there is a danger of confusion with the eastern red-footed falcon (*amurensis*) which also winters partly in that area from its breeding home in eastern Asia. The two birds are very much alike and the males can only be distinguished in the field—if and when the underside of the wing can be seen !—by *F. vespertinus vespertinus* having black under the wing, whereas in *F. vespertinus amurensis* the under wing-coverts and axillaries are white. The females are less difficult to distinguish from one another. Some authorities, notably Doctor Chapin and Doctor Austin Roberts, treat each as a full species in their principal publications.

HABITS : Owing, no doubt, to the scarcity of this most attractive falcon in western Europe, to which it is an accidental visitor, the literature about it in our language is very scanty, and the British ornithologists who are familiar with it are equally scarce. It was one of the birds which I hoped to see this year (1954) when studying bird migration in Cyprus, and in that I was not disappointed. I had read somewhere that the red-footed falcon loves nothing so much as wide flat plains where the grass is short or absent and the birds can run about freely in search of locusts or other winged insect prey. It was in just such a place that we first came upon it in Cyprus— a vast plain where flocks of grazing sheep and goats had eaten down the scanty growth and the hot sun had baked the earth as hard as a billiard table. We were accustomed to pay this particular plain a regular visit, for there was fresh water to be had where the flocks were watered in some artificial pools caused by the villagers of Patriki cutting out clay with which

---

[1] Chapin, *Birds of the Belgian Congo*, i, p. 638.
[2] The type of *Falco pyrrhogaster* Reichenow.
[3] Austin Roberts, *The Birds of South Africa*, p. 47.
[4] Mr. Jourdain gives no evidence in support of this statement and the occurrence of the bird as a nesting species so far west in Europe must be considered extremely rare.

to make bricks. The passing migrants must have known these pools of old, and at almost every visit we found some newly arrived migrant resting after its long flight from Africa or Syria. It was on 26th April as we approached the pools that we saw the red-footed falcons coming in, presumably from overseas, for they were still arriving and circling high over the plain. One by one most of the birds came to earth, though some remained soaring overhead. They were accompanied by many lesser kestrels in whose company they may have crossed the sea, for there were many more *Falco naumanni* present than we had seen on this plain on former visits. The red-footed falcons were either very tired or remarkably tame, for they allowed fairly close approach.

The falcons and kestrels together had attracted to the scene a number of *Corvidae*, for there were in close attendance on the falcons four ravens, two jackdaws and at least a dozen Cyprian hooded crows, all of which seemed to be taking the greatest interest in the newcomers. The falcons were resting in all manner of places, some perched on large stones, others on the bare earth, where we noted they could run with ease, while many more kept wheeling about in the air with the crows, some ascending to a considerable height. These birds had obviously arrived in the same party and we noted that the numbers of males and females were about equal. No case here of segregation of the sexes during migration.

Three days later quite a number were still on the same plain, though a few had obviously continued their journey. Our last visit was paid to the spot on 2nd May, when the falcons had all departed and with them the various members of the crow family which like ourselves had found the passage of these little falcons through the island of absorbing interest. We were at pains to note that the falcons hovered in the same way as kestrels, though not to the same extent as the common kestrel does. The flight of the falcons was peculiarly graceful and as they floated round with the larger birds they appeared very small and elegant by comparison. When all had gone the plain seemed very empty, for the presence of the falcons added a charm to the scene which no words can express. We never saw these falcons "hawking like swallows", as Major W. M. Congreve witnessed in Transylvania.[1] In the spring of 1929 two well-known English ornithologists, Claud Ticehurst and Hugh Whistler, made a tour through Jugoslavia to study the bird-life and make collections, and on almost the identical day when we witnessed the passage of red-footed falcons through Cyprus in 1954 the same thing, only on a much greater scale, had been taking place in Jugoslavia twenty-five years earlier. No doubt the birds arrive punctually year after year both in Jugoslavia and in Cyprus but the similarity of the dates when we had made our observations struck me as peculiarly interesting after an interval of so many years.

[1] *Ibis*, 1929, p. 482.

Writing in the *Ibis* of their experiences Ticehurst and Whistler observe :[1]

This delightful little falcon we found swarming on the Podgoritza plain from 28th April to 2nd May,[2] after which none was noticed. Several might be seen sitting on each tree and bush in the neighbourhoods that they frequented, now and again flying down to the ground to take their prey (black ants, grasshoppers, etc.). They were fairly tame and usually allowed a close approach. Telegraph wires were their favourite perch, and where a line crosses the plain a hundred or more might be seen sitting like a row of bee-eaters. They frequented only absolutely open plain, but many collected to roost in a grove of trees round the hospital. When the flying ants were out we saw many red-footed falcons catching them over Podgoritza town, sharing the feast with the Alpine swifts. These ants are very deftly taken with the foot, and eaten on the wing.

Adult males very largely predominated.

Although the breeding area of the western red-footed falcon lies further north and east than Italy, the bird appears some years in Sicily in considerable numbers towards the end of April and beginning of May. J. I. S. Whitaker frequently saw numbers of them among the olive plantations and orange groves in the Royal Park near Palermo, where an abundance of insects was believed to be the attraction. The Italians must be well acquainted with the red-footed falcon to have bestowed upon it the name " falco cucculo ", and it would be interesting to discover the destination of the birds which pass through that country, for a direct route to their breeding grounds would surely pass to the east of the Adriatic. The birds are, however, not uncommon in Tunisia during the spring migration, arriving in flocks towards the end of April and beginning of May, to depart again northwards after a short stay. The shortest sea crossing from Tunisia to eastern Europe would then be via Sicily and the toe of Italy. The late Joseph Whitaker wrote that numerically the passage of these birds through Tunisia varies greatly, the falcons being particularly plentiful in some years and their numbers insignificant in others. He also observed that in many parts of Italy, particularly where open tracts of low-lying country and marshy plains abound, the species is numerous during the spring, although none remain to nest.

Apart from this apparently normal passage through Tunisia, Sicily and Italy, which to me seems very surprising, this falcon is sometimes found hundreds of miles out of its normal range. Why, it may be asked, should it ever be heard of in Nigeria or Adamawa ? and even more surprisingly in the Canary Islands ? On 25th April 1890 a good many visited the valley of Orotava in Tenerife, and a specimen obtained by E. G. B. Meade-Waldo on 7th May of that year is preserved in the British Museum in

[1] *Ibis*, 1929, p. 684.
[2] The passage through Cyprus began on 26th April and ended on 1st or 2nd May.

support of the occurrence. On at least two other occasions Tenerife has been visited by *Falco vespertinus*, as I recorded myself in the *Ibis*, 1919, p. 492. They have also been reported from Morocco and from localities in Algeria. The explanation of these wanderings in Africa may be found in the presence of locust hordes and of termites, of which the falcons are especially fond, and locust swarms are by no means unknown in the Canary Islands, although Meade-Waldo made no mention of a plague of locusts when the birds invaded Tenerife. The bird is even reported to straggle or rare occasions to the Balearic Islands and to turn up in Andalusia and in Tangier " when the locusts arrive ".

What would appear to be a much more direct route from their main winter quarters in the Sudan and further south takes the birds through Egypt, and of that passage we learn from Colonel Meinertzhagen [1] that they are of regular occurrence in the Delta and Wadi Natrûn on spring and autumn passage between 11th and 29th May, and again between 7th and 28th October. The falcons pass through Sinai commonly in autumn, there being many records between 7th August and 21st December, but curiously enough there are no spring records, Sinai being evidently missed during the passage south. It is noteworthy too that whereas the red-footed falcon is seen in the Sudan during the months of September and October, often in very considerable flocks, it is much less noticeable on the return migration in the spring.[2] The birds evidently take an entirely different route on their northern passage. From the rather scanty data available it is not possible to form a very clear picture of their movements in Africa ; moreover the numbers appear to fluctuate annually for no very obvious reason. We have still much to learn about the migrations of the western red-footed falcon and the problem is not made any easier by the presence in Africa in the non-breeding season of the eastern race.

From Russian sources [3] I learn that spring migration in the Ukraine takes place about mid-April, in the northern portions of its range in the first half of May in some years, or near Molotov (Perm) in the second part of May.

In the year 1930 these falcons were observed in the Minussinsk steppe on 21st April and they arrive in western Siberia and in the vicinity of Krasnoiarsk in early May.

The autumnal migration begins in August and continues until the middle or the end of September. The bulk of the migration has been noted in eastern Europe during the latter part of September and is at its height during the period from 20th to 25th September.

Madame E. Kozlova, to whom I am indebted for this information,

[1] Nicoll's *Birds of Egypt*, ii, p. 378.
[2] Grant and Praed, *Birds of Eastern and North-Eastern Africa*, 1952, i, p. 146.
[3] This information has been sent to me from the Leningrad Academy of Sciences by Madame E. Kozlova.

writes that in Russia the red-footed falcon is mostly an inhabitant of the plains in the steppe and forest-steppe zones. It is to be found in cultivated districts, gardens and parks and is sometimes found breeding in towns, as at Poltawa. It occurs commonly in river valleys with typical river-bank vegetation. The falcon avoids dense woods but in the north it is of common occurrence on old burnt areas in open parts of woodland. It normally avoids mountainous country but has been found by Professor Sushkin in the Altai range at heights of up to 1000 m. (3300 feet) and occasionally up to 1500 m. (4950 feet).

The following has been recorded in Russia as the red-footed falcon's food : mostly insects, which are caught with the claws in the air or on the ground—mainly orthoptera and coleoptera. It also captures small mammals : *Mus musculus*, *Stenocranius gregalis*, *Lagurus* and young *Citellus pygmaeus*, and *Sorex*, as well as lizards, *Lacerta* and *Eremias*. This list varies but little from that published in *The Handbook* from European sources.

In its winter quarters Doctor Austin Roberts found that in eastern Cape Province it fed almost exclusively on insects such as locusts, grass-hoppers and flying termites, serving a good purpose in keeping down these pests and therefore protected by sentiment as well as by law in the Union of South Africa.

In Britain, where it turns up periodically, the comparative scarcity of insect-life compels it to subsist largely on shrews, mice, poultry chicks (when obtainable !), dragonflies and beetles, as the late F. C. R. Jourdain has recorded.

BREEDING HABITS : It is well known that the red-footed falcon has a strong tendency to nest in close proximity to others of its kind, but as it builds no nest of its own, it is forced to use the old nests of other species in which to lay its eggs. Being addicted to colonial nesting when possible, it is not surprising to find it making use of the nests of other colonial-nesting species and the nests of rooks are consequently in great demand. If for any reason the rooks are late in breeding, the falcons have to wait until the young rooks have flown. Von Nordmann has described (as quoted in *The Handbook of British Birds*) how the red-footed falcons indulge in remarkable social evolutions before nesting commences, the birds flying to and fro for hours over the same beat, turning sharply at fixed points. The evolutions were seen to begin about 4 p.m. at a high elevation, the birds gradually descending lower as evening approached.

Madame Kozlova informs me that in eastern Europe and western Siberia the nests of crows and kites are utilized in addition to rookeries—old magpie's nests are used too in eastern Europe. Sometimes the falcon nests in the holes of trees and in stumps, and it has also been found nesting in bushes at Caragana, so Madame Kozlova assures me ; occasionally it has been known to lay its eggs in burrows.

Eggs may be found in eastern Europe and western Siberia in the second half of May and in the region of Krasnoiarsk in early June. In Russia full clutches normally consist of three to four eggs but on rare occasions one or two only are laid.

In the east of Hungary, where the red-footed falcon is very common, its arrival in its breeding quarters was witnessed by Mr. Gerald Tomkinson, who has kindly supplied me with the following note on his experiences :

We found *Falco vespertinus* nesting in any old nests of magpie, crow or rook and although we found quite a lot nesting in the old nests of magpies and crows, by far the most interesting was our discovery of vast numbers literally taking over the whole of a rookery. The falcons used to sit in the tree close to the rooks' nests waiting for the young rooks to quit, and as soon as the young rooks left the nest, they took possession. This we found in two rookeries, neither of them very large and both quite close to the Hortobágy plain, not far from Debrecsen. In the one case the rooks' nests were in fairly large trees and very easy to get at, but the other rookery was in small trees about thirty feet high and not easy to get at as they were very thin and whippy. The falcons would sit for some days on the tree until the young rooks had flown.

The falcons breeding in the rookeries were later in laying than the falcons which made use of the old nests of the magpie or crow, for in the latter case they had nothing to wait for. We found that these had eggs about 25th May, whereas the falcons nesting in the rookery were at least a week later.

We found that the eggs were very like those of the lesser kestrel (*naumanni*), with variations, some resembled those of the hobby (*subbuteo*), others those of the merlin (*columbarius*), while others are like small eggs of the kestrel (*tinnunculus*), but they are never likely to be confused with the eggs of the kestrel as they are so much smaller.

Mr. Tomkinson draws my attention to a statement in Dresser's *Birds of Europe* that the clutch is often five or sometimes six, but in his experience he never saw more than four eggs in a clutch and very often the birds were sitting on three eggs. At least thirty full clutches were examined and nearly all were a few days incubated. In this respect Mr. Tomkinson in Hungary and Madame Kozlova in Russia have had similar experiences.

In the *Catalogue of Birds' Eggs in the British Museum* a number of eggs are listed taken in Hungary, the Volga district and southern Russia. These are barely distinguishable in markings from the eggs of the common kestrel but are distinctly smaller. Most are dark in colour, rich reddish-brown predominating on a white ground. The average of 100 eggs (after Jourdain, forty by Ray) measure $36 \cdot 8 \times 29 \cdot 22$ mm. Max. $41 \cdot 5 \times 30 \cdot 5$ and 40×32 mm. Min. $33 \cdot 8 \times 29 \cdot 4$ and $36 \cdot 5 \times 27 \cdot 3$ mm.

Continuing her account of the nesting habits, Madame Kozlova writes :

Both parents incubate, but at night, and at the end of the incubation period—the female only. The incubation period is twenty-eight days.[1]

---

[1] In *The Handbook of British Birds* it is stated that the incubation period is unknown.

The first young are hatched in the Ukraine usually in the middle of June but in the northern portions of the range in eastern Europe and in western Siberia at the end of that month.

The male alone provides food for the young whilst they are small but after ten to twelve days both the parents hunt. When the young are two weeks old the parents were observed to bring them food fifty-seven times a day.

The young falcons have been recorded leaving their nests in the Charkow district of the Ukraine on 22nd June, near Tchkalow, Orenburg, by the end of June and near Minussinsk on 16th to 22nd August. As already noted, the autumn migration sets in in August in Russia.

Since the above essay was completed from information then available I have received from Doctor L. Horváth of the Hungarian National Museum a resumé of his work on the life of the red-footed falcon in advance of publication of the full story, which is due to appear in the *Proceedings of the Tenth International Ornithological Congress*. The observations were made in the forest of Ohat, Hortobágy, Hungary, and afford interesting comparison with the information supplied to me from British and Russian sources.

As regards the occupation of nests in the forest of Ohat, Doctor Horváth found that possession was taken of the rooks' nests two or three weeks prior to egg laying by the falcons. No repairing of the nests was seen. It was found that 80 per cent. of the falcons selected nests in the rookery at a medium height from the ground. Thirty-two nests out of a total of one hundred and fourteen in this forest were kept under special observation. Of these thirty-two nests, fourteen were in trees which held other nests and it was seen that where several nests were available the falcons preferred the higher ones. Another point noticed was that the height of the nest selected was related to the height of the tree and amount of foliage available above the nest.

Doctor Horávth discovered that the number of breeding falcons is always in proportion to the number of nests in the rookery, thus :

Serial number of rookery	Total of rooks' nests	Number of nests occupied by falcons	Percentage
1	168	22	13
2	334	45	13·04
3	84	10	11·9
4	278	35	12·05
Total	864	112	12·9

The number of breeding falcons had no relation to the height or age of the nesting trees, but all the falcons attempted to congregate within the area of the rookery.

Out of 114 falcons' nests in the forest of Ohat, sixty-five were examined to ascertain the number of eggs. These sixty-five nests held in all 226 eggs. These were divided as follows : six clutches of two eggs ; twenty-four clutches of three eggs ; thirty-three clutches of four eggs ; two clutches of five eggs. The comparatively low average of clutches was due, it was thought, to the females having been mostly young birds, which was proved by their markedly light-coloured underparts and also by their somewhat delayed breeding.

Some curious facts emerged from the study of these eggs. It was noted, for instance, that the first egg to be laid was paler-coloured, and the last egg laid more richly coloured as a rule. Moreover, the first-laid eggs were found to be the smallest in the clutch and the last-laid the biggest. Compared with those of the kestrel the eggs of the red-footed falcon are less profusely and variedly coloured and in view of the fact that small clutches showed poorer colouring it was assumed that as a rule young birds laid paler eggs than old birds. The measurements of the eggs (presumably 226) showed an average of 37·04 × 29·57 mm. Max. 40·0 × 33·4 and 39·4 × 33·9 mm. Min. 33·0 × 25·7 mm.

Doctor Horváth considered that brooding was shared equally between the sexes and that incubation commenced as soon as the first egg is laid. It was found that incubation lasted twenty-two to twenty-three days, though in abnormal cases it lasted twenty-seven days due to special causes. In one clutch it was ascertained that a period of twenty-eight to thirty-seven hours elapsed between the successive hatching of the eggs. Juvenile birds remained in the nest for twenty-six to twenty-eight days, an average of twenty-seven days. For the first ten days the male bird provided the food, which was fed to the young by the female. Later on both parents brought food to the nest, though not during the early hours, when this duty devolved on the male entirely. Prey was always killed before being carried to the nest. Egg shells and other extraneous matter were invariably removed from the nest and carried to a considerable distance.

I am greatly indebted to Doctor Horváth for preparing these notes specially for incorporation in this volume.

REFERENCES : Original Description. *Falco vespertinus* Linnaeus, Syst. Nat., 12th ed., 1766, p. 129. " Ingria ", *i.e.* Province of St. Petersburg, Russia.

PLATE 16

GOLDEN ACRE

PLATE 15

GOLDEN EAGLE

Aquila chrysaëtos chrysaëtos (Linnaeus)

Family *ACCIPITRIDAE*

Genus *AQUILA* Brisson

GOLDEN EAGLE   PLATE 15

Aquila chrysaëtos chrysaëtos (Linnaeus)

Resident in the Highlands of Scotland and on the Inner and Outer Hebrides ; absent from the Orkneys and Shetlands. Elsewhere in Scotland very rare but nests spasmodically in the south-west. In Ireland exterminated around 1915, but has nested once very recently. Formerly bred in some districts of northern England and in the Snowdon district of Wales but has long been exterminated south of the Border. Vagrants appear at long intervals in non-breeding areas.

IDENTIFICATION : The sexes of the golden eagle are alike, but the females are somewhat larger than the males. Adult birds total thirty to thirty-five inches in length and have an enormous wing-span. They exhibit considerable variation in plumage, mainly owing to the length of time which it takes for the species to become fully adult—at least four years and possibly as much as six. When its final plumage has been attained the golden eagle is an exceedingly handsome bird. The upperparts are dark brown, against which the much paler head and nape are in strong contrast, the lanceolate feathers of the crown, nape and sides of the neck having bright tawny-buff edges and tips which wear much paler to a pale golden-buff. The underparts are brown like the back but are paler and the breast feathers incline to tawny, giving the general appearance of being golden-brown. The body feathers are liable to much variation in tone through abrasion. The tail of the adult bird is blackish-brown crossed with three irregular greyish-brown bars, the tips of all the rectrices almost black. The wings are brownish-black. The long feathers of the legs are yellowish-brown. The iris is yellowish-brown or hazel, the bill black, paler at the base. The cere is rich yellow and the exposed legs and feet are the same colour ; the claws are black.

Immature golden eagles are darker in general colour than adults. Young birds may be distinguished by the tail being white with a broad black band at the tip and by more white at the base of the wing. In this plumage they are liable to confusion with the white-tailed or sea eagle.

Distinctions between the adults of these two eagles have been mentioned under *Haliaëtus albicilla*.

The huge size of the golden eagle with its immensely powerful bill and talons should proclaim its identity at close quarters, but when seen soaring the outline of its broad wings with upturned primaries and fingers spread and the relatively longer tail should enable it to be distinguished from the buzzard when its greater size is not so apparent.

There is no white on the shoulders, as there is in the imperial eagle, and at a distance the whole bird appears blackish unless one is sufficiently close to see the golden crown and mane of some individuals. It is much less easy to identify a golden eagle in the mountain ranges of Europe and North Africa than it is in the Highlands of Scotland, but even so there is room for error should a white-tailed eagle be paying us a visit.

LOCAL DISTRIBUTION : Practically now confined to the Highlands of Scotland and the islands, with one or two other exceptions north of the Border, the golden eagle had been totally exterminated as a breeding species in the rest of Britain for many years until the dramatic appearance of a pair in Northern Ireland. Formerly, as *The Handbook* tells us, " resident in Derbyshire some two hundred years ago, in the Cheviots over one hundred years ago and in the Lake District towards the end of the eighteenth century " and apparently too in Yorkshire, it is unlikely to re-establish itself in any of these areas.

In Wales, where it is now only a very rare vagrant, recorded from Carmarthenshire, it once bred regularly in the Snowdon district. The fact that it has not colonized its ancient haunts on Snowdon (of which the old name is Eagle Mountain) is used as a strong argument by Mr. Seton Gordon that the Scottish golden eagles are not migratory as they are in Europe. It had been suggested to him that the eagle might be re-introduced into Wales, and certainly, as he states in recent correspondence with me, the project would be more likely to succeed than the attempts made to persuade the ospreys which pass through the Scottish Highlands on their way to Lapland and Sweden to check their northern journey and make their nest near some Highland loch where their species nested long ago !

The sudden reappearance in 1953 of a pair which nested successfully on the Antrim coast and reared two young, to be followed by another success in 1954 when one, and possibly two, young were reared successfully, also in Antrim,[1] is an event of great importance to all naturalists. It gives cause to hope that the golden eagle may perhaps be allowed to return to that country, where it nested extensively a century ago in the higher ranges of Munster, Connaught and Ulster.[2] Who can tell whether, with the stricter laws of protection now on the statute book, it may not return to Wales as well ?

Regarding its status in Scotland opinions are still divided. The general idea prevalent to-day that the bird is increasing in numbers needs to be accepted with caution. I have good authority for the statement that the

[1] *Irish Bird Report*, 1953, p. 9, and 1954, p. 12.

[2] In the *Irish Naturalist*, 1915, p. 63, Richard M. Barrington describes how in a taxidermist's shop in Dame Street, Dublin, in early January (presumably of the year in which he wrote) he found to his surprise and horror a freshly-killed golden eagle—a fine old male weighing 8½ lb. whose extended wings measured six feet three inches. It had been shot near Ardara, Donegal. Barrington considered it probable that this was the eagle—almost certainly the last in Ireland—which Ussher told him he had seen in 1913 on the Donegal coast north of Slieve League. It had had no mate for some seasons and was said to have inhabited the district for forty years (see also *British Birds*, xix, pp. 211 and 258).

eyries now in use have been used for centuries, and we have definite knowledge of 111 pairs and nineteen single birds which might be paired. It
is estimated by those best able to know the facts that this represents two-
thirds of the present population in Scotland. The wastage by shooting,
trapping, etc., is considerable and probably represents five to ten per cent.
per annum.

There is no need to specify the counties in which the known eyries
are situated. With possibly two exceptions, all those on the mainland are
north of the Clyde and Firth of Forth. The wilder and more inaccessible
the country the more likely is it that a pair or more will be in occupation.
Excluding North Uist, South Uist, Benbecula, Lewis and Harris, in all of
which islands the eagle breeds sparingly, I have a list of ten islands of the
Inner Hebrides where pairs are known to nest, but only in three mainland
counties does the number of pairs run into double figures.

The golden eagle has never been a native in the Shetland islands and
it apparently ceased to breed on Hoy in the Orkneys about 1840,[1] though
a pair is reported to have returned in 1901.

It would seem therefore that the status of the golden eagle in Scotland
has not changed a great deal in the last hundred years. It must be
remembered that when it was being freely said that it was on the verge of
extinction Harvie-Brown knew of over a hundred eyries.

As a vagrant it occurs from time to time in localities far from any
known nesting place, but whether these are first-year birds driven from their
birthplace or genuine visitors from abroad it is not easy to say. The
reports of " golden eagles " which appear from time to time in the press
usually turn out on closer investigation (when that is possible) to be white-
tailed eagles, which are more likely to occur as oversea migrants at rare
intervals than the subject of this essay. Young Scottish golden eagles
are more likely to disperse over the Highlands and Islands and to seek
new homes in Britain than to go overseas, but there is a strong probability
that the pair which have recently established themselves on the north coast
of Ireland were Scottish-born birds. There is no proof that the old-
established pairs ever go very far from where their eyrie is situated unless
very exceptional circumstances compel them to leave their accustomed
haunts for a comparatively short period.

On the continent of Europe, especially in the extreme north, this rule
does not apply, and as birds from that area regularly migrate south there
is nothing to prevent an odd one or two visiting the British Isles.

DISTRIBUTION ABROAD : The typical race of the golden eagle described
by Linnaeus from " Europe ", with restricted type locality Sweden, ranges
throughout Europe generally, except in the Iberian Peninsula, where
another race, *homeyeri*, occurs. Its eastern range extends beyond the

---

[1] *Ibis*, 1943, p. 8 : Eagle Clarke gives the year when it apparently ceased to breed in
Orkney as about 1850.

Urals to western Siberia, where in the region between the Rivers Ob and Yenisei the race *kamtschatica* takes its place. We in Europe ally our British golden eagles with the Swedish birds, but other opinions have been expressed, notably by Russian ornithologists, who, in their standard work on the birds of the Soviet Union, apparently follow our countryman Kirke Swann in considering British golden eagles better kept separate under another Linnaean name, *A. c. fulva*,[1] described somewhat doubtfully from Derbyshire and Wales. It will be noted that for the purposes of this book I follow Ernst Hartert in uniting British golden eagles with *Aquila chrysaëtos chrysaëtos*, as this is no place to argue the Russian point of view. As Colonel Meinertzhagen perhaps tactfully wrote in a recent work[2] : " The golden eagle breeds in various very similar races from the British Isles to Japan and North America and south to the Atlas Mountains and the Himalayas."

Being a bird which requires a very specialized environment in which to rear its young it is naturally not to be expected in lowland areas, and from such countries as Denmark, Holland, Belgium—with the possible exception of the Ardennes—and northern France it is naturally absent save as a vagrant or passage migrant. It is, however, generally distributed in the mountainous areas of France.

In the north of its range it would appear to be a great deal rarer than in former days. For instance, in Esthonia, where it is protected by law, it is now considered a rare species, and in 1946 was to be found in only three of the larger uncultivated areas where the forested country alternates with vast bogs. Just previous to that date only six occupied nests were known.

In Norway the golden eagle was undoubtedly at one time more plentiful and more widely distributed than it is to-day. It is equally certain that the change in the bird's status can largely be attributed to the disastrous law of 1845 which authorized the payment of " head money ". Though the campaign of destruction no longer receives official encouragement, " head money " for " vermin " having been abolished in 1932, there is as yet no sign of the golden eagle gaining lost ground, if indeed the number of breeding pairs does not continue to diminish.

In southern Norway the bird breeds sparingly throughout the higher-lying forested regions. According to Doctor Hagen it still does so a little to the south of latitude 59°, near Tovdal and Bygland in Aust Agder. There are eyries about the inner reaches of several of the great western fjords, but none anywhere along the coast-line, where the sea eagle alone breeds. Beyond the Trondhjem Fjord the golden eagle ranges north-wards to the 70° parallel, in East Finmark, descending in that province almost to sea-level. It does not, however, breed anywhere amongst the great chain of islands that fringes the coasts of Arctic Norway. While

[1] See H. Kirke Swann, *Bull. Brit. Orn. Club*, xlv, p. 64.
[2] *Birds of Arabia*, 1945, p. 346.

in Norway the adult golden eagles are practically sedentary, the young birds moving away from the breeding haunts in October. At that season they appear even in the most southerly coastal districts, as well as in Lofoten.

HABITS : To know the golden eagle in all its varying moods, to have watched it at all seasons and in all weathers in the Highlands and Islands of its native Scotland, to have in fact lived with the King of Birds on one's doorstep and, moreover, to have the facility to describe the romantic setting in which the eagle makes his home, has been the fortune of few men, and to none have such opportunities come more happily, or been used to better advantage, than by that great Scottish naturalist Seton Gordon, of the Isle of Skye.

In the following account of the golden eagle which he has prepared for inclusion in this book, Mr. Gordon takes us to many of the haunts of the eagle which he has known during a long life. In one passage he draws a picture of the Cairngorms in time of war, when the wild life of that romantic area—a favourite haunt of the golden eagle—was bound to suffer from an unnatural invasion of its solitudes. His plea made in this essay to the custodians of our first National Park to protect the nesting eagles from the too friendly attention of visitors, and especially from photographers, will be heartily endorsed by every naturalist in the land, for in this comparatively accessible hill country future generations should enjoy wonderful opportunities of seeing golden eagles in superb surroundings and under better conditions than ever before, *provided* the birds are allowed to breed undisturbed.

Mr. Seton Gordon's essay is the fruit of his experiences of many years and is told in his own inimitable style.

THE GOLDEN EAGLE IN SCOTLAND

CONTRIBUTED BY SETON GORDON, C.B.E.

I have often thought that the golden eagle is the very spirit of the Scottish hills and glens, and of the high moorlands plateaux. No hill country is quite the same without the King of Birds, a fact which was borne in upon us during two seasons in recent years in Switzerland. There can be few more beautiful hills in the world than those which rise from the Zermatt valley and though my wife and I were on these hills daily in 1949 and 1953 we came to realize that the skies were almost always lonely here. We never saw an eagle, but heard that one pair did indeed nest each spring in the Zermatt valley. We were told that hunters had climbed very early in the morning three days running to the eyrie, to shoot the parent eagle as it brought in food for the young. They were unsuccessful and had to be content with shooting the eaglet, then feathered. Yet the golden eagle in that canton is protected—on paper ! There was no secrecy made of the killing of the eagle ; we were told that it preyed upon hares and marmots, the quarry also of the local human hunters, who presumably grudged it a share. Scotland is fortunate in having a considerable population of golden eagles ; it is perhaps because they are usually unmolested that they are comparatively approachable.

One of the grandest haunts of this superb bird is the Cairngorm Hills, which have now (1955) become a National Park. This area, almost more than any in Scotland, felt the impact of the Second World War. It was a training ground for the British Army, and latterly for the Norwegian forces also. Indian cavalry galloped through Rothiemurchus Forest. That great mountaineer, the late F. S. Smythe, led commando units through the passes and over the tops in winter blizzards, the severity of which, as he later told his friends, exceeded in fury and intensity anything he had experienced on Everest. It is idle to pretend that the wild life of the district did not suffer from these unusual activities. Ptarmigan were shot for the pot, sometimes on the nest ; the rattle of machine guns disturbed the golden eagle at his remote haunts. Tanks prowled over the foothills and even attempted (unsuccessfully) to cross Lairig Ghru. In 1945 there was scarcely a golden eagle to be seen in the Cairngorm area, but during the last few years they have returned, although not in their earlier numbers. It is to be hoped that the National Park authorities will see that the golden eagle is not only efficiently protected, but is not visited and disturbed during the incubation season, when even a friendly visit may cause it to desert its eggs.

I like to recall the old days, when the Forest of Mar was a deer forest in the true sense of the word, when the Duke of Fife and the Princess Royal had their home at Mar Lodge, when MacDonald was head stalker, and Charles Robertson the deer watcher lived in the Corrour Bothy, to be succeeded by John Macintosh the Piper. The forest paths were kept in good order in those days and the golden eagle's position seemed more secure, for there were few people who wandered over the hills. It was from the door of Corrour Bothy that I watched, one summer day, a golden eagle rise in spirals on the north wind until it had become invisible to the unaided eye and continued to rise until it became invisible even in the field of a stalking glass of twenty-six magnifications. I have often wondered to what height the eagle had attained. It must have been the best part of two miles above me—at least 10,000 feet. The day was fine and clear, and I have sometimes pondered what hills, at that height, were visible to the eagle. He must have seen without difficulty the Cuillin Hills in the Isle of Skye, and perhaps the islands of Mull and Jura ; northward his view must have extended across Caithness to Orkney. That was an exceptionally fine summer, much of which I spent studying the snow bunting (and incidentally the golden eagle also) at his singing station almost 4000 feet above the sea. There was no darkness in those June nights in the country of the eagle and the snow bunting, and long before the eagle was astir the snow bunting was singing his strong, melodious song. As the sun strengthened I could see, across intervening hills, the snow-beds on distant Ben Nevis gleaming in sun on the western horizon. More rarely the cone of Cruachan above the Atlantic fjord Loch Etive could be seen, and the even sharper peak of one of the Sisters of Kintail.

It was in the Cairngorm area that I witnessed, from a hide, a most thrilling approach of a golden eagle to his eyrie, built on the crown of a very old Scots fir. The eagle had been hunting over the high tops and was approaching in a steep slant. His approach was literally breath-taking. From an aeroplane an eagle has been timed to exceed ninety miles an hour in level flight and in this steep slant, with the extra weight of a ptarmigan in his claws to help him, his downward rush must have well exceeded the speed of 120 miles an hour. How thrilling it must be, even for a golden eagle, to make approach to his home at this speed !

In the Western Highlands and Hebrides of Scotland the country of the eagle is of a different character from that in the Central Highlands. Here, in the Isle of Skye and on the mainland of Wester Ross, the high hills closely approach the ocean, and in five minutes' flight the golden eagle may glide from a country of unbroken snow to the blue deeps of the Atlantic. One imagines that to a flier of the calibre of the golden eagle the Minches and the North Channel which separates Scotland from the north coast of Ireland constitute no barrier at all. There is in my mind no doubt that the children of the eagles which have recently nested successfully in the Mull of Kintyre area are the eagles which have made a home for themselves and have reared young on the north coast of Ireland. In the same manner the eagles which have colonized the Outer Hebrides may have crossed the Minch (which they could do in ten minutes) from the Isle of Skye.

I have so far written of the spring and summer quarters of the golden eagle. In northern Europe, and in North America, there is a definite south migration of this bird in autumn—for example, almost all the young golden eagles leave Lapland as winter sets in—but in Scotland there is no definite southward flight. Indeed in most parts of the Highlands and Islands the eagle may be considered a firm resident. Exceptional weather conditions and a consequent scarcity of food may cause them for a short time to move from their accustomed haunts, as, for instance, during the exceedingly hard weather in February 1947, when a most stay-at-home pair of golden eagles in the Isle of Skye disappeared for a month from their accustomed haunts. Yet even in the high ground of the Central Highlands, where it is usual for snow to lie for long periods, the golden eagle is not a migratory bird.

Surprisingly little is known of the habits of the young eagles after they have been driven away in October or early November by their parents.

There are a few pairs of eagles in which the family bond is so strong that the young eagle (I have not known this to happen where two have been reared) remains with its parents until the close of the year, but the general rule is that the young are driven from the parental territory in October. Where do they go? The reports of wandering eagles in England in winter almost always refer to the white-tailed or sea eagle. It would seem that young golden eagles distribute themselves, their first winter, over the Scottish Highlands. As I write this December day, there are reports of a young golden eagle taking shelter in the wooded grounds of Viewfield House, near Portree in the Isle of Skye, and of being remarkably tame. The golden eagle is not supposed to be fully mature until it has reached the age of four years, but from my personal observations I am convinced that a pair of eagles may mate, but not actually lay, while they are still immature, and may wander together before they have actually chosen a nesting territory. The old-fashioned Highland stalker had the comforting belief that young golden eagles crossed the sea to Norway—why, he could not explain. Much knowledge of the movements of young birds has been gained by ringing, or banding as it is termed across the Atlantic, but very few young golden eagles have been ringed, and I have not heard of a single recovery.

Like the buzzard, the golden eagle may choose either a tree or a ledge of rock in which to nest. In the Central Highlands of Scotland the nesting site often is in a tree. In the West Highlands a ledge of rock is almost always the site of the eyrie. Most pairs of eagles have two eyries; some have three, and the changes are rung regularly between them. By the end of the nesting season an eyrie has become fouled by much prey lying in it, and by leaving the nest for the cleansing action of two winters it is more acceptable to the parent birds. A tree eyrie, being more sheltered from the elements than a rock eyrie, and being added to each alternate spring, some-times becomes a very large and bulky structure. The largest eyrie I know is in the Forest of Mar. I have watched this eyrie grow since 1909, and when I last saw it, in 1952, I estimated its height from base to crown as approxi-mately fifteen feet. I have never seen a rock eyrie of anything like this size. The nesting tree is almost always a Scots fir, but one pair of eagles I used long ago to watch in Inchrory Forest nested in a birch. The eyrie in time fell to the ground, and the eagles did not again nest in the tree.

The nesting material, in a tree eyrie, is usually branches of Scots fir. Large dead branches are used as foundations of the eyrie and the platform is made of fresh fir shoots, their green needles adding a touch of beauty to the structure. It is the almost unvarying rule that the cup of the nest is lined with leaves of the great wood rush, *Luzula sylvatica*. Have birds an æsthetic sense? It would appear that the eagle has one. Why else should she carry to the nest, at intervals after the eaglets have hatched, rowan branches in full leaf, often with flowers on them? Why should she rarely, if ever, at this stage, bring the green-needled branches of fir which, earlier in the spring, she had intertwined to form a platform to hold the nesting cup ? I have seen the mother eagle lay a rowan branch in delicate leaf gently across her eaglet's back, and then step back a pace to admire the effect. Who can fathom the mind of a bird ? Certainly not those who give it credit for no intelligence.

The platform of the eyrie and the small cup in the centre having been skilfully constructed—both sexes may share this work—the female eagle lays her first egg. In the Highlands of Scotland the first egg is occasionally laid as early as 4th March, and one pair which I have studied closely in the West Highlands have eggs regularly around 8th to 11th March. A more normal date is around 16th March. Some eagles do not lay until near the end of the month, and, exceptionally, April is the laying season for a few pairs, perhaps young birds laying their first clutch. An interval of several days may elapse between the laying of the first and second egg. The usual clutch consists of two ; occasionally three are found, and one West Highland eagle of my acquaintance laid three eggs and reared three young each season for at least six years and probably more. There is a single instance of a Scottish clutch of four.

At most eyries it seems that the incubation duties are performed by the female bird with no help from her mate, but in the light of my own observations, over a number of seasons, of one West Highland pair, it may be that the male takes a greater part in the duties of incubation than is generally imagined. Careful and prolonged observations at an eyrie before the eggs hatch are rarely easy, for the golden eagle is liable to desert if disturbed. The pair of golden eagles which I have been able to study closely are perhaps a model pair—at all events the male bird, which I have come to know well, both from his small size and from his characteristics, rarely allows his mate to brood for more than two hours before flying in to the eyrie and standing quietly on the edge until he has persuaded his mate to rise and allow him to take a spell of duty on the eggs. Sometimes, when she is comfortably settled and is reluctant to rise, he bends forward, his head close to hers, and quite obviously does his best to persuade her to make way for him. This in the end she almost always does and then, before himself brooding, he often escorts her a little way on her flight.

From the careful observations of more than one observer the incubation period would seem to be forty-one to forty-two days. The eaglets take a good many hours to break the thick, polished shell, light brown in ground colour and more or less thickly spotted with rusty-red markings at the larger end. The white down which clothes the baby eaglets remains for three weeks, at the end of which time the dark quills of the earliest feathers begin to show. During the first days of its life the eaglet is closely brooded, but at the end of a week, when it is still small and helpless, it may be left by both its parents for several hours if the day be fine and calm. Considering that a pair of ravens often share the cliff with the eagles and that there is no love lost between the two species, the eagles appear to be taking a risk in leaving their small young unguarded. I have known a pair of eagles mysteriously lose their eaglet, and I should not be surprised if the eaglet had provided a tasty meal for one of the ravens. The young golden eagle is feathered for some considerable time before it takes its first flight. This it does when it is approximately eleven to twelve weeks old. It may remain in the neighbourhood of the nesting site for at least two months longer and may be fed at intervals by its parents long after it is apparently as skilled in flight as they are.

The blue or mountain hare was formerly the chief prey of the golden eagle in Scotland, but this animal has decreased in a remarkable manner, and now (1955) I should say that the chief article of food is the rabbit. What will happen if myxomatosis, the fell rabbit disease, destroys the rabbit population of the Highlands ? In the hilly region there is little appearance of it as yet, but if and when it arrives both buzzard and golden eagle will find their main source of food cut off. Next to hare and rabbit, I should put the red grouse and ptarmigan as the eagle's prey. For less than a month in the year lambs may on occasion be taken. This I have seen happen, yet I say confidently that there are many pairs of golden eagles in the Highlands which have never taken a lamb. Indeed in the Central Highlands lamb-slaying by the golden eagle is the exception.

On one occasion in the Isle of Mull a friend of mine on visiting a golden eagle's eyrie found no fewer than six grey crows laid out, neatly plucked, as prey. I have frequently seen stoats at an eyrie, and have been told by other observers that they also have found them, so it would seem that this small animal, most destructive to game, is the eagle's habitual prey. At an eyrie in the old Caledonian Forest near Aviemore squirrels were brought in on several occasions during the weeks when my wife and I kept an almost daily watch. Although I have not seen a mouse brought to the young, I have seen the male bird catch and carry in a mouse for his mate, and I have frequently seen both adult and immature golden eagles hunting mice. Unusual prey was a full-grown heron which was carried in to the eyrie by a golden eagle nesting on a comparatively low rock close to a well-known salmon river on the west coast.

During the twelve weeks the eaglets are in the nest the parent eagle— it is the male bird that does almost all the hunting—must cover thousands of miles, and it is perhaps not surprising that towards the end of the fledging period he seems to lose interest in his offspring. During the last fortnight the eyrie may not be visited more than once in the day with food—sometimes not even that. Once the eaglet has become airborne its parents appear to take more interest in it. In August and September one often sees the family party of eagles sailing together, like a small flight of aeroplanes, and food continues to be brought in for the eaglet when it is almost indistinguishable in the air from its father and mother.

SUPPLEMENTARY NOTES FROM OTHER SOURCES : In the foregoing account Mr. Seton Gordon has confined himself to his own personal experiences, which cover a large field, but a bird such as the golden eagle has attracted many naturalists and around it there has grown up a considerable literature. It is to some points in that literature that I would now draw attention.

In Scotland, as Mr. Gordon has shown, the principal food of the golden eagle consists mainly of mountain hares, ptarmigan, grouse and particularly rabbits. That diet is supported by the evidence of Mr. Duncan Macdonald,[1] who enters into the endless controversy as to whether this eagle normally destroys lambs. He has examined many eyries in western Scotland and only once was a lamb brought to the eyrie, and that at a time when there had been much snow and hard weather, which might account for the lamb's death from exposure. In correspondence with me Mr. Seton Gordon cites a small island of the Inner Hebrides upon which two pairs of eagles nest regularly and where they say they have never lost a lamb ; with his unrivalled experience he writes : " I think the lamb-killing by occasional eagles is greatly magnified and that many, indeed most, of the lambs taken are found dead on the hillside." Only twice in his life has he seen a golden eagle carry off a living lamb. That occasionally a rogue eagle will take to lamb-killing in earnest cannot be doubted—a recent case in Lewis has been widely publicized in the press—and if the facts are proven the culprit met with his deserts, but that is no reason why the whole population of golden eagles should suffer. I am firmly convinced that the majority of Scottish eagles have never touched a living lamb and that unless other food entirely fails them, they are nothing like the menace to the sheep-farmer that they are reputed to be. With the white-tailed eagle it was different, and many of the crimes of that bird must have been placed at the door of the golden eagle, whose reputation suffered in consequence. Captain H. A. Gilbert and Arthur Brook had more opportunities than most naturalists in bygone days to assess the danger to lambs from the golden eagle and their opinion may here be quoted. " Undoubtedly," they wrote, " still-born lambs which weigh little more than a large hare are often picked off the hillside and carried to the nest, but living lambs are rarely attacked." Only five cases of the golden eagle carrying off a living lamb came under their notice in many years and in three of them the lamb was attacked within an hour of its birth. They quote the opinion of Highland shepherds that a lamb is quite safe after it is from ten days to a fortnight old.

The castings of a golden eagle which nested within recent years in south-west Scotland were found from analysis made at the Royal Scottish Museum to contain[2] fragments of a fox, carrion crow, pheasant, teal and mountain hares. The capture of a curlew by an eagle, as recorded by Mr.

[1] *British Birds*, xix, p. 219.
[2] *Scottish Naturalist*, 1951, p. 67.

D. Macdonald, must be very rare. In northern Europe the eagle's fare is probably more varied and some surprisingly large birds appear to be taken. In Esthonia, for instance, among the species of animals and birds brought to a nest by the parents for food [1] were *Erinaceus europaeus*, *Putorius putorius*, *Martes martes*, *Strix aluco*, *Grus grus* (!) and *Tetrastes bonasia*.

There cannot be many who have had the opportunity which fell to General Sir Philip Christison of witnessing a fight between a golden eagle and a wild cat. The encounter took place near Mam Ratagan in Kintail in January 1909, when just after dawn Sir Philip and a shepherd named John McRae saw through the glass a wild cat making a meal of a white hare. There was frozen snow on the hill at the time. Suddenly an eagle swooped down several times and then alighted a few yards from the cat. It then sidled up to it and the cat went for it. A struggle ensued and the eagle raised flight by hopping to the edge of a small cliff with the cat hanging on. The eagle flattened out and began to gain height. When very high— Sir Philip estimated 1500 to 2000 feet above the hill—he and his companion saw the cat coming down and found it dashed to pieces on the rocks. Next day word that a sick eagle had been seen about three miles away brought them to the scene, where a golden eagle terribly wounded inside the thigh and unable to stand or move was discovered. The bird was put out of its misery and was eventually, as a mounted specimen, offered to the Royal Scottish Museum. [2]

Few accounts which I have read of the golden eagle make mention of its cry. Duncan Macdonald describes it as a yelling bark but acknowledges that he has only heard it once, uttered by a bird which resented his presence near its eyrie. The birds are usually silent once they have become airborne but when in the nest the young eaglets utter faint squeaks which turn later to yelps in a shrill edition of their parents' voice.

Nearly all raptorial birds when hunting for prey have their own particular beats, and the golden eagle is no exception. Colonel Meinertzhagen had a good example of this in Ross-shire, where a pair of golden eagles breeding on the estate had a territory of about eight miles from the nest, and there many opportunities of watching them occurred, both in winter and in summer.

In Corrie Fiola on Ben Wyvis they would always hunt in the morning in clear weather from about 11 a.m. to 2 p.m. In mist or rain they would come lower down and could always be found on the south shoulder of the mountain, either soaring for grouse or hunting low for hares. With snow on the ground they had a different technique : they would hunt the summit of Wyvis for ptarmigan and hares in the early morning and in the afternoon would come lower down for grouse between 2 and 3.30. Their roost was on a cliff on the north side of the mountain.

[1] Mait Zastrov in *Vär Fågelvärld*, 1946, summary, pp. 79-80.
[2] *Scottish Naturalist*, 1949, No. 2, p. 121.

They would sally out about an hour after sunrise in fine weather, but an hour later in rain or fog. Both would start out together, gain height, have a good look at the weather and prospects, circle round the summit and then begin the day's work. As Meinertzhagen here describes, the routine was regular, and by posting himself at the proper place he could always rely on seeing them. A hare drive in winter was a sure attraction and the eagle would come to the sound of the guns and join in by picking up wounded animals.

Keepers on the big grouse moors have good cause to fear the arrival of an eagle when a grouse drive is in progress. I have experienced that catastrophe only once, on the moors above Dunkeld belonging to the Duke of Atholl. We were all in our butts and the beaters had begun the drive; birds were plentiful and coming nicely towards the guns when suddenly a golden eagle appeared over the crest of a hill. In a moment all was panic. The approaching birds scattered in every direction, doubling back and breaking away, and no amount of frantic flag-wagging by the flankers would turn them. The drive was virtually at an end before a shot had been fired.

Much has been written of the eagle's superlative flight. As Meinertzhagen has recorded, " they can catch hares in a rough-and-tumble flight through peat hags, turning and twisting like a terrier after a rat; they can come down on ptarmigan or grouse like a thunderbolt, and they will take birds on the wing as large as wild geese ". On the ground they are naturally handicapped by their weight but for all that they can move with facility when they wish. Seton Gordon tells elsewhere of an experience he had with an eagle in bygone days. He was watching a male bird standing on short grass with sheep grazing around him. Suddenly to his surprise the eagle ran forward about ten yards with the same motion as a feeding starling, the feet being moved alternately, the steps short and made quickly. The eagle did not hop.

Aerial displays such as the one witnessed in Inverness by Miss Winifred Ross and communicated by her to *British Birds* [1] are not seen every day and the performance must have been remarkable. The date was 7th June and the young had already hatched and were believed to be still in the eyrie. The female parent was seen to come over the hill from the direction of the nest and was joined by the male from the opposite direction. They circled round each other, spiralling a little but not gaining much height. Then, suddenly gaining speed, they approached each other and appeared to be going to collide head on, but at the last moment both birds put out their legs and the female dropped below and turned over on her back; the legs touched for an instant exactly as an acrobat touches his partner for balance, and she completed the turn. Circling recommenced and the next time they met she did two complete turns, the legs touching at

[1] Vol. xxxv, pp. 82-83.

each turn when she was on her back. They then began to gain height in spirals and at the final meeting they flew towards each other at very high speed. The female performed three turns and as she finished the third the male did a complete turn above her. The turns were done with extraordinary rapidity and, as Miss Ross describes, it was a fine sight against a blue sky with brilliant sunshine lighting up every feather. After the display both birds spiralled to a great height and, flying towards the headwaters of the stream where their eyrie was situated, disappeared behind the hills.

Performances of the kind described are probably confined, when they do take place, to the breeding season. Desmond Nethersole-Thompson has contributed additional notes on this subject which have been incorporated in Witherby's *Handbook*.

In this essay Mr. Seton Gordon has already described the favourite nesting sites of the golden eagle in the Scottish Highlands, but it may perhaps be mentioned that in north-west Russia Colonel Meiklejohn found its nest at the top of a very tall pine. In the field notes which he left me he observes that whereas in Britain he usually found the nest on the ledge of a cliff as already described, abroad the reverse was the rule, for there the eagle often nests in very tall trees. Eggs which came under his notice varied a good deal, which is not surprising.

In the British Museum collection there is a fine series of clutches of the golden eagle taken in various localities in Europe from northern Scotland to the Taurus Mountains and these represent most of the types which the golden eagle lays. They are well described by Oates as broadly oval, elliptical or spheroidal in shape; the shell is rough and devoid of gloss. The ground colour varies from white to a dingy pinkish-buff and the markings are extremely varied. A certain number of eggs are plain white and others are very sparingly marked, but the majority are very handsomely spotted, blotched and smeared with various shades of rufous, brown, purplish-grey and brownish-pink. In one common type the shell is covered with spots and well-defined small blotches of rufous; in another the markings consist of specks and blotches of rufous which form a confluent cap at the larger end. In another type the egg is thickly smeared and blotched with chocolate-brown. A few specimens are very thickly smeared and streaked with brownish-pink, while others are densely blotched with reddish-brown and underlying purplish-grey. The golden eagle is single-brooded. If the first clutch is taken the birds may breed again but by no means invariably. Very shy at the eyrie, it is easily made to desert.

100 British-taken eggs of the golden eagle measured by F. C. R. Jourdain have an average of 77·02 × 59·48 mm. Max. 88·9 × 66. Min. 70·3 × 56 and 77·6 × 51 mm.

REFERENCES : Original Description. *Falco chrysaëtos* Linnaeus, Syst. Nat., 10th ed., 1758, p. 88. Europe. Restricted type locality Sweden.

GREATER SPOTTED EAGLE   PLATE 16

Aquila clanga Pallas

A rare Accidental Visitor which has occurred about fifteen times

IDENTIFICATION : It is not possible to be sure of the identity of this eagle unless critically handled, for the similarity of the species to the lesser spotted eagle, *Aquila pomarina*, is such that only an expert is likely to be able to tell them apart. The very pale to white upper tail-coverts, considered by A. Quednau to distinguish the present species from *A. pomarina* even in the field, have been shown to be an unreliable character, for, as Bernard Tucker has pointed out, " though birds showing well-marked white (upper tail-coverts) can be accepted as *A. clanga*, those having a little dingy white or none may be either, and the character must be used with caution ". That applies only to the adult bird. In general *A. clanga* is darker brown than *A. pomarina* and in adult dress the plumage of both species is uniform. Only immature birds are spotted, and the name " spotted eagle " is therefore most misleading once *A. clanga* and *A. pomarina* have assumed fully adult dress, which apparently does not take place until they are four to four and a half years old. The younger the bird the more intense is the spotting of the upperparts, the juvenile in its first year having on the feathers of the back, rump and scapulars broad central spots or streaks of light buff.

Young birds of *Aquila clanga*—to quote Tucker once more—differ from the young of *Aquila pomarina* in being of a darker colour, and in having no rust patch on the nape, usually a well marked area of white or whitish at the base of the tail, and more conspicuous development of the pale spots and streaks of the upperparts.

There is no particular reason why the lesser spotted eagle should not some day figure on the British List as a straggler, and, as Mr Witherby pointed out [1] so long ago as 1921, " while there is no clear proof that the lesser spotted eagle (*A. pomarina*) has ever occurred in the British Islands, some of the records of the spotted eagle are so wanting in essential details that it is impossible to say to which species they refer ".

Another unfortunate misnomer is the *lesser* spotted eagle, for the measurements in each sex overlap. We must therefore fall back on the comparative distinctions which Mr Witherby pointed out—the " considerably darker coloration of the upper parts of *A. clanga* at all ages, and, in immature examples the larger spots on the mantle than in *A. pomarina* ". It may be that the round-shaped nostrils exhibited by both the spotted eagles will distinguish them from the other eagles (which have slit-shaped nostrils) with which they may be confused. This character is rightly given prominence in *The Handbook of British Birds*.

[1] *British Birds*, xiv, pp. 180 and 209.

The following is a technical description of *Aquila clanga* by Colonel Meinertzhagen borrowed from his *Birds of Arabia* :

Nostrils round or rarely square, never longer than broad ; seventh primary usually not more than 60 mm. shorter than the tip of the longest and with the outer web more abruptly and deeper notched than in *A. pomarina*, the lesser spotted eagle. Adults, sexes alike. Whole plumage dark brown, with a plum-like gloss in very fresh plumage ; under parts slightly paler than mantle ; tail blackish brown, with sometimes indications of greyish barring. The immature bird is darker than the adult, feathers of crown and nape with buff tips ; rest of upper parts streaked or spotted buff or white ; under parts broadly streaked buff ; tail with slightly more barring than in adults ; between this plumage and that of the adult every inter-gradation of plumage occurs according to age. Fully adult plumage is probably not acquired until after four years. Third primary usually 10-20 mm. shorter than the longest. Wing 495-560 mm. Iris greyish brown.

OCCURRENCES [1] IN GREAT BRITAIN : Ireland : In January 1845 two spotted eagles were shot at Youghal, Co. Cork, one of which is in the National Museum.[2] This is the only record for Ireland, if indeed it proves to be *A. clanga* as suspected.

Scotland : Mr. Witherby listed this bird as " One probable Aberdeenshire Sept. 1861 ", but it seems that a specimen of the spotted eagle in the City Museum, Leeds, is the bird in question, shot on 20th September 1861 by the Speaker of the House of Commons. For further details see *Birds of Scotland*, 1953, p. 300, where the name is enclosed in square brackets. The evidence given certainly points to the bird having once been obtained in Scotland.

England : Cornwall, December 1860 ; Cornwall, November 1861 ; Hampshire, December 1861 ; *Berkshire, October 1872 ; Walney Island†,

* Examined by H. F. Witherby.

† See Clifford Oakes, *The Birds of Lancashire*, p. 187, and Macpherson, *Fauna of Lakeland*, p. 186.

[1] The late Harry Witherby took great pains to examine every specimen within reach of the spotted eagle reputed to have been taken in Britain and in *British Birds*, xiv, 1921, pp. 180-182 and 209, went into great detail of the history of each specimen said to have been killed. Eleven are there enumerated and mention is made of another taken at sea off the Norfolk coast. I have therefore copied the list given in *The Handbook* for which Mr. Witherby was responsible, which brings the list up to date to the end of 1942, for there were no additions to the records published in the Supplement to the 1938 edition. Any which may have occurred *since* that date will be included in their proper place.

[2] " This bird has never been critically examined." It seems an extraordinary thing that the statement to that effect made in 1921 by Mr. Witherby is merely copied by the authors of *The Birds of Ireland* (1954) and that not one of the four authors of that important work —Colonel Scroope in particular—appears to have examined the specimen. They are content to observe : " As other British-taken examples appear to have been of this species it seems probable that those above [the Youghal examples] were similar." They add that one of these specimens, the only one preserved, is now in the National Museum.

PLATE 16

GREATER SPOTTED EAGLE

Aquila clanga Pallas

Upper Figure . . Adult
Lower Figure . . Immature

PLATE 10

GREATER SPOTTED EAGLE

Aquila clanga Pallas

Upper figure . . . Adult
Lower figure . . . Immature

Lancashire, 1875 ; Northumberland, October 1885[1] ; Essex, October 1891 ; Essex, November 1891 ; *Suffolk, November 1891 (one shot, one seen) ; Suffolk, January 1892 ; †Norfolk, October 1907 (140 miles from coast in North Sea) ; *Essex, April 1908 ; *Hereford, November 1915.

In addition to having wandered to Britain this eagle has been recorded as a vagrant in Sweden, Denmark, Holland, Belgium (six times at least), Luxembourg, France, Germany, Austria, Italy, Sicily and once apparently in Algeria.

DISTRIBUTION ABROAD : In very general terms the greater spotted eagle has been known to nest from Finland (spasmodically) and the Baltic States eastwards to the Ural Mountains. In Germany [2] it is known to have bred regularly only in eastern Prussia. It has also been found nesting in Galicia, Hungary and Croatia. The breeding record from Macedonia seems open to doubt, and this species has never occurred as a breeding bird in Greece or Albania, so Doctor E. Stresemann informs me. Of its distribution in Czecho-Slovakia I have no recent information. To Italy it is a rather rare migrant which may very exceptionally remain to nest. It is reported to occur in eastern Jugoslavia, whence its range extends eastwards north of the Black and Caspian Seas. In the extreme west of its range, i.e. in Finland, it has been known to breed in two districts : about Vasa and Björneborg. Nests were found in 1884, 1885 and 1886, and a young bird was killed in 1887. Another nest was taken in 1892 and others were found as late as 1916. Whether it has bred since then no one apparently knows. The *lesser* spotted eagle is very rare in Finland and does not breed.

Owing to the kindness of Madame Kozlova I am now able to give the range of this eagle in the U.S.S.R. with much more precision than would otherwise have been possible. From the limits of its northern range in the Baltic States, the greater spotted eagle extends to Leningrad, Onega Lake and probably to the eastern shores of the White Sea, in the region of which an adult bird was procured on 20th June 1941 near Holmogory in the Archangel district. It ranges thence to the middle course of the

---

* Examined by H. F. Witherby.

† Specimen captured and sent to London Zoological Gardens, where examined by J. H. Gurney (cf. *Zoologist*, 1908, p. 131).

[1] Doctor Blair assures me that this is the only example known to have been obtained in Northumberland. The history of this specimen is to be found in Bolam's *Birds of Northumberland and the Eastern Borders*. The bird remained in the possession of the Cresswell family until 1925-26, when it was presented to the Hancock Museum. Doctor Blair writes that it was beautifully mounted and is fully as handsome as the two immature spotted eagles selected by Lord Lilford as subjects for Thorburn. Hancock examined it himself.

[2] As recorded in a personal letter to the author from Professor Erwin Stresemann of Berlin, dated 3rd November 1954.

Petchora River, to latitude 60° N. in the Ural Mountains. In western Siberia the northern limit of the range of this eagle acquires a slight southern trend. It is to be found breeding throughout the forest-steppe zone, mostly in birch plantations and penetrating no further north than Surgut and Tomsk on the River Ob. Still further east its northern range extends to the regions of Yenisseisk on the Yenisei River and Kirensk on the upper reaches of the Lena, while summer records exist from Irkutsk, not far from the south-west shore of Lake Baikal.

The greater spotted eagle breeds also in southern Transbaikalia, north to Tschita and Srietensk on the Onon River, a tributary of the Amur. It has been obtained in the Kentei Mountains of northern Mongolia on 29th June. There are summer records from the mouth of the Kumara River—a tributary of the Amur—and from the mouth of the Ussuri, but it has definitely been found breeding only in the southern parts of Ussuri Land, *i.e.* on the lower reaches of the Iman River.

The southern limits of the range of this eagle in Soviet territory are not well defined, Madame Kozlova informs me. Its southern boundary extends apparently through the northern portions of the Ukraine south to the Pripet River (a tributary of the Dnieper north of Kief) and Charkow Government to the middle reaches of the Volga and Ural Rivers. Along the valley of the Volga this eagle seems to penetrate south to the river mouth. From the southern region of the Ural Mountains there are summer records from the upper reaches of the Rivers Bielaya and Sakmara and from the vicinity of Troitsk, in the eastern offshoots of the Ural Mountains.

Further east the boundary passes approximately along latitude 54° N. to the Altai Mountains, where the spotted eagle has been found during the summer months by Professor Sushkin.

Aquila clanga is known to breed sporadically south of the southern limit of its range as here defined—in the Zaissan Depression and on the lower Syr-Daria River. There are also summer records from the Caucasus but breeding is doubtful.

It must be added that in the Altai Mountains the greater spotted eagle ranges to about 500 metres above sea-level.

HABITS : Madame Kozlova's field observations have special reference to the bird's habitat in Russia ; she writes as follows : " The spotted eagle is a denizen of open lowland woods, with meadows and fields in the vicinity and marshy meadows near the forest-rim. It is often found nesting in forested river valleys. In southern Siberia it frequents mostly birch groves in the forest-steppe zone, but is occasionally found nesting in the semi-desert, as, for instance, on the lower Syr-Daria in Turkestan, where riparian vegetation—willows, poplars, saxaul (*Haloxylon*), etc.—abounds." As already noted it is found in the Altai up to 500 metres altitude.

Regarding the eagle's movements in various parts of its range Madame Kozlova observes : " First arrivals have been noted in the Ukraine near

Charkow from 22nd March to 28th April in different years. In the south
Ural Mountains in April. In the Zaissan Depression from 27th April to
2nd May and in the region of the Aral Sea and in eastern Siberia in early
April.

" The spotted eagle leaves the Ukraine in early September, some years
not until late October, while on the lower Dnieper belated individuals
were recorded on 4th November. Near Krasnoiarsk the last eagles depart
by the end of September, in Transbaikalia about 23rd September and in
Ussuri Land between the 11th and 25th of that month."

Only twice during her extensive travels has Madame Kozlova observed
Aquila clanga on the outskirts of Kentei during her stay in northern
Mongolia. The first occasion was in June on the lower reaches of a
mountain river. The upper belt of the gently sloping mountains bordering
the river valley was covered with bright larch woods which did not descend
to the river bed but thinned out to steppe. The eagle perched on a dry
branch of a larch on the forest edge. From there the bird had a wide
outlook over the steppes and meadows below. Madame Kozlova succeeded
in securing this specimen but never saw any more of the eagles in the same
valley. Her second specimen was obtained in September in another region
of Kentei. The bird was first seen soaring above a steppe river valley
with no trees in the vicinity, and was evidently on migration.

Discussing its prey in the notes which she has sent me Madame
Kozlova observes that in eastern Europe, Transbaikalia and eastern Siberia
the food of this eagle consists mainly of rodents—marmots, *Alactaga*,
Ochotona, *Citellus*, *Cricetulus*, *Microtus*, etc., together with hares and
squirrels. Insectivora : *Sorex* (Transbaikalia). The following birds are
also recorded : *Anatidae* of various species, *Lyrurus tetrix*, *Corvus
frugilegus*, *Corvus corone*, *Pica pica*, *Asio flammeus* and *Emberiza* of
various species. Young larks just out of the nest are sometimes caught and
it has been observed that this eagle will go to considerable trouble *running*
after the young birds which are not able to fly, but seldom succeeds in
catching them. Sometimes fish have been recorded as appearing on its
menu. There are actual records of this from Tshkalow (formerly Orenburg), Ussuri Land and the Syr-Daria River in Turkestan. Frogs, lizards
and large insects are often captured.

The feeding habits of the spotted eagle have been the subject of
contributions by E. Moltoni to an Italian quarterly [1] and he gives a long list
of mammals, birds, reptiles, frogs and toads, a fish, insects and molluscs
upon which this eagle has been known to prey.

BREEDING HABITS : Very little has been published concerning the
nesting of the greater spotted eagle, at any rate in works accessible in this
country, and I therefore include in this account the fresh notes on the
subject which I have received.

[1] *Rivista Italiana di Ornithologia*, xii, 1943, pp. 97-100.

Asia : Madame Kozlova's notes, compiled from Russian sources, are as follows :

Nests of the greater spotted eagle are found in tall trees—pines, oaks, willows, poplars—and in the valley of the Syr-Daria River on saxaul (*Haloxylon*), with its stout, crooked trunk and branches. Most nests are placed eight to twelve metres from the ground but in western Siberia, where this eagle builds in willow trees, sometimes not above three metres.

Full clutches have been found in the Charkow Government on 8th and 10th May and fresh eggs have been taken in the region of Ufa on 6th and 10th May. The full clutch consists of two eggs only, rarely only one.

Downy young have been found in the Witebsk Government on 15th June ; the period of incubation is about six weeks and incubation begins with the first egg.

Europe : The late Colonel R. F. Meiklejohn has an account in his diary—now in my possession—of finding a nest of *Aquila clanga* in Esthonia on 13th May 1921 in a huge almost primeval forest of pine and fir with some silver birch. The eagle was seen to leave its nest in the top fork of a dead pine which leant over at an angle and presented a difficult climb. The eyrie was a bulky structure of sticks lined with grass, soft material and bits of fur. It contained two eggs, almost fresh. They were beautifully marked, one egg being reddish-brown with purplish ashy-grey, the other having all the lower half suffused with reddish-brown, culminating in large blotches of this colour at the larger end. After the eggs had been taken the male returned to the nest with a rat in its beak and sat for several seconds on its edge. Later on the same day, 13th May, Colonel Meiklejohn found, only some fifteen feet from the ground in the fork of a very large fir, another eyrie which appeared just ready for eggs. This nest was almost two miles distant from the first he had found. In May 1926 another eyrie was discovered near Matzul Wiek, Esthonia, about thirty feet up in a tall thick fir in a large forest, but unfortunately the female had been shot as she was completing building.

Colonel Meiklejohn states that subsequent investigations, including a specimen from the locality to which his first notes referred, proved the bird to be the greater spotted and not the lesser spotted eagle as first suspected.

The eggs of the greater spotted eagle in the British Museum collection, although slightly larger than those of the lesser spotted eagle, are nevertheless quite inseparable. Many of the eggs taken in Europe are richly coloured, though others are paler, being marked with light rufous and purplish-grey. F. C. R. Jourdain describes eggs which he personally measured as having a ground colour of greyish-white, frequently unmarked and without gloss, but at times rather sparingly spotted or blotched with dark brown and some ashy shell markings. Fifty-six eggs, mostly from Transcaspia, show an average measurement of $68 \cdot 23 \times 54 \cdot 15$ mm. Max. $74 \cdot 6 \times 55 \cdot 6$ and $74 \cdot 4 \times 58$ mm. Min. $64 \cdot 4 \times 52 \cdot 8$ and $67 \cdot 2 \times 51 \cdot 2$ mm.

REFERENCES : Original Description. *Aquila clanga* Pallas, Zoogr. Rosso-Asiat., i, 1811, p. 351 : Russia.

PLATE 17

ROUGH-LEGGED BUZZARD
Buteo lagopus lagopus (Pontoppidan)

Genus *BUTEO* Lacépède

ROUGH-LEGGED BUZZARD PLATE 17

Buteo lagopus lagopus (Pontoppidan)

An Irregular though fairly frequent Visitor in autumn and winter, mainly to Scotland. Occasional in Northern Ireland. At rare intervals arrives in Britain in considerable numbers.

IDENTIFICATION: The rough-legged buzzard somewhat exceeds the common buzzard in measurements but this difference is too slight to serve as a useful distinction in the field. Of the two the former is generally the lighter, white or cream predominating in the handsome pattern on the plumage of the lower parts, and the crown and nape being often so slightly streaked as to appear almost hoary. Particularly striking, as the bird soars overhead, are the bold contrasts on the underside of the wing of the sharply-defined carpal patches and the black tips of the primaries against the otherwise light feathering of the underwing. Members of the genus *Buteo* are, however, subject to considerable variation: in some of the darker examples of *Buteo lagopus*, for instance, the breast and abdomen are of an almost uniform deep brown, the feathers of the head being heavily streaked with the same colour, while, on the other hand, largely white individuals occur amongst the more extreme varieties. The only reliable, as well as the most readily noted, means of distinguishing the rough-legged buzzard is to be found in the conspicuous light tail with its broad dark terminal band. In flight the feathered tarsi rarely appear in view, apart from brief glimpses upon arising and alighting, and even when the bird is at rest they may be almost concealed, the plumage of this northern hawk being looser and softer than that of the trimmer-looking common buzzard.

OCCURRENCES IN GREAT BRITAIN: To most of the eastern counties this fine bird is an irregular autumn visitor. One or more appear in the latter half of October or in November, and if permitted to remain unharmed will stay over the winter, returning north again in March or April to their breeding places in Scandinavian countries. Even to the south coast this buzzard will repair and we read in *A History of Sussex Birds* that hardly ever does a winter go by without tidings of a rough-legged buzzard or two being present in the county. On occasions it will even visit Cornwall but on the whole it is a rare bird in the west of England and Wales, though not infrequently reported from the Midlands. The migration of rough-legged buzzards to eastern England, and especially to Norfolk, during the winter of 1915-16 was the largest and most important influx of this species that had been recorded for several years. In these words J. H. Gurney reported the immigration[1] to the Norfolk and Norwich Natural History Society, observing that one pair at least was seen by Jim Vincent as early as September but that owing to the presence of common buzzards as well, it was

[1] *Trans. Nat. Soc. Norwich*, 1916, pp. 168-170.

not until October that the rough-legs were positively certified. As regards numbers, Mr. Gurney believed that Norfolk was not visited by less than forty, and Suffolk and Lincolnshire possibly by half that number. It was remarked that the birds generally seemed to keep two together and a pair remained at Hickling all through the winter. Examples were seen up to 24th April, which date would nearly mark the date of their departure, though one was seen as late as 5th May.

Previous to the visitation in 1915 which so impressed John Henry Gurney, and which happens also to have been the last to date on such a scale, there were other years when the rough-legged buzzard arrived in these islands in exceptional numbers, these being 1839-40, 1858-59, 1875-76, 1880-81, 1891-92, 1903-04 and 1910-11. Since the winter of 1915-16 no special influx has been noted but occasional examples turn up even in the Midland counties ; a rough-legged buzzard was reported in Warwickshire in March 1949. Farther west, in Wales, it is but rarely seen and the same applies to north-west England ; in Lancashire, for instance, there has been only one record during the present century.

In Scotland this buzzard appears more regularly but still can only be termed a rare visitor. Miss Baxter and Miss Rintoul, authors of *The Birds of Scotland* (1953), have been at pains to give a summary of its distribution and state that the incidence of the rough-legged buzzard in Scotland in winter is not quite what one would expect, the bird occurring most frequently south of a line from Dumbarton through Perth and Angus as well as in parts of Inverness-shire and in Caithness. They inform us that in Aberdeen and south-east Sutherland it is more or less regular on passage but appears not to stay the winter. From the Inner Isles it has been recorded only from Arran, Mull and Skye. It is absent from the north-west Highlands and there are only four records from the Outer Hebrides.

To Orkney it is an uncommon visitor, though it occasionally winters. It was unknown in Shetland until 1884 and there are few subsequent records. Mr. Kenneth Williamson, writing to me in August 1954 from Fair Isle Bird Observatory, states that in his opinion the rough-legged buzzard is a rare bird either on passage or wintering in the Shetland area. There are, he informs me, very few records for Fair Isle. From details which he has kindly supplied it appears that the first to be identified on Fair Isle was seen by the authors of *The Birds of Scotland*, between 12th and 14th September 1925. The following year the same two ladies observed two or three between 14th and 22nd October and on 5th-6th November. Ten years later, on 29th August 1936, Mr. L. S. V. Venables observed one —a remarkably early date. Mr. Williamson adds that buzzards are seen annually on Fair Isle and are commoner than they were, but all those which he has up to date identified with certainty have been examples of the common buzzard, *Buteo buteo*, and he has never seen *Buteo lagopus* to be sure of its identity. That from so astute an observer certainly points to the rough-legged buzzard being a very rare visitor to Fair Isle.

In Ireland there have been some twenty-five occurrences in all between 1837 and 1954, dated from September to February. According to Colonel C. F. Scroope in *The Birds of Ireland* (1954), Ulster is the most favoured area, with ten instances. Leinster, in which Wicklow claims most of the records, has at least eleven, while Connaught has two and Munster only one. The capture of a specimen on the northern boundary of County Galway on 5th September 1950 is of interest as being the first September record for Ireland.

DISTRIBUTION ABROAD IN THE BREEDING SEASON : The rough-legged buzzard inhabits the greater part of the boreal zone of the Holarctic Region, birds from the various parts of this extensive range differing sufficiently *inter se* to allow of the recognition of three local races. The typical form— the only one so far encountered, or likely to occur, in Britain—breeds from Scandinavia eastwards to the valley of the Ob in Siberia. In sub-Arctic Norway, Doctor Blair informs me, it is mostly restricted to the upper slopes of the fjelds from latitude 59° northwards, but an odd pair has from time to time been found nesting in the lower-lying eastern districts. It becomes rather scarce in the west, breeding in small numbers on the heights between and around the heads of the great fjords, and never on the actual seaboard. In most seasons this is the most plentiful of the birds of prey in Arctic Norway, where it occurs both at sea-level and at high altitudes, and as commonly along the coast-line, including some of the larger islands, as in the more inland districts.

In Sweden, Count Nils Gyldenstolpe informs me, the rough-legged buzzard breeds in north-western Delecarlia, in the provinces of Härjedalen, Jämtland and Norrbotten, and in northern and southern Lapland. *It is said* to have been found breeding in the provinces of Småland and Hälsing-land, as well as on the island of Gotland in the Baltic. During the migration season it is found in other provinces. The migration period in Sweden starts in the middle of September and continues until the first part of November in a south-western and south-eastern direction to central and eastern Europe. The bird is regularly—though sparsely—found wintering in southern Sweden when the weather is not too severe. The above was the accepted status of *B. lagopus* in Sweden in 1949 and it is unlikely to have altered since.

It is common in northern Finland, and has also been recorded as nesting outside the Arctic Circle, as at Kuussamo and Pudasjarvii, its distribution here overlapping that of the common and honey buzzards.

When studying the rough-legged buzzard in Finnish Lapland [1]

---

[1] The notes in this paragraph which refer to Finnish Lapland are taken from Carl Finnilä's " Studies of *Archibuteo lagopus* in Finnish Lapland " which he published in *Fauna och Flora* (1916); they have been kindly translated from the original by Count Nils Gyldenstolpe of the Royal Swedish Museum.

some forty years ago, Carl Finnilä found that it bred more or less commonly throughout the pine-forested region, but was more characteristic of the birch forests along the uppermost forest edge. In Finnish Lapland Finnilä considered it fairly rare in what he terms the " regio alpina ", for during his visit to Utsjoki in the summer of 1915 not a single nest was found in that area, although about twenty were discovered in the birch and pine zones.

Beyond the Finnish border the typical race of the rough-legged buzzard ranges throughout the northern governments of Russia onward to the limits of its distribution on the Ob, birds from further east being referred to the paler race known as *Buteo lagopus pallidus*. The rough-legged buzzard has not yet been found nesting on either Kolguev or Novaja Zemlya, but it does so in limited numbers on Waigatz. In the north of Canada this buzzard is represented by a darker form, *B. l. sancti-johannis*, and a closely allied species occurs in the western United States.

The winter quarters of the rough-legged buzzard are not very clearly defined. Thus Jourdain in *The Handbook of British Birds* observes that the typical subspecies migrates south to " Middle Europe and the Black Sea region ", and to western Asia. He notes that it is a casual visitor to northern Spain, France, Switzerland, northern Italy, Jugoslavia, Malta, Greece, Asia Minor and northern Persia. Jourdain also included Egypt but on erroneous information. Nicoll himself never obtained an example in Egypt and no one else has ever met with it there. The bird is unknown from any part of northern or tropical Africa.

MIGRATIONS : While rough-legged buzzards have, with one or two exceptions,[1] been encountered in Sweden only during the breeding season or on migration, a few spend the winter in Norway, some of them as far north as Finmark. For the most part, however, these hawks quit Scandinavia on the approach of the cold season. The earlier amongst them leave towards the end of September, and the emigration continues throughout October, odd stragglers being seen in Norway in November and, more exceptionally, in December. According to Collett, the emigrants spend little time on the Norwegian lowlands, but in Sweden they usually fly low enough to allow of their easy recognition, and travel rather slowly, often halting for a day or two in places where field mice happen to be plentiful. There the autumn flight may assume imposing proportions. One hunter, employing an eagle-owl as a decoy, killed as many as seventeen of these buzzards in an hour in South Oland, while in Skaane an even greater number has often fallen to a single gun in the same space of time. As might be expected from the winter distribution of the species, the majority

---

[1] In *Fauna och Flora*, 1917, pp. 44-45, Carl Fries records seeing a rough-legged buzzard on the Tåkern Lake in the Province of Östergötland (which is known to the present writer) just after Christmas Day in 1915 ; the lake was frozen and the ice covered at the time (28th December) with snow. Only one previous record of *B. lagopus* being seen in midwinter at this lake exists : a bird identified in January 1892 in the vicinity of Hofgården.

of the migrating birds follow a south-easterly rather than a due southerly course, and in Norway they are always most numerous eastward of Lindesnes.

Further evidence of the eastward trend of the autumn passage is forthcoming in accounts of the recovery of birds ringed in Sweden. Of 154 ringed about Kiruna, Lapland, in 1912-13, three were killed in Sweden, two of them on the east coast; two to the south of Uleaby in Finland; seven in north-central Germany or nearby Poland; one at Moscow; and nine in Austria or Hungary. On the other hand, the late Doctor Einar Lönnberg in his English introduction to the *Birds of Sweden* recorded three rough-legged buzzards ringed in the Swedish province of Jämtland which were later recovered in Scotland, Denmark and Silesia, south-east Germany, respectively, showing a fairly wide dispersal of Jämtland birds. The example recovered in Scotland was ringed in Sweden on 13th July 1926 and found less than six months later in Inverness.

It is early in April, or more rarely late in March, that the first home-coming rough-legged buzzards cross southern Norway and Sweden. Further influxes occur during April, and it is not exceptional for a straggler or two to be seen about Oslo in the opening days of May. The incoming birds soon pass by, pressing on to their summer haunts with little delay and usually at a great height. One of the first of the summer visitants to return to the north, the rough-legged buzzard may be expected at breeding stations on the Arctic Circle towards the end of April, and at about the same time, or in early May, in Finmark. In the latter district, according to Wessel, it appears sooner in vole or lemming years than at other times, having been recorded under those conditions as early as 25th March.

HABITS IN GREAT BRITAIN : Although the rough-legged buzzard cannot be considered a particularly rare visitor to Britain, surprisingly few of our county ornithologists have much to tell of its habits here. Those who do go beyond chronicling local occurrences describe these visitors from the north as preferring open country—moorlands along the Borders and in Yorkshire, heaths, commons and broads in East Anglia, and in Kent the marshes along the Thames estuary. Some of the birds, however, take up their quarters in wooded districts, such as the larger Suffolk parks. It is remarked by several authors that wintering rough-legged buzzards tend to keep in pairs—to employ the word in its wider sense—the two birds regularly hunting the same moor or common and often roosting together in some plantation or quarry. For several winters in succession, as C. B. Ticehurst learned from F. R. C. Jourdain, two of these buzzards slept every night on a window-ledge of an untenanted Suffolk mansion. Ticehurst must surely be right in his surmise that it was the same pair of birds which returned each year to so unusual a roosting place.

When first they arrive here rough-legged buzzards are sometimes, in George Bolam's words, very careless of their safety. Bolam himself knew of a captive bird that had been picked up by hand while gorged and apparently asleep. He also tells of four or five particularly fearless buzzards which arrived together one November on Holy Island, where they boldly followed tame pigeons into the gardens and streets of the village. One indeed was so tame as to allow a gunner bent on its destruction to approach within such close range that when it rose he missed it with both barrels !

Occasionally a rough-legged buzzard that has been here for some time will show itself equally lacking in caution. Following a heavy snowfall in December 1878, one bird, emboldened no doubt by hunger, regularly visited a Berwickshire stackyard in pursuit of mice ; this is recorded by Muirhead in his attractive work on the birds of that county. Nelson, so long the recorder of Yorkshire ornithology, heard of an especially rash buzzard raiding the domestic pigeons about a moorland house, the home of no less a person than the local gamekeeper.

Earlier in date than any of these records is the extract from an old manuscript volume which concludes the account of this species in Stevenson's *Birds of Norfolk*. According to this " curious anecdote ", a party of gentlemen shooting near Holkham on 16th December 1816 " were followed during the greater part of the day by a bird of prey, which constantly attended their motions, and was repeatedly fired at while hovering over their heads, without betraying the smallest symptoms of apprehension and alarm, even though the shot was heard to rattle on its feathers. In the afternoon it descended on a tree, where it allowed Mr. Coke, attended by a boy holding a pheasant dangling in his hand, to approach sufficiently near to get a shot at it, which brought it to the ground. It proved to be a most beautiful specimen of that rare bird the *F. lagopus*, or rough-legged buzzard, measuring nearly five feet across the wings, and two feet one inch in length. The male bird had attended the chase at Wighton, just in the same manner, two days before, and had boldly carried off from a heap of game two partridges. "

A most interesting account of the rough-legged buzzard, based largely on the writer's experience in the field, is to be found in George Bolam's *Birds of Northumberland and the Eastern Borders*. After spending many hours watching one or more prowling over the moors, Bolam came to the conclusion that " the flight of these birds bears considerable resemblance to that of the common buzzard, the circling sweeps with which the ground is quartered being ever and anon interrupted as the bird ' brings itself to ' in mid air, where head to wind it hangs poised like a large kestrel for a few seconds while it examines some likely cover beneath. A pounce is made very suddenly, and with almost closed pinions, the bird dropping like a stone on its prey, head foremost, and the wings being only again spread as, within a few inches of the ground, the position is suddenly reversed and the talons thrust forward." While agreeing that small mammals constitute the chief food of this species, Bolam early remarked its fondness for pigeons. In winter when these hawks were not uncommon on some of the Border moors, he frequently noticed one, or sometimes two, stooping at wood pigeons as they came in to roost in a fir plantation. The procedure, he remarks, was always the same :

As soon as a flock of pigeons had settled amongst the trees, a buzzard would begin beating over the wood, at a height of perhaps thirty to fifty feet above the tree-tops, and presently stoop with more than half-closed wings upon its hoped-for prey, but never make any attempt to follow it when the pigeon took wing. After each unsuccessful stoop the buzzard generally rested for a few minutes on the top of the low wall surrounding the wood, apparently with the object of allowing the pigeons to settle again before making another attempt upon them, and this game used frequently to be kept up till almost dark, when one of the buzzards would wing its way across the valley to Whitsunbank, where it roosted, almost nightly, on the face of a high quarry, for several months. Although I never saw a pigeon captured on these occasions, the resolute manner in which the attack was maintained seemed to indicate a considerable belief in their prowess on the part of the buzzards, and the remains of pigeons, frequently found near their favourite perches, bore further testimony to the fact that their efforts were often crowned with success.

Besides witnessing rough-legged buzzards attacking pigeons, Bolam disturbed one feeding on a water vole, and saw another carry off a young rabbit. An example shot in Northumberland contained " seven mice nearly whole " (probably voles) and a second the remains of an old cock grouse, while two others had made meals of stoats. John Hancock, who preserved one of these last, discovered evidence of a severe struggle between the captor and the captured, for a considerable strip of skin, with the feathers of the throat, had been torn away.

Most other county historians describe this buzzard as feeding largely on rabbits and rats, and, like Claud Ticehurst, dismiss its poaching offences as trifling. Nelson alone, on the evidence before him, refused to acquit it of the charge of killing game, and cited various instances of examples being surprised, and sometimes shot, while devouring grouse.

Rough-legged buzzards, it is sad to relate, readily fall victims to the trapper, particularly if rabbits are laid out as bait. To-day these fine hawks come and go unmolested in many counties but it is not so very long ago since Claud Ticehurst had to complain that in Suffolk every keeper's hand was against them. While no reasonable person could object to the collecting of a rough-legged buzzard in an unusual phase of plumage, the indiscriminate destruction of such useful and attractive birds cannot be too strongly condemned. It remains to be seen how far this and other raptorial birds will benefit by the new protection laws.

Rough-legged buzzards appeared in quite unusual numbers in the Scottish Border counties during the vole plague which devastated so many hill pastures in 1876-77. The birds concentrated about the farms most hardly hit, one shepherd counting seven on the wing at the same time.

Contemporary accounts speak of the buzzards being " attracted " to the affected countryside.   No one can doubt that such an abundance of easily-won prey would induce the birds to linger in the vole-infested districts, but an explanation for the magnitude of the immigration must be sought in the countries where it originated.   Records kept by Scandinavian naturalists show that the Border vole plague had its counterpart, covering a far wider area, in northern Europe.   In Norway alone, voles of four different species, and lemmings besides, swarmed from the southernmost highlands to the Russian frontier.   That birds of prey bred freely that year can be concluded from the marked increase in the amount of " head money " paid for their destruction, which exceeded that for the previous year by more than a third. Such rewards were supposed to be paid for eagles and goshawks only but, as Sigurd Johnsen discovered, most of the so-called " eagles " brought to the authorities were in reality rough-legged buzzards.   After so successful a breeding season it was only to be expected that the autumn migration would be in great strength, and that more buzzards than usual would find their way to Britain.

During the more prolonged vole plague of 1891-93 rough-legged buzzards were at times common enough about the Borders, if not so plentiful as in the previous outbreak.   Here again we find that voles had been very abundant in some parts of Scandinavia, and that the number of birds of prey for which head money was claimed had risen sharply.

HABITS IN NORWAY[1] :   Towards the southern limit of its range the rough-legged buzzard keeps largely to the heights on and above the tree-line—wildernesses of naked stony fell interspersed with marshy levels thicketed with dwarf birch, willow and juniper ; only a minority breed within the fringes of the birch woods.   Within the Arctic Circle this hawk, while far from uncommon amongst the great pine forests, is always most numerous in open country, and in Finmark it breeds in many coastal districts, often within a mile of the sea, and sometimes in a cliff overhanging one of the fjords.   If left unmolested rough-legged buzzards will occasionally build close to villages, and Doctor Blair knew of a nest, occupied in most vole years, in a little cliff within a few minutes' stroll of the town of Vadsö, where he often paused to watch one of the birds circling over the streets in the early hours of the morning.

Rough-legged buzzards sometimes return to landscapes almost as wintry as those of December, the fells swathed in foot-deep, hard-crusted drifts, the little rivers silent under a casing of ice.   On the blustery days so typical of this changeable season, when one snow flurry after another blots out every landmark, the buzzards spend little time on the wing.   Let the sun break through, however, and every bird will soon be outlined against the grey clouds.   Later the males vary their soaring with a display of wing-

[1] Doctor H. M. S. Blair is responsible for this account, in which he has made considerable use of Doctor Hagen's researches in Norway, as well as of his own.

power closely resembling the spring flight of the common buzzard. Suddenly drawing in his wing, the great bird hurtles down in a stoop as imposing as that of a falcon. He mounts again until, so swift and steep has been the ascent, his body hangs upright between his half-closed wings. Then he swings forward and plunges downwards once more.

In those early spring days, rough-legged buzzards can hardly be over-looked. Once the females have completed their clutches, all become less obtrusive. As the males pass the greater part of the day on guard near their sitting mates, the presence of a pair of these large conspicuous-looking hawks may remain unsuspected unless the nest is approached closely enough to arouse their resentment. Even in a vole year one can ramble over a stretch of fell about which maybe half a dozen pairs are nesting and yet see no more than one or two of the birds. Perhaps one will appear well overhead, taking full advantage of every current and eddy of air as it soars in majestic spirals, its widely separated quills rigid and motionless. Another passes by at a more moderate height, quartering the ground in wide sweeps as a harrier will. Keenly alert for any movement below, the questing bird moves slowly forward with deliberate, almost laboured, wing-beats, and then glides easily along for as much as a hundred yards before bringing the pinions into play again. From time to time—and certainly more frequently than a common buzzard—it swings into the wind to hover on rapidly moving wings over some promising covert.

In the breeding season, as at other times, small rodents are the favourite prey of the rough-legged buzzard. *Microtus ratticeps*, the " fjellrotte " (mountain rat) of the Norwegians, and our own field vole are the commonest victims in their seasons of abundance, and the buzzards also levy toll upon *Clethrionomys rufocanus*, a grey and red vole closely allied to the bank vole. Recent investigations have shown that, contrary to widely held belief, lemmings do not figure nearly as prominently in the bill of fare as voles do. The bank vole has been still less frequently identified amongst the captures of this hawk, and the Scandinavian representative of the water rat only rarely. Other mammals recorded as taken by the rough-legged buzzard include the common and water shrews, the squirrel, the hare and the ermine.

In Arctic Norway sportsmen generally condemn rough-legged buzzards as very destructive to game but in this less prejudiced, and perhaps more trustworthy, observers do not concur. Both Wessel and Schaanning emphasize their failure to discover any evidence of these hawks feeding their young on birds in Finmark, where Doctor Blair saw avian remains near only two of the many nests he visited. One of these was a partly-eaten Arctic skua, perhaps struck down while trespassing on the buzzards' territory rather than selected as a prey. Two years later, the feet and tarsi of a small goose—either brent or barnacle—were found beside a nest on the same fell, but these may have been picked up about a nearby fishing village.

References to feathered prey appear in most accounts of the nesting of the rough-legged buzzard in sub-Arctic Norway, one writer going so far as to declare that he " never " examined a nest without finding willow grouse chicks amongst the young buzzards' provender.

In his invaluable monograph Doctor Yngvar Hagen has tabulated and reviewed over 2000 records of prey taken by Norwegian rough-legged buzzards, the great majority of them extracted from his own diaries. A summary of these reads as follows :

Lemming (*Lemmus lemmus*)	.	131
Water rat (*Arvicola terrestris*)	.	8
Field vole (*Microtus agrestis*)	.	509
Mountain vole (*M. ratticeps*)	.	617
Grey-sided vole (*Clethrionomys rufocanus*)	. . .	103
Bank vole (*C. glareolus*)	. .	66
Small rodents unspecified .	.	368
Total small rodents	. .	1,802
Common shrew (*Sorex araneus*) .		12
Shrews unspecified	. . .	15
Stoat (*Mustela erminea*)	. .	23
Squirrel (*Sciurus vulgaris*)	.	1
Hare (*Lopus timidus*), chiefly young		18
Total mammals	. . .	1,871
Hooded crow (*Corvus cornix*)	.	3
Reed bunting (*Emberiza schoeniclus*)		2
Meadow pipit (*Anthus pratensis*)		7
Pipits unspecified	. . .	11
Fieldfare (*Turdus pilaris*)	.	19
Song thrush (*T. ericetorum*)	.	1
Thrushes unspecified	. .	4
Wheatear (*Oenanthe oenanthe*)		2
Cuckoo (*Cuculus canorus*)	.	3
Short-eared owl (*Asio flammeus*)		4
Long-eared owl (*Asio otus*)	.	1
Kestrel (*Falco tinnunculus*)	.	1
Rough-legged buzzard (*Buteo lagopus*), young . . .		3
Raptores unspecified, young	.	1

Golden plover (*Pluvialis apricarius*)	2
Common sandpiper (*Actitis hypoleucus*)	1
Snipe unspecified . . .	6
Pintail (*Anas acuta*) . .	1
Teal (*Anas crecca*) . . .	2
Ducks unspecified . . .	5
Willow grouse (*Lagopus lagopus*)	61
Ptarmigan (*L. mutus*) . .	1
Grouse unspecified, chiefly chicks	46
Black grouse (*Lyrurus tetrix*), one female	1
Black grouse, chicks . . .	12
Capercaillie (*Tetrao urogallus*), female	1
Capercaillie, chicks . . .	2
Chicks, capercaillie or black grouse	8
Birds unspecified . . .	21
Total birds	232
Frog (*Rana temporaria*) . .	10
Salmon (*Salmo salar*) . .	1
Grasshoppers (chiefly *Acridier*) .	11
Beetles of genus *Carabus*, adults	4
Burying beetles, adults . .	3
Burying beetles, larvae . .	16
Beetles unspecified . . .	67
Insects unspecified . . .	many
Spiders unspecified . . .	many

It will be seen that the smaller rodents constitute 85 per cent. of the total number of vertebrates, with the voles of the genus *Microtus* greatly predominating, and the lemming considerably in the minority. Birds are outnumbered by mammals by more than eight to one, and many of the species appearing in the list are included on the strength of one or two records only. It appears that while rough-legged buzzards can, and do, kill birds, they seldom prove very expert in such hunting. Yet some have shown themselves able to cope with prey worthy of a goshawk or peregrine, such as the capercaillie and pintail. To birds of prey captured by rough-legged buzzards can be added the hawk-owl, recorded by Finnilä in Finland. Cannibalism Doctor Hagen considers to be more frequent than the list suggests. Of the three buzzards he found partly eaten about nests of their own species, one was very small and still down-clad, one half-feathered and one nearly fledged.

As frogs occur as far north as Finmark, it seems remarkable that their remains, and those of lizards besides, should have been so rarely identified amongst rough-legged buzzards' rejecta.

In the course of his researches Doctor Hagen has confirmed that the proportion of " feather " amongst the kills of rough-legged buzzards varies from year to year according to conditions. Even when voles swarm on the hunting grounds, these hawks take birds to supplement their mammalian captures while feeding their rapidly growing broods. The number of birds brought to a nest in such a season will, however, be relatively small.

That the rough-legged buzzard continues to prefer mammals as prey after the breeding season was conclusively demonstrated by the researches of Rörig and Greschik in the species' central European winter quarters. In the material collected in the course of these, small rodents amounted to 93 per cent. of the 1933 animals identified, other mammals to 5 per cent., birds to 2 per cent.

Like all its allies, the rough-legged buzzard is the object of much unwelcome attention from other birds. As the big hawk soars over the forest a pair of hooded crows will tumble and caw about it or a merlin will accompany it for perhaps half a mile, repeatedly teasing it with half-playful stoops. Over the fells it may be the centre of a crowd of screaming Arctic terns, and skuas of both species find the sport of buzzard-baiting very attractive. Sometimes the persecutors are clearly intent, not so much on merely annoying the hawk as on robbing it of a recent capture. One unfortunate buzzard, homeward-bound with some prey dangling in its talons, was sorely pressed by no less than three greater black-headed gulls and two Arctic skuas. Within their own territory a pair of rough-legged buzzards will brook no intrusion, and even the more formidable of their neighbours prefer to observe its limits. According to Scandinavian accounts rough-legged buzzards at all seasons display towards the eagle-owl an antipathy little short of hatred—a weakness of which unfair advantage is taken by gunners devoted to the destruction of birds of prey.

The long-drawn wailing call of this hawk differs from the common buzzard's mew only in being somewhat louder and lower-pitched. Nor can the sexes of the former be recognized by note alone. As a female leaves

the nest, cramped and tired by incubation, her protests are at first noticeably weaker than those of her mate, but they soon gain strength, and within
a few moments this transient distinction between the two disappears.

BREEDING HABITS : While a few of the rough-legged buzzards resorting
to wooded districts nest on rocks amongst the forests, by far the greater
number prefer trees, either pines or, less frequently, birches or spruce-firs.
Sometimes a pair will utilize an old hooded crow's nest as a foundation for
their home, or they may appropriate the deserted eyrie of an eagle or osprey.
A rather unusually sited nest filled the hollow in the top of the broken
trunk of a massive spruce. In more open country the rough-legged buzzard
generally builds on a ledge of a cliff or rock, often at no great height.
The descent to a nest can sometimes be negotiated only with the aid of a
rope and many are remarkably easy of access, being placed on low outcrops
or about the shaly walls of the gullies cut by the little rivers, often on one
of the topmost ledges, perhaps even on the cliff-head itself. By the time
the snow has melted, if not before, it is sometimes possible to walk directly
up to such a nest, and one is apt to regard the site as very carelessly selected.
Earlier in the season, however, it will be obvious that the birds had no
other choice, the cliff-head being the only dry spot available. The nest,
besides, may then be as much out of reach as any built in a sheer precipice.
A steep glacis of smooth hard snow hid every foothold beneath one visited
at the end of May, while from above the approach—so easy later in the year—
was cut off by an ice-crusted drift some eight feet in thickness at the point
where it almost overhung the sitting bird. Of other nests seen in Finmark,
some were on steep slopes, others on top of flat boulders, and one was on
the crown of a sand-hill. No fewer than four—two of which had been
abandoned when complete—lay on level ground, in just such situations
as gulls would choose. While buzzards always avoid a damp ledge, instinct
does not warn them against occasionally building on foundations even less
suitable, such as the " layer of ice about six inches thick immediately
under the new grass-lining " of a nest described by the late Alfred
Chapman.

In Finmark it was found that most rough-legged buzzards built a
fresh nest each spring, sometimes close to that of a previous season, and
in one case actually touching it. While none of these was known to be
reoccupied in the following year, the birds at times repaired—or rather
added to—an older structure, deserted perhaps for more than a decade.
Some old nests had been so long in existence, and so frequently refurbished,
that they had become low mounds overgrown with moss and creeping
plants, and one or two supported vigorous foot-high birch saplings. Newly-
constructed nests vary in size. Measuring from 60 cm. to a metre overall,
they are built up to a thickness of between 15 and 20 cm., with inner cups
of between 15 and 25 cm. by 7·5 to 10 cm. Those on the Finmark fells
were built of branches of dwarf birch—some of them quite large—and

crowberry ling, the turf often still attached to it, with some moss and lichen ; crowberry was also intermixed with the dry grass lining. In one large nest a number of raven's feathers had been worked into both the outer framework and the bowl, which included besides a piece of brown paper. A fragment of newspaper was found in the lining of a nest seen by Olstad, who notes that in Oyer dwarf birch branches are supplemented by those of juniper and willow. In the forests the nests are largely constructed of pine branches and lined with the black hair-like lichens (*Usnea*) which drape the conifers in these latitudes. Nests on the ground are usually very simple structures. One was no more than a scrape in the peat, lined with dry grass and moss, with a few dwarf birch twigs carelessly placed around the rim. Another, which had been deserted, was most peculiar in that beside it, and partly interwoven into it, lay two small supplementary nests. Like some other raptorial birds, rough-legged buzzards commonly add fresh material to the nest as long as it holds eggs or young. These " decorations " are laid on the side of the nest or in the bowl, and may be either freshly plucked shoots of living pine, birch or crowberry, or fragments of moss, generally reindeer moss.

When food is scarce a pair of rough-legged buzzards will now and then get no further than building or repairing a nest. They will nevertheless keep watch over the empty nest until well into June, and, which is more remarkable, continue to decorate it. Less frequently one of these barren nests is the work of an unattached bird, and here too greenery is sometimes added long after the nest is completed.

Rough-legged buzzards normally begin laying in the latter half of May—most frequently on dates between the 18th and 25th—or in the opening days of June. Very rarely a bird will be sitting by mid-May ; eggs on the point of hatching have been found on 7th and 8th June. Late nests occur rather more frequently. Harvie-Brown obtained two fresh eggs on 25th June in 1871, Alfred Chapman four on the same date in 1885. The former also received from his collectors clutches said to have been taken on 21st and 22nd August. Six eggs, the contents of four nests, found on 8th and 10th September, Collett described as " fresh ", but Hagen points out that they were bleached of colour and may have been addled.

If a rough-legged buzzard's clutch consists of four or fewer eggs, the bird generally lays every twenty-four hours. With larger clutches the last egg or two appear at longer and more irregular intervals. Collett records an altogether exceptional nest in which the second and third eggs were not laid until their predecessors had hatched, all three young being duly reared.

As earlier mentioned, many rough-legged buzzards do not lay if voles and lemmings are nearly absent from the fells and marshes in the spring. When the little animals are more numerous, though still not abundant, most of the buzzards have three, or perhaps only two, eggs, though sets of four are common enough, particularly within the Arctic Circle. In outstanding vole years, and especially if weather conditions in April and May are favourable, the birds become more prolific. Many then lay five eggs, every other nest holding that number in some years, and sets of six are not very rare. Recently two clutches of seven eggs have been recorded for this hawk, one from the neighbourhood of the Varanger Fjord, the other from Finland.

A series of rough-legged buzzard's eggs recorded by Jourdain averaged $55\cdot03\times43\cdot59$ mm., the largest measuring $62\times49\cdot5$ mm., the two smallest 48×41 mm. and $57\cdot8\times39\cdot2$ mm. Eggs in the same nest may differ strikingly in this respect, and one remarkable pair might well have been mistaken for the produce of different birds, the first-laid measuring 52×40 mm., its fellow 57×44 mm.

The markings on these variable eggs range through tints from pale ochraceous to rich reddish-brown and sepia, and the beauty of many is enhanced by underlying markings of lilac or even purple. On some of the more handsome the markings take the form of large boldly defined blotches ; others are prettily clouded or smeared, while others again are thickly freckled. The less attractive may show no more than a few scattered spots or fine, hair-like streakings of colour, but immaculate eggs are exceedingly rare with this species. The proportion of heavily pigmented eggs, always large, appears to increase in vole years ; all but one of several clutches found in 1934 were well coloured, and some very handsome. One or two almost fresh eggs found by Doctor Blair in Finmark were distinctly, if slightly, smeared by the black lichens with which the nests were lined, while another was spotted with juice from the bruised fruit on a strand of crowberry brought as a " decoration ". Such adventitious markings should suffice to identify an egg with certainty. Otherwise eggs of the rough-legged buzzard cannot be distinguished from those of the common buzzard, although in a series they appear the more boldly marked.

Should either of a pair of rough-legged buzzards be killed, the survivor sometimes finds a new mate, as so often happens with birds of prey. Whether the male of this species takes his turn on the eggs regularly, if at all, has yet to be ascertained, but the major share of the duties of incubation undoubtedly falls on the female. Unless away hunting, the male keeps a sharp look-out from a vantage point near the nest, and soars out to challenge an intruder still a good quarter of a mile from the site, if not earlier. The female rises from fifty to a hundred yards ahead, or, though less frequently, she may persist in brooding until the last moment. Sometimes she is the more demonstrative of the pair, at others her mate shows the greater concern. As long as their unwelcome visitor remains on the scene the two circle overhead, occasionally swooping earthwards, perhaps to alight, sometimes together, on a boulder, and all the while keeping up an incessant wailing which now and then rises to a distracted squealing. For the most part the anxious birds keep their distance but one female—whose eggs were almost fresh—closed in a succession of magnificent half-stoops, two of which she pressed to within twenty feet of the nest. While the young are leaving the shell, and for several days afterwards, the parents become much bolder and are sometimes never out of gunshot. One female lingered by her brood until the cliff was almost scaled and another only shifted to a boulder twenty yards from her home.

With few exceptions rough-legged buzzards begin incubating before completing their clutches, generally as soon as the first or second egg is laid. In the wild weather that so often ushers in June a sitting buzzard must endure much hardship as she covers her exposed nest. One bird, surprised in a blizzard, was almost mantled in snow, which fell from her wings in masses as she took to flight. Olstad gives the incubation period for this species as thirty-one days, which is somewhat longer than with the common buzzard. The young appear at intervals, breaking the shell— at least in clutches of up to four—on successive days, and remain in the nest for about six weeks. Hagen had found that, as is so often the case with birds of prey, the males of a brood leave the nest before the heavier females. At one nest a male fledgling made his first venture when only thirty-four days old, and proved strong enough on the wing to avoid capture. A female, however, kept to the nest until her fortieth day, while the third youngster, whose sex was not ascertained, was still incapable of flight at forty-three days. Until the young are well-grown, and perhaps until they fly, the female stays about the nest, the male doing all the hunting and dropping the food to her. According to Collett, the latter will rear the brood if his mate is lost. It is said that the young are fed " in strict rotation ", but in some nests the last-hatched dies of starvation. On 15th July one year, a nest which had been found on 25th June with a newly hatched bird and three eggs appeared to hold only two large and well-feathered young until a miserable squeaking led to the discovery that they were sitting on, and entirely concealing, a third—a very small weakly creature with no quills showing. In another nest, seen two days later, the smallest of the four young was already dead. Such weaklings are no doubt the first victims of cannibalism in bad seasons. Höst gives an account [1] of a pair of rough-legged buzzards dropping food beside the bodies of their young for several days after the latter had been killed and thrown from the nest.

The mortality amongst rough-legged buzzards' eggs and young is considerable. A late May frost can addle many of the first-laid eggs, as Doctor Blair found in 1926, when nearly every nest held an addled egg, and one as many as three. Doctor Hagen, who stresses the importance of this wastage of offspring, gives some interesting figures for the forty-three nests he located and studied on the Dovrefjeld in the course of an eight-year

[1] *Trekk av Dyrelivet på Hardangervidda*, p. 50.

period, which included both good and bad seasons. From the 152 eggs laid in these nests 124 young emerged, but only seventy-six reached the flying stage—exactly half the number of eggs laid. Even in " vole years " the number of nestlings perishing from one cause or another often amounted to a fifth, and once even to a half, of the total hatched. The mortality becomes yet higher when the vole population, as sometimes happens, suddenly declines after the buzzards have set about nesting.

REFERENCES : Original Description. *Falco lagopus* Pontoppidan, Danske Atlas, i, 1763, p. 616 : Denmark.

PLATE 18   **COMMON BUZZARD**

Buteo buteo buteo (Linnaeus)

A Resident, breeding in the west of England, in Wales and in Scotland but not in Orkney or Shetland ; also a Bird of Passage. Practically exterminated in Ireland as a breeding bird.

IDENTIFICATION : Those who are so fortunate as to live amidst surroundings where the buzzard is to be found have no difficulty in recognizing the bird from a considerable distance. Its large size, though it is considerably smaller than an eagle, with which it may be confused by the novice, broad wings and rounded banded tail, and particularly its habit of soaring above well wooded country in large spirals, should proclaim its identity. When so engaged the tips of the wings are strongly upturned and the fingers wide apart. At sufficiently close quarters the pattern of the underside may be seen and the pale markings in the middle of the breast are then conspicuous against the dark brown sides and the less noticeable dark patches in the region of the carpal joint. The silhouette of a buzzard is really unmistakable, owing to the breadth of its wings in comparison with those of other birds of prey such as peregrines, harriers and sparrow-hawks. It is less easy to write of its colouring, for buzzards show a great amount of individual variation in their plumage. On the upperside they are usually dark brown with some rufous on the plumage, old birds being usually very dark. The tail is evenly barred grey and brown, there being about a dozen brown bars ; the terminal band is broader than the others. The underparts show a mixture of white and brown or rufous-brown, the amount of white on the breast varying considerably, but few British examples show as much white as do some Continental birds.

The yellow legs are bare of feathers. When at rest the buzzard sinks its head low upon its shoulders and as the feathers are often erected and the tail is not very long, its appearance is that of a heavy bird which when disturbed rises sluggishly and moves away with slowly flapping wings. Not until it is soaring on high does the buzzard appear to the best advantage and then its flight is seen to be easy and graceful. Its mewing cry carries

PLATE 18

COMMON BUZZARD

Buteo buteo buteo (Linnaeus)

a long distance and is often the first indication one has that a buzzard is in the vicinity. The females are larger than the males but otherwise resemble them in appearance. Young birds are paler than adults. In total length an adult buzzard measures from twenty to twenty-three inches and has a wing expanse of about forty-eight inches or more.

LOCAL DISTRIBUTION: How near to vanishing the buzzard became in the nineteenth century may be gathered from W. H. Hudson, who, writing in 1897, expressed the opinion that " this once common bird is now almost unknown in England and must be sought for in the wildest forest districts of Wales and Scotland ".

Previous to 1845 the buzzard was a native of Norfolk and Suffolk, and not very rare. In both these counties game of all kinds abounded, but with the increase in game preservation and the indiscriminate destruction of every bird of prey, quite regardless of its specialized habits, the buzzard was doomed, and when in 1866 Henry Stevenson wrote his *Birds of Norfolk* he stated that the bird had probably ceased for some years to breed in the county, adding that when the term " common " was really applicable to the species, it was frequently known to nest, the large woods at Hethel and Ashwelthorpe being instanced as among its former haunts.

To take another part of Britain where the buzzard might have expected less persecution, we have Selby's word for it—writing in 1831— that in the hilly districts of Selkirk, Dumfries and Peebles the buzzard was very numerous during the breeding season and almost every precipitous dell or rock contained an eyrie. Forty-three years later, in 1874, Hancock wrote of the Border counties that it was fast disappearing everywhere, under the influence of the gamekeeper's gun and trap. And so the melancholy tale was told in almost every district of England and the Borders where the buzzard had once reigned supreme.

The blame for this state of affairs must be laid squarely at the doors of the owners of sporting estates who permitted their keepers to shoot and trap any member of the " hawk " or owl tribe, disregarding the feeding habits of their victims or their usefulness to the land.

Wales has always been the buzzard's stronghold, even when game preservation threatened its extinction elsewhere in the nineteenth century. Indeed it was not until the First World War that it had any chance of recovery from the cruel treatment it had endured for so long. But in Wales I doubt if the bird was ever really in danger of extermination. In 1914 a well-known writer stated in his book [1] that so numerous was the species in certain parts of Cambria that during walking tours of three or four days only he had seen upwards of fifty buzzards in early spring, and that if the west country was traversed it was nothing unusual to see twenty or more in the course of a single day. In those days, previous to the First World War, the Welsh counties in which the buzzard could be counted

[1] *Field Studies of Some Rarer British Birds*, by John Walpole-Bond, 1914, pp. 154-174.

common were Brecon, Radnor, Cardigan, Carmarthen, Merioneth and Caernarvon, but according to the authority quoted buzzards were especially numerous in Cardigan and Carmarthen.

The country where it thrives best, and is likely to continue to do so, is largely given over to sheep-rearing, and the shepherds have no cause to dislike the buzzards and therefore do not molest them. Only in the game-rearing areas were the birds ruthlessly destroyed by keepers who seldom took the trouble to enquire beyond the fact that they were birds of prey, and as W. H. Hudson expressed it, " the larger the ' hawk ' the worse it must necessarily be ! "

Very satisfactory to-day is the status of the buzzard in the south-west corner of England, where, as recently as 1920, the late T. A. Coward wrote that in addition to Wales and Scotland " a few pairs find sanctuary in Devon and Cornwall and the Pennines ". Now a very different tale would be told, for in Cornwall [1] alone it can be reckoned almost common, the bird having spread into every part of the county and established itself even in the Land's End peninsula. In Devon it is certainly the commonest bird of prey after the kestrel, especially perhaps along the northern coast-line. Its breeding range in that county appears to be influenced to some extent by the nature of the rock, for it has been shown,[2] unless circumstances have altered in the last twenty-five years, that east of the Start the buzzard is found as far as Berry Head near Brixham, but not farther along the coast where the Devonian rocks are replaced by Permian and Triassic sandstones. During an ecological survey [3] of the buzzard's status in the spring of 1929, the bird was found to be very numerous on the coast, twenty-two pairs nesting between Plymouth Sound and the Start and twenty-five pairs between the Cornish boundary and Westward Ho ! There is no reason for the numbers to have decreased since the census was made. It has been suggested that the great increase of the buzzard in Cornwall is due to the increase in the rabbit population and to the consequent use of gin-traps, for, as a writer on Cornish bird-life has expressed it, buzzards like carrion as well as rabbits and the gin-trap provides carrion.

Replying to my enquiry as to the status to-day of the buzzard in the north of England, with special reference to the Pennine Range, and the counties of Northumberland and Durham, Doctor Hugh Blair has kindly sent me the following note :

Since the buzzard has become more firmly established just beyond the county boundary, in Westmorland, some of these fine birds have crossed the watershed into West Durham every winter or spring. Until very recently such visitors were forth-with hunted down in the interests of game-preserving. There is now, happily, less inclination to give buzzards short shrift, and the sight of one or more over the moors

---

[1] *Bird Life in Cornwall*, by B. H. Ryves, 1948, p. 98.
[2] V. C. Wynne-Edwards, *Bull. B.O.C.*, l, 1930, p. 65.
[3] By the Devon Bird-Watching and Preservation Society.

around the head of the Tees is by no means unusual. Nests have been built on both sides of the march between Durham and Yorkshire, but, as far as is known, eggs have been laid in the latter county only. There are clearly good grounds for hoping that the buzzard may soon be once more included amongst the regular breeding birds of Durham. Elsewhere in the county it can only rank as a casual visitant.

Over much of Northumberland also buzzards must still be regarded as rarities. They are most likely to be encountered along the Cumberland border, in South Tynedale, beyond which there are breeding stations within easy flight for such powerful birds, both further up the river and across the divide on the Eden side of the Pennines. Here too, given tolerance, the species may, in the not distant future, extend its range sufficiently to add Northumberland to the list of counties in which it nests.

On the western slopes of the Pennines the buzzard succeeded in maintaining a footing until the withdrawal of the gamekeeper from many districts in 1914-18 allowed it to widen its local distribution. To-day the number of pairs breeding between the Tyne Gap and Mallerstang runs into two figures, several appearing in new sites during the recent war. One nest, in which several broods have been reared, is built in a pine no more than thirty yards from the highroad that links the Tyne and Eden valleys. In Lakeland the buzzard has rightly been described as a " familiar resident ". It is the commonest bird of prey in some dales, and in one three nests can be visited in half an hour's walk.

Before discussing the distribution and status of the buzzard in Scotland and Ireland I am able, through the courtesy of Mr. W. B. Alexander, Librarian of the Edward Grey Institute of Field Ornithology, to give the following details of the buzzard's status in 1952-53 in England and Wales. Mr. Alexander has compiled this list from the local bird reports of the years stated, which now cover almost the whole of England and Wales.

Status of Buzzard in England and Wales (1952-53) :

Counties or Parts of Counties where it is Generally Distributed and Breeds Abundantly

Cornwall	Merioneth	Brecon
Devon	Westmorland	Radnor
West Somerset (Exmoor)	Cumberland	West Hereford
Pembroke	Carmarthen	Lancashire
Montgomery	Cardigan	(north of the sands)

Counties or Parts of Counties where it Breeds Regularly but is still somewhat Local

Central Somerset (Quantocks, Mendips)	Monmouth
	East Gloucester (Cotswolds)
Dorset (except Portland)	East Hereford
South-west Hampshire (New Forest)	North Shropshire
South Wiltshire	Denbigh
Glamorgan	Caernarvon

Counties or Parts of Counties where it has been Reported in Summer
and One or More Pairs have been Known or Suspected Breeding

North Somerset
North Wiltshire (three or four pairs nested in 1952)
Mid-Sussex
South-west Surrey (deliberately introduced)
Kent
Berkshire (one pair known to have nested in 1952)
South Oxfordshire (Chilterns, nest not yet found)
West Oxfordshire (Cotswolds, perhaps ranging from Gloucester)
Worcestershire (nested in 1952)
Warwickshire (nested in 1952)
South-west Staffordshire
South Shropshire
Derbyshire (attempted to breed in 1953)
Yorkshire (three pairs nested in 1953, presumably in Pennine Range
    but localities kept secret)
South Lancashire (one area)

Mr. Alexander informs me that there were only a few records for Durham[1] (Upper Teesdale) and only one or two in Northumberland,[1] so it is unlikely that it breeds in either of those counties. He was unable to find any recent information from Flint or Cheshire. He further observes that in the counties east of and including Notts, Lincs, Northants, Bucks and Middlesex occasional buzzards are seen, chiefly in winter, but it is often doubtful whether they are *Buteo buteo* or *Buteo lagopus*.

STATUS OF BUZZARD IN SCOTLAND AND IRELAND : The history of the buzzard in Scotland has been set out clearly by Miss Baxter and Miss Rintoul in their book on *The Birds of Scotland* (1953), where they wrote :

In the early part of the nineteenth century the common buzzard bred plentifully over the greater part of Scotland from the Border northwards. About 1830 or so, persecution of the species became intense, and in the next fifty years the numbers were seriously diminished and in some places the birds were exterminated. The sad words " used to breed " have to be written for Dumfries, and all the counties in Tweed as well as Caithness. In the Highlands, especially in the west, however, a breeding stock always survived and owing to better protection the species increased again and is now quite common in certain parts.

Many of the islands off the west coast of Scotland are inhabited by one or more breeding pairs or have been so in the last twenty-five years, but the distribution of the buzzard in the islands at the present time is not so easily discovered save in the larger isles such as Arran, Mull and Skye,

[1] See Doctor Hugh Blair's remarks on the buzzard's status in these counties quoted on pp. 146-147.

Islay and Jura, in all of which it may be on the increase. Of the smaller islands in which it is known to have bred within recent years mention may be made of Bute, Tiree, Coll, Eigg, Canna, Lunga, Iona, Raasay and Tanera.

The status of the buzzard in Deeside is discussed by a correspondent in the *Scottish Naturalist*,[1] where it is pointed out that from 1870 or 1880 until 1947 the bird was rarely seen in the area, but from that year onwards, during the late autumn and winter months it has been observed in some of the glens and on some of the higher hills. In 1950 a pair was seen on several occasions during the spring and summer and on 26th July 1952 five were observed together quartering the slopes of Creag Liath. The presence of the buzzards on Deeside has since been confirmed by Mr. Seton Gordon, who has become accustomed to seeing the species in the Dinnet and Braemar area, where previously they were never seen. That the buzzard is now resident in Middle Deeside there seems little doubt, although breeding had not been confirmed up to August 1952.

For further details of local distribution *The Birds of Scotland* by Miss Baxter and Miss Rintoul should be consulted.

Of late years the buzzard has colonized the Outer Hebrides and is apparently well established.

There are no breeding records from the Orkneys or the Shetlands. A straggler is reported to have been seen in Unst in 1936, but the bird is more often recognized in Fair Isle. Writing to me in August 1954, Mr. Kenneth Williamson, Director of the Fair Isle Bird Observatory, tells me that he sees buzzards annually and they are undoubtedly commoner than they were. He believes that practically all of those seen are *Buteo buteo*, and certainly those which he was able to identify were of this species.

As a breeding bird the buzzard was nearly extinct in Ireland. Lieutenant-Colonel Scroope in the recently published work on that country[2] observes that it was formerly resident and bred in Ulster, but was almost exterminated between 1880 and 1890. A pair bred in Antrim in one year between 1905 and 1915, and another pair in 1933. In 1951 a pair was present but proof of breeding was not obtained, while in 1952 " at least one pair bred in another locality ". All the records given by Ussher and Warren [3] over fifty years ago of its breeding refer to the four maritime counties of Donegal, Londonderry, Antrim and Down.

Apart from the few instances of nesting within recent years which I have quoted above on the authority of Colonel Scroope, the buzzard prior to 1953 was only a rare visitor to the country. Listing the occurrences since 1900 it was possible to include only eighteen records up to October 1952. For details *The Birds of Ireland* (1954) should be consulted.

[1] Alex. Tewnion, vol. lxiv, 1952, p. 177.
[2] *Birds of Ireland*, 1954, p. 101.
[3] *Birds of Ireland*, 1900, p. 123.

We now have encouraging news that in 1953[1] three pairs bred in one locality in Antrim and one pair elsewhere in that county, while in the following year, 1954,[2] ten pairs were computed as breeding in Antrim. For a bird considered to have been all but extirpated in Ireland this is cheering news indeed.

DISTRIBUTION ABROAD : The common buzzard breeds throughout western Europe extending in Norway[3] to 65° N. and in Sweden to central Norrland. East of the Vistula its eastern range is ill-defined but H. G. K. Molineux[4] includes the Baltic States and East Prussia within its breeding range as well as Austria, Czecho-Slovakia and Hungary. In the Mediterranean countries it occurs from the Iberian Peninsula to the western shores of the Black Sea, and is also reported from western Asia Minor. Races of the buzzard have been described from the Azores (*rothschildi*), Madeira (*harterti*), the Canary Islands (*insularum*), the Cape Verde Islands (*bannermani*) and Sardinia (*arrigonii*) ; with this last race the buzzards from Corsica, Elba and the Tuscan Islands have been united. There is no resident buzzard in the Balearic Islands, nor is there one in Cyprus. To the Balearic Islands *Buteo buteo* is a scarce winter visitor.[5]

There are occasional reports that the common buzzard crosses the Straits of Gibraltar. Howard Irby himself wrote that he had seen it crossing the Straits between 11th and 24th March, and quotes Favier that the birds are to be seen on the Tangier side " in flights " in March and April. As Favier says the same of practically every bird, we need not put much faith in his assertion. Irby, however, was careful about similar statements which he made. More recently Colonel A. J. S. Tuke, Nature Correspondent of the *Gibraltar Chronicle* from 1950 to 1953, published a small brochure on Gibraltar birds[6] and stated therein that " many [common buzzards] can be seen crossing the Straits in spring and autumn in company with honey buzzards, kites, etc ". That statement struck me as so unlikely that I got in touch with the author, who informs me that, in the light of what I was able to tell him, he considers a mistake in identification was made. Although I have travelled extensively in northern Africa, especially in Morocco, I have never seen a common buzzard on the African side of the Straits, and the late J. I. S. Whitaker, with years of experience in Tunisia, wrote that he too had never met with a common buzzard in that

[1] *Irish Bird Report*, 1953, p. 9.

[2] *Irish Bird Report*, 1954, p. 12.

[3] Doctor Yngvar Hagen has stated that in Norway at the present day (1953-54), the buzzard, though greatly reduced in numbers through persecution, occurs chiefly in the east and south, but breeds northwards to Trondelag and about latitude 65° in the interior of Helgeland. It ranges no further west than Setesdal.

[4] *A Catalogue of Birds, giving their Distribution in the Western Palæarctic Region*, 1930, p. 210.

[5] P. W. Munn, *Novitates Zoologicae*, xxxvii, p. 98.

[6] *An Introduction to the Birds of Southern Spain and Gibraltar*, 1953, p. 71.

country and throws doubt on the few Algerian records which came to his notice.

On the other hand, thanks to Monsieur le Docteur Jean Panouse of the Institut Scientifique Chérifien at Rabat, and his assistant M. Georges Pasteur, I have been able to trace the very few instances when *Buteo buteo buteo* has been recorded from Morocco. These are as follows :

1. The first mention of the common buzzard from Morocco is contained in the very valuable contribution made by H. and A. Vaucher in their " Liste des oiseaux observés au Maroc de 1884 à 1914 ",[1] where these authors under the heading of *Buteo vulgaris* (Bechst.) observe : " Nicheur. Très rare, tué en janvier 1905 à Tanger. Collection Vaucher, Genève (femelle adulte)."

2. The next mention of the species is contained in the Report made by Rear-Admiral Lynes on his collecting expedition to the mountains of the Spanish Province of Yebala, north-western Morocco.[2] He wrote under the heading *Buteo buteo buteo* (Linnaeus) : " We have the following two reliable records of the common buzzard ; in both cases seen at short range :

at Quitsan, March 19 ;
at El Bijut (two miles S.W. of Apes Hill), May 11.

The latter was very likely breeding in one of the cork trees of the El Bijut ' wooded jungle '."

Lynes is very unlikely to have made any mistake as to the identification of the birds which he saw and it is to be noted that both he and Vaucher agree that the bird is likely to *breed* in these mountains. If that is the case, in these little known mountains, which have never been satisfactorily explored, it does not point to the buzzards being *migratory*, at any rate to the mountainous area which fringes the northern coast-line. On the other hand, there is in the collection of the Institut Scientifique Chérifien one specimen which M. Pasteur definitely assigns to the common buzzard of Europe—a female obtained at Tiflèt on 21st October 1951, but not adult—and possibly another (? female) obtained in the Forêt de la Mamora on 3rd February 1935, but whose small measurements suggest that it is a male.

We can, I think, state with some assurance that if Spanish examples of *Buteo buteo buteo* or birds from northern Europe ever cross the Straits of Gibraltar they must do so in negligible numbers and certainly not to the extent suggested by Favier and Colonel Tuke. The resident buzzard of Morocco is *Buteo refinus cirtensis*.

HABITS : Were he alive to-day W. H. Hudson could take comfort from the fact that the fate which he foretold for the buzzard in Britain

---

[1] *Revue Française d'Ornithologie*, iv, 1915, p. 95.
[2] *Novitates Zoologicae*, xxxi, 1924, p. 88 (no. 171).

has fallen far short of reality. Referring in his very charming book entitled *British Birds* to the status of the buzzard in Britain at that time (1897), Hudson wrote: " My one consolation in this sad portion of my work, which tells of the noble and useful species whose ' *doom is sealed* ', is that I am not writing for grown men, but for the young, who are not yet the slaves of a contemptible convention, nor have come under a system which has been only too mildly described as ' stupid ' by every British ornithologist during the last five or six decades."

It required the passing of another generation before the words which Hudson addressed to the young men of his day bore fruit, but in the times in which I am writing (1954) there is a very real recognition by the public, and especially by sportsmen and farmers, of the inestimable benefit which birds convey to an island population which has to try and live on its own resources. One of the chief scourges to-day in Britain, especially in Scotland, is the plague of rabbits which infests the land, and the greatest disservice which man can do—and has done—is to destroy the birds which destroy the pests. Unhappily, the buzzard takes a long time to recover from incessant persecution, for its presence in greater numbers in the south-west of Scotland would be a boon indeed. The bird is all too seldom seen in the counties which border the Solway where it once used to flourish and which are now overrun with rabbits.[1]

In addition to the vermin mentioned, rats form a considerable part of the buzzard's food supply, but it does not scorn smaller prey and moles, voles, slow-worms, earthworms, molluscs, toads, frogs, beetles, dung-beetles and the larva of the privet hawk-moth are recorded on good authority in this country. Carrion is also known to be eaten when opportunity occurs.

In Sweden buzzards have been seen on several occasions to kill dragon-flies. The birds watch until the insects settle and then capture them.

A very complete investigation into the feeding habits of the buzzard was undertaken in Germany between the years 1900 and 1909 and the results published by G. Rörig.[2] No less than 1237 buzzards were examined, both in summer and in winter, and the result of the analysis, so far as the stomach contents could be determined, showed the following creatures to have been consumed :

  1906 voles, mice and water voles,
    64 larger rodents from brown rats to squirrels,
   219 shrews and moles,
    28 leverets and rabbits,
    20 remains of carrion, including hare and roe-buck,

[1] Since this sentence was written myxomatosis has *nearly*, but not entirely, exterminated the rabbit population of the Solway. The presence of buzzards to put the finishing touches to this rabbit plague would have been a godsend to the country.

[2] G. Rörig, " Magen- und Gewölluntersuchungen heimischer Raubvögel ", *Arb. Kaiserl. Biol. Anst. Land- u. Forstwissenschaft*, vols. iv, v and vii, 1903-10.

* {
18 partridges and 11 pheasants,
6 pigeons and 4 domestic fowls,
44 other birds, including the young of crows, jays, magpies and thrushes,
}

* [It is almost certain that while some of these birds were captured by the buzzards themselves, others had been found dead and a few fetched from the eyries of peregrines and goshawks whose nests the buzzards had raided.]

40 lizards,
32 slow-worms or snakes,
186 amphibians, mostly frogs but also a few toads,
6 fish.

Insects were found in 245 stomachs, often in such abundance that they could not be counted. There must have been several thousands of insects in all. In one stomach there were found 144 larvae of different sorts.

The buzzard's method of hunting is nothing like as spectacular as that of a falcon. It quarters the ground in long sweeps from a fair height and when a victim has been selected the bird pounces upon it. It is not often seen to chase its prey in the manner of a sparrow-hawk, but as it has been clearly seen to do so it may indulge in this type of hunting more commonly than is suspected. The instance to which I refer took place in April 1948 when Mr. I. S. C. Robinson was watching a common buzzard flying across the estuary at Dale, Pembrokeshire. A flock of six starlings passed below it, but despite its advantage in altitude the buzzard made no attempt to stoop on the smaller birds. Instead it flew rapidly after them and took one of the starlings in its talons. It then alighted on the opposite shore but was lost to sight.

Although it is a very much smaller bird, there are many who still mistake the buzzard for a golden eagle, and in parts of Scotland where the King of Birds is looked upon with more than suspicion by the Highland shepherds, the buzzard often pays the penalty for the oft-quoted misdeeds of its larger relative. The grouse know better, for whereas the appearance of an eagle will clear a moor in the twinkling of an eye, the arrival on the scene of a buzzard evokes no such panic. To watch a pair of buzzards soaring in the heavens amidst mountain scenery is a most inspiring sight. With motionless wings and widespread tail the birds seem almost to float upwards, crossing and re-crossing each other's course as they mount higher and higher until they are mere specks in the sky. It is this soaring habit of the buzzard which will enable it to be identified from afar and will often betray its presence when it is at too great a distance for its mewing cries to be heard. When rising from a post or branch it appears to be a clumsy bird but once properly on the wing such an illusion is quickly dispelled. In countries where they are not molested buzzards will permit much closer inspection than they do in this country, and I have more than once walked up to within thirty yards of a resting bird.

It seems to be inferred by the authors of *The Handbook of British Birds* that all British buzzards are sedentary, remaining in these islands the whole year round. The statement is based on the fact that a number of buzzards ringed as nestlings have been recovered in their country of origin, and that none, apparently, has been recovered abroad. Considering what a small proportion have been ringed and recovered this seems rather too hasty an inference to draw, and it seems to me perfectly possible that *not* all the buzzards which quit our shores in autumn are those which have wandered across the North Sea before continuing their way south. When discussing the buzzards which nest on the Cornish cliffs Colonel B. H. Ryves makes the interesting statement that after early November it is unusual to see more than one or two birds at a time until early spring, and voices a strong suspicion that a proportion of buzzards migrate from the county for a short period in December and January. In some winters their usual haunts are entirely deserted.

Buzzards have occasionally been seen passing south in September and October in the Isle of May and it is recorded as a passage migrant " in very small numbers and of somewhat uncertain appearance " in the early autumn along the Suffolk coast. We hear of them too in Kent, usually immature birds, and in other south coast counties where they are not known to breed, the inference being that those encountered are on their way to winter quarters beyond our shores. It has been suggested by more than one writer that these birds may be of Continental origin, for it is well known that the buzzards from the north of Europe wander south on the approach of bad weather.

Writing many years ago (1895) from Heligoland, the old German naturalist Gätke recorded that the common buzzard visits that island throughout the whole year except in June and July, for the most part in small groups of three, four or more examples, though—and this is instructive—" sometimes during the autumn migration these numbers are increased almost up to hundreds, and should a sharp frost set in later on during the winter, solitary examples of this species are to be met with almost daily ". It seems more than likely that a small proportion of these birds would drift across the North Sea and reach our eastern coast-line. That disaster has at times overtaken them during the crossing is recorded by the late C. B. Ticehurst, who recalls in his *History of the Birds of Suffolk* the great immigration of birds of prey which took place in 1881—a year in which the common buzzard was extraordinarily abundant. On that occasion a number, together with honey-buzzards and other species, were overwhelmed in a severe gale in the North Sea ; many were washed ashore and others driven inland.

The spring passage of the buzzard in the British Isles passes almost unnoticed.

That European buzzards sometimes make considerable journeys is proved by the bird ringed as a nestling near Berlin which was recovered the following March in the province of Ciudad Real in Spain [1] and by another example of which I have a note, ringed in May 1924 in Bavaria, recovered in March 1929 in Switzerland.[2] Both these buzzards were examples of the typical subspecies. The late Professor Einar Lönnberg [3] found that the common buzzard breeding in southern and middle Sweden appears to winter in the north-western parts of the continent of Europe from Wismar in the east through Westphalia to Belgium and northern France. As a rule it was found not to extend its migrations further south than Paris, and an example which was recovered as far south-west as the Department of Deux-Sèvres during the severe winter of 1928 was looked upon as having journeyed exceptionally far.

That buzzards which habitually frequent the higher mountainous areas of Europe leave their haunts in severe weather is quite understandable, for food is then difficult to come by and the birds must seek lower altitudes if they are to survive. The Spanish writer Castellarnau [4] has stated that the common buzzard emigrates from the sierras of central Spain in autumn to return at the end of February or early March, and observes that he has several times seen them in flocks of twenty or more. As is well known the winter months on the high sierras can be extremely severe. How far south these buzzards wander is not known but on the Spanish side of the Straits of Gibraltar common buzzards are reported to be very abundant from November to the end of February, and it is said that these visitors do not remain to breed. More than likely these are the buzzards which have descended from the sierras further north and it does not appear that they have any necessity to proceed beyond Andalusia, or from the other southern provinces of Spain. The statement copied from one book to another that the common buzzard winters as far south as north-west Africa can, I think, be discounted, except in very exceptional circumstances.

Now that the buzzard is much more commonly seen in the west of Britain (excluding Ireland) the opportunity has been taken by many naturalists to study its habits and many excellent notes upon it have been published [5] or been sent to me from different parts of the country.

[1] *Ibis*, 1928, p. 639.   [2] *Bull. Soc. Vaud. Sci. Nat.*, lvii, 1929, p. 57.
[3] Introduction to his *Swedish Birds*, 1929, p. xii.
[4] J. M. Castellarnau in *Anales de la Soc. España de Hist. Natural*, vi, 1877, pp. 151-209 : " Estudio Ornithologico del Real Sitio de San Ildefonso ".
[5] Apart from a small book, *The Buzzard at Home* by Arthur Brook, *The Lure of Bird Watching* by E. W. Hendy and various nesting notes in *British Birds*, I have made special use of the accounts of the buzzard in Colonel B. H. Ryves' *Bird Life in Cornwall* and of Mr. E. Blezard's *Lakeland Natural History*, to the authors of which I wish to make full acknowledgment.

Unless aroused to anger by repeated attacks the buzzard is a peace-loving bird and does not easily retaliate. Crows and rooks persecute it unmercifully, ravens chase it with fury and gulls stoop at it. Usually it submits quietly to their molestations but when on rare occasions it does retaliate, there are no half-measures. Thus has it been succinctly described.

A terrific battle between a buzzard and two ravens was once witnessed in Cornwall by Colonel Ryves, the ravens making a determined onslaught " with murder in their hearts ". The combat lasted a whole hour and the honours appear to have been divided at the finish, when the fight was broken off from sheer exhaustion on both sides. Considering the antipathy which undoubtedly exists between the buzzard on one side and ravens and crows on the other, it is curious how often they nest in proximity. It is worthy of note that buzzards and peregrines share no such unfriendly feelings towards one another.

Buzzards pair for life, but unlike ravens they do not combine against their enemies. Indeed, if one of their number is the subject of attack, its mate may be seen to vanish discreetly. Should, however, a buzzard lose its mate during the breeding season, it does not at once take a fresh one but may even wait until the following season, showing in this way a nice regard for its previous partner. Even so, companionship of the sexes is never so marked as in the raven.

Buzzards are known, moreover, to have strong social tendencies and in Cornwall—and no doubt the same may be said of other districts where the bird is common—an assemblage of birds may be witnessed ; as many as fifteen have been counted. The latter part of August is a favourite time for these gatherings to occur but they may be seen at any time from early spring to autumn. It is difficult to suggest a likely explanation other than pure sociability, for there can be no analogy between the flocking of buzzards and the flocking of ravens, to which reference is made in my first volume.

The courtship flight of the buzzard may be witnessed in March and early April, when the great birds float round and round in circles, with their tails spread wide to show off their bars, screaming at times as the male circles above his intended mate. Humphrey Gilbert describes [1] seeing no less than six pairs in the air at once performing these courting evolutions on the Pembrokeshire coast, all displaying at the same time. That this is not the only method employed was observed by Colonel Ryves, who on several occasions saw the same pair of birds indulging in a very different flight. One of the birds flew up and down the edge of a wood with long ungainly strokes of the wings, which were raised well above the body at the upward stroke and lowered well below it at the downward, giving the impression of a large bird jerking itself through the air. This is a very different motion from that used when the bird is flying, as it does, rather slowly to roost with quick, short steady wing-beats, without a single alternating glide.

[1] *Watching and Wandering among Birds*, p. 49.

Buzzards may often be seen, as I have constantly observed, almost stationary over a given spot, and though not in the same class as the kestrel, they can hover, under favourable circumstances, on motionless wings.

The more normal display flight of the buzzard is not necessarily confined to the period of courtship, as Colonel Ryves observes, but may often be seen in spring and sometimes in autumn, and he has seen it at the change-over during incubation :

The incoming bird soars above the nest and dives obliquely like a falling star. The sitting bird shuffles clumsily to the edge of the nest and leaps into space. With outstretched wings it catches the wind and soars gracefully skywards. When it has climbed to a height of two or three hundred feet, it shoots upwards, and at the top of its vertical rise, backwards, giving the impression that it is going to turn on its back—but checking itself without visible effort, it tilts forward and the next moment dives almost headlong fifty or sixty feet. Staying its fall by opened wings, it repeats these evolutions several times. Finally it soars into space and is lost to sight.

BREEDING HABITS : It is exceptional to find eggs of the common buzzard much before the middle of April, and even in Cornwall [1] 5th April is the earliest date on record, though the 29th of that month is said to be abnormally late, first eggs being usually deposited between the 9th and the 20th. In Lakeland [2] the first buzzard's eggs can generally be found about mid-April, and most of the birds have full clutches by the end of the month. In very backward springs some nests do not hold eggs until well into May. Buzzards begin nesting operations much earlier than the above dates would indicate and their nests are completed long before they lay their eggs. In Cornwall Colonel Ryves has seen a nest completed— lining, decorations and all—by 10th February, but normally nests are constructed in that county during March. Both birds collect and bring sticks to the nest but the hen apparently does most of the decorating.

Lakeland and Pennine buzzards nest both on rocks and on trees. Some nests are in cliffs which would satisfy the peregrine, but others are in outcrops so low that the eggs can be inspected without the trouble of climbing, and one or two have been practically on the ground, on waterside banks.

In Cornwall it has been found that the buzzards show a preference for a particular kind of tree in which to build, such as a pine marooned with one or two others in a wood of beech. Some pairs select a larch, while others will nest only in elms. Buzzards normally prefer to build in trees, but once they take to cliff-nesting they are said not to revert to trees again.

The nest of the buzzard is usually an elaborate affair and no better

[1] *Bird Life in Cornwall*, p. 110.
[2] The notes on Lakeland and Pennine buzzards have been supplied by Doctor Blair unless otherwise stated.

description has been given of it than that in *Lakeland Natural History*,[1] where the authors write :

The composition of the nest varies from a few scraps of plant-stalks surrounding a hollow in turf to a bulky and well-lined collection of sticks and heather stems. Among the grassy fells, and failing other materials, the nest is mainly made up of turf, the basal parts of grass clumps, and dead stalks of thistles, nettles or umbelliferous plants. One nest so formed, and used two years running, was for the second time merely scraped out and scantily lined with woodrush, grass and green moss. Dried grass, woodrush and dead bracken are the common lining materials. There is sometimes an additional tuft or two of sheep's wool and one exceptional nest was lined mostly with this material.

Marked differences are shown in the buzzard's habit of decorating the nest with freshly plucked foliage. Now and then a nest is embellished with a spray or two before laying has begun ; some nests are half smothered in greenery at the time they hold eggs while others appear to receive very little during the whole of the incubation and fledging periods. Sprays of rowan or mountain ash leaves, occasionally with blossoms, are oftenest used, other kinds noted being cherry, spruce, larch, ivy, heather and willow-herb—*Epilobium montanum L.* In addition are lady fern, young fronds of bracken and catkin-bearing twigs of willow. One nest had a mixture of raspberry and rose-bay when it held incubated eggs, and another, an adopted raven's nest, had three long flowering stems of rose-bay—*Epilobium angustifolium L.*—at the time the single young buzzard in it was about ready for leaving. On a grassy knoll, one of the typical places where prey is broken before being taken to the nest, a fresh spray of rowan leaves lay among the remains of young rabbits. The decorations of rowan in the nest, which held two half-grown young, were all withered at the time.

Colonel Ryves inclines to the belief that " decoration " is the wrong word to use. Rather he considers that the so-called decorations are really an attempt to camouflage the exterior of the nest in order to make it more like its surroundings. Tree-nests are always very bulky and in Cornwall we are told that some pairs—very far from all—build one or more spare nests and camouflage both so that it is not always possible to guess which will eventually hold eggs. Tree-nests are built of stout sticks with a comparatively shallow cup in the centre, lined with grass, bracken or ivy leaves. A wide platform extends well beyond the cup to provide space for the young birds. In Scotland many buzzards have perforce taken to cliff-nesting and in the late Colonel R. F. Meiklejohn's diary, which is in my possession, he notes that *all* the nests belonging to buzzards which he saw in Scotland were in cliffs. It is certainly not true of all Scottish buzzards.

It is far from uncommon to find four eggs in a buzzard's nest on the Pennine or Lakeland fells, and several clutches of five have been recorded. In some years, however, such large numbers will be looked for in vain. In 1952, for example, some buzzards were incubating solitary eggs in one

[1] *Lakeland Natural History*, 1946, by E. Blezard *et al.*

dale, two being the largest clutch seen there. The previous winter had been very mild, and the mortality amongst the fell sheep trifling, which suggests some correlation between average clutch size and food supply. The authors of *The Birds of Lakeland* remark that in 1940 clutches were uniformly small under rather similar conditions, very few sheep having perished in the winter despite a spell of very hard weather.

Doctor Blair has contributed the final paragraphs to this essay, dealing with clutch size in general, and variation in the eggs which to some extent may be correlated with the locality in which they are laid. He writes as follows : At one time a clutch of four buzzard's eggs was considered worthy of record. As the species has become more plentiful, such large clutches have naturally become more frequent, especially in some districts. Large clutches appear to be more numerous in Great Britain than elsewhere in the buzzard's range. They are particularly common in Somerset, where several sets of five have been recorded, besides one undoubted set of six— so far the only one to be found in Britain. Yet in Cornwall buzzards content themselves with two or three eggs.

In shape buzzard's eggs vary considerably, the majority being ovate, some almost round, and others elongated or even elliptical. Their ground colour is white with, in the thinner-shelled examples, a slight bluish tinge. Many show markings of lilac or violet-grey where pigments have been deposited on the deeper layers of the shell. The more superficial markings range in colour from pale yellowish- or reddish-brown to deep chocolate, or even sepia, and in character from streaks and spots to extensive blotches or smears. The majority of specimens must be described as sparingly marked, and a few lack even a trace of pigment, but on some the rufous blotches and cloudings almost hide the ground colour. While the colouring matters are generally concentrated towards the larger pole of the egg, they are sometimes evenly distributed, or they may, more rarely, form a zone. Seebohm describes a very striking type of buzzard's egg in which " the rich brown colouring matter is covered with a thin coating of lime, giving the egg a beautiful delicate lilac-pink appearance ". It is exceptional to find a buzzard's clutch evenly marked, one egg generally being considerably lighter than the rest. It has been said that the colouring of a buzzard's eggs becomes richer as the bird grows older.[1]

In large series buzzard's eggs will be found to vary according to locality. Amongst British birds, those in Somerset undoubtedly produce the most handsome clutches, rich and bold markings being the rule there. Compared with these an egg typical of a wide area in North Wales seems quite unattractive with its few spots and streaks of yellowish-brown.

The average of 100 British-taken eggs (after Jourdain) is $56 \cdot 8 \times 45 \cdot 44$ mm. Max. $61 \times 45 \cdot 6$ and 59×49 mm. Min. $52 \cdot 1 \times 43$ and $53 \cdot 1 \times 42 \cdot 5$ mm.

[1] *Coloured Illustrations of the Eggs of British Birds*, vol. i, p. 25.

Incubation lasts from twenty-eight to thirty days.   The fledging period lasts from six to seven weeks.

The buzzard is single-brooded.   Both parents bring food to the nest but at first the female alone feeds the young.

Food brought to young buzzards by their parents in the Pennines one season included young rabbits, a meadow pipit and a wheatear.   Under a Lakeland nest, which contained large young, lay a number of mutton bones and, singularly enough, the wings of several carrion crows.

Dead lambs are certainly taken but there is no instance known of a buzzard attacking a live lamb.

It cannot be too strongly emphasized that the buzzard is an entirely beneficial species and well worthy of encouragement on anyone's property.

REFERENCES : Original Description. *Falco buteo* Linnaeus. Syst. Nat., 10th ed., 1758, p. 90 : Europe. Restricted type locality Savoy.

PLATE 19   **STEPPE OR EASTERN BUZZARD**

Buteo vulpinus Gloger

A rare Accidental Visitor which has been recognized once only

IDENTIFICATION : It is practically impossible to give a satisfactory description of the steppe buzzard owing to the extreme variability of its plumage even in adult examples.   Colonel Meinertzhagen attempted to do so in *The Birds of Arabia* and his description, which is applicable to many specimens, reads as follows : Whole upper parts dark brown, the feathers normally with rufous edges and very rarely without.   Under parts very variable, sometimes uniform rufous with whitish streaks on chin and throat, sometimes whitish with large drop-shaped pale brown streaks, sometimes almost barred brownish and sometimes whitish with pale rufous bars and streaks.   The tail is always barred and the tarsus is bare and unfeathered.

In the *Birds of East and North-Eastern Africa* the authors considered the following to be the salient characters : Above dark brown edged with chestnut ; below chestnut or ash brown more or less barred ; underside of wings white ; under wing-coverts chestnut or ash brown, more or less barred ; several bars on tail.   Sexes alike.

The young bird is described as brown, below deep buff with blobs and streaks of brown.

Captain Grant and Mr. Mackworth-Praed observe that this buzzard has a very dark brown and also a blackish phase of plumage.

It is a matter of opinion whether the steppe buzzard is considered to be a race of the common buzzard, *Buteo buteo*, or whether it is given full specific rank.   As the breeding area of the two birds appears to overlap, I prefer the latter course.   Admittedly these two buzzards are so much alike in appearance that there has been endless confusion over the records.

PLATE 19

STEPPE OR EASTERN BUZZARD
Buteo vulpinus Gloger

With a view to disentangling the errors of identification into which many writers have fallen when recording buzzards from western Europe, three well-known ornithologists [1] examined no less than 383 specimens in the various collections of Europe, particularly Holland, and were able in consequence to make at least a suggestion as to how the two birds may be recognized. The following extract from their contribution to an English periodical [2] summarizes the main differences between the buzzard and the steppe buzzard as determined by these authorities :

The well-known strongly developed individual variability of the common buzzard (*Buteo b. buteo*) makes it hard to give an exact plumage description of the two races,[3] but we may recall the fact that steppe buzzards can be recognised by the rufous or buffy-brown general colouration of upper- and underparts, which is especially noticeable on the head and mantle. Moreover head and mantle of the steppe buzzard are often of a lighter yellowish-brown colouration than the remainder of the body. The irregular cross-bars on the underparts are mostly rufous-brown, the under tail-coverts usually have rufous cross-bars, and the rectrices mostly have a rufous-brown ground colour. Nevertheless a pure greyish colour occurs at least in the central rectrices of a few adult specimens from Wladikawkas, Caucasus, which in all other respects are typical *vulpinus*.

The authors proceed to point out that " dark rufous-brown buzzards with a relatively dark brownish-red head and neck, with dark brown instead of rufous-brown cross-bars on the under tail-coverts, and extensive dark earthy brown bases to all small feathers of the upperside, represent the rufous-brown variety of the common buzzard, *Buteo buteo buteo* ".

They further state that in literature west European buzzards with rather small dimensions have been referred in the past to *vulpinus*, but after measuring a very large series they came to the conclusion that no exact difference in wing-length exists between *B. b. buteo* and *B. vulpinus*, although there is a general tendency for *vulpinus* to be a trifle smaller.

OCCURRENCES IN GREAT BRITAIN : The steppe buzzard has been recognized only once in these islands : an example was killed at Eversleigh, Wiltshire, in September 1864 by J. C. Hawkshaw and recorded by Gould in the *Birds of Britain*, vol. i, p. xxx. It is preserved in the British Museum collection.

Other examples had been tentatively assigned to this species in Great Britain but Mr. H. F. Witherby took great pains to examine those available and was convinced that they were specimens of the common buzzard. He concluded therefore that the inclusion of the steppe buzzard in the British List must rest upon the Wiltshire specimen of 1864 alone. (Cf.

[1] Doctor K. H. Voous, P. A. Hens and J. G. van Marle.

[2] *British Birds*, vol. xli, 1948, pp. 77-82.

[3] It must be borne in mind that the authors in their work cited treat *vulpinus* as a race of *Buteo buteo*, and when they write of two races they are referring to *B. buteo buteo* and *B. buteo vulpinus*, *i.e.*, *Buteo vulpinus* Gloger.

British Birds, xiv, 1921, p. 183, in which Mr. Witherby gives a history of all the specimens examined.)

It is worthy of note, to quote Mr. Witherby's description, that the Wiltshire specimen in the British Museum has the upperparts broadly edged rufous, the tail tinged rufous and the underparts with the centres of the feathers brownish-rufous ; the under tail-coverts and axillaries are barred rufous, and the underparts are more rufous than any example of *Buteo buteo buteo* that Mr. Witherby had ever seen. The measurements are given as wing 363, tail 200, tarsus 76 and bill 20 mm. The sex of this specimen was not ascertained.

DISTRIBUTION ABROAD : The type locality of Gloger's *Buteo vulpinus* is South Africa, the name having been given to the bird in its winter quarters.

The range of the steppe buzzard has been closely worked out by Russian scientists and, thanks to Madame Kozlova of the Leningrad Academy of Sciences, I am able to give for the first time in western literature the newly-accepted Russian distribution. In this review Elizabeth Kozlova has made full use of the work of Dementiev. She writes as follows under date July 1954 :

The steppe buzzard inhabits the forest and forest-steppe zones of U.S.S.R., north of Leningrad, Onega Lake, Archangel (near the south-eastern shores of the White Sea) ; 66° N. latitude in the basin of the Petchora River ; about 62° N. latitude on the eastern slopes of the Ural Mountains and in western Siberia north to about 60° N. latitude.

The eastern limits of its range pass through the regions of Krasnoiarsk on the Yenisei River, the western Sayan Mountains and the upper reaches of the Yenisei region (adjoining the north-western borders of Mongolia). It is found breeding in the forest zone of the Altai Mountains up to 2200 m. From the Altai this buzzard ranges south along mountain ranges to eastern and central Tian-shan, where it has been found in the vicinity of Djarkent, Alma-ata (formerly Wierny) and the Issyk-kul Lake.

The southern boundary of the steppe buzzard's range in western Siberia coincides with the southern limit of the forest-steppe zone, extending from east to west along 54-55° N. latitude to the middle course of the Ural River and rather north of Stalingrad on the Volga. The southern limit of its range in eastern Europe extends from the northern Caucasus westwards to Chersson (Kherson) on the lower Dnieper, and Moldavia, *i.e.* Bessarabia.

In the forested mountains of the Crimea (Krim Peninsula) we have *Buteo buteo menetriesi* Bogd.

According to a recent review of the subspecies of *Buteo buteo* by Dementiev (1951) an extensive region of eastern Europe—from Vitebsk, Vilna and the Prut River in the west and south-west, to about Charkow in the east—is inhabited by birds of mixed population : (1) intermediate individuals *buteo* × *vulpinus* ; (2) birds which do not differ from *Buteo buteo buteo* ; and (3) birds which are similar to *Buteo buteo vulpinus*.

It would appear that the examples which Dementiev would place in the third category are those which are reported to breed in the north and east of Sweden and in Finland. Whether these steppe buzzards from the north-west migrate, as we should expect, across Europe in a south-easterly direction does not appear to be known. It seems that this buzzard is of more regular occurrence in the Netherlands and Belgium than had hitherto been guessed until Doctor Voous and his collaborators called attention to the fact and were able to assign twenty-seven specimens of Dutch and Belgian migratory buzzards to *Buteo vulpinus* on account of plumage characters only.[1]

Lending colour to the view that a more direct route to Africa is taken by certain steppe buzzards may be instanced the bird ringed in the province of Norrbotten, northern Sweden, which was shot in the Department of Hérault in southern France, close to the Gulf of Lyons, in the first week of October. Professor Lönnberg, who recorded this specimen in his *Review of Swedish Birds* (1929), was of opinion that had it not been killed it would have crossed the Mediterranean to North Africa, but the bird was very far to the west of the route usually taken by migrants of this species when normally proceeding to their winter quarters.

Mr. Witherby had further examples in mind when he wrote in *The Handbook of British Birds* that vagrants have been reported from France, the Iberian Peninsula and Sardinia.

This buzzard winters in East and South Africa. It is reported to have been found breeding once in Arabia but on what appears to be slender evidence.[2] There are numerous records of it passing through the Aden Protectorate[3] in November, December and April, and it has been obtained in December at Sharaya in Arabia[4] not far from Jedda. Either the typical subspecies or a closely allied race (*intermedius* Menzbier) has been reported from the Sudan[5] and *Buteo vulpinus* is reported from the Belgian Congo,[6] where Chapin states that while nowhere common in the Congo, it comes not only to the savannas of the Uelle and eastern frontier but even to clearings in the Equatorial Forest. It was never seen during the period of northern summer. More will be told of its migrations through Africa in the next section.

Madame E. Kozlova informs me that a few individuals winter regularly in the vicinity of Lenkoran in south-east Transcaucasia, and occasionally in the Kopet-tag Mountains in southern Turkestan near the border of Iran.

---

[1] *British Birds*, xli, 1948, p. 82.
[2] Cheesman and Ticehurst, *Ibis*, 1925, p. 24.
[3] Grant and Mackworth-Praed, *African Handbook of Birds*, 1952, i, p. 194.
[4] Bates, *Ibis*, 1937, p. 58.
[5] Stresemann, *Journ. für Ornithologie*, 1925, pp. 295-309.
[6] Chapin, *Birds of the Belgian Congo*, 1932, i, p. 612.

HABITS AND MIGRATIONS : The steppe buzzard disappears from the northern portions of its range about the middle of September but some individuals linger near Pskow till early October, according to Madame Kozlova. On the autumnal migration many pass through the Balkan States, Sinai and Egypt, but very few examples have been collected and in its passage through Egypt there is difficulty in distinguishing it from the long-legged buzzard (*Buteo rufinus*). Considering that it must pass through Arabia on passage and has been obtained, so Sir Geoffrey Archer assures me, on several occasions in the Arussi country of Abyssinia,[1] it is remarkable that of nearly thirty buzzards which he collected in British Somaliland, not one turned out to be a steppe buzzard. Perhaps their main line of flight lies farther west.

It is known that large numbers of steppe buzzards pass through Kenya and Uganda on their spring and autumn journeys, and when Colonel C. R. S. Pitman was farming in the Nzoia Valley, some thirty miles east of Mount Elgon, he had several opportunities of observing the birds on passage. Describing one of these flights he wrote :

On 13th October 1922 a flock of from 200 to 300 birds appeared in the late evening wheeling at a great height. They were evidently on south-west migration, though the actual movement at that time of the day was north-east. There is little doubt that the flock was searching for a suitable roosting place for the night, and apparently the forests of the higher Cherangani Hills appealed to the birds more than the sparse cover of the plains. The flock continued to wheel and circle at a great height and then the individuals dropped one by one almost to the ground as if preparatory to taking up quarters for the night. As the low-flying birds passed me, I managed to secure a specimen which proved to be a female, but on the whole I found them extremely wary. Each time the flock abandoned its dizzy wheeling in order to descend abruptly, the birds would follow some accepted leader as they would sail majestically north-east towards the hills one after the other.

These migrations pass over the great Rift Valley and its flanking escarpments, and on the western side the hills attain an altitude of nearly 12,000 feet. Special attention should be drawn to the fact that both specimens secured were females.

Four years later to a day, on 13th October 1926, Colonel Pitman again encountered a migration of this buzzard, this time in southern Ankole, where at 9.15 in the morning he observed a flight of fully 150 birds near the Kagera River and the Tanganyika border, moving slowly to the south-west at no great height. The position was 0° 45′ S. and 30° 48′ E. In the South African summer the bird is not uncommon in open and savanna veld, where it may be seen perched on telegraph poles and other conspicuous posts, from which it can dart upon its prey.

Doctor Austin Roberts in his *Birds of South Africa* (1940) does not make any mention of this buzzard's date of arrival in, or departure from, the Union.

[1] *Bateleur*, 1929, i, pp. 38-40.

On its spring passage north the steppe buzzard has come under notice on several occasions in Kenya, the Nzoia Valley east of Mount Elgon again being the point of observation. Colonel Pitman wrote : " On 17th March 1922, just as dusk was falling, a steady, low-flying stream of these birds was observed moving slowly in a northerly direction and a female was secured for identification. The specimen, with others, was roosting for the night in a tall tree in the dense cover on the banks of a water-course. On 29th March of the same year, another fairly large flight passed northerly in the forenoon ; while on 7th April quite a number were seen feeding on flying termites."

It was next observed in the Nzoia Valley on 20th March 1923, when a small flock of about thirty birds was seen slowly moving northwards. No autumn movement was observed for the next three years, and in 1925 Captain Pitman, as he then was, took up his appointment as Game Warden in Uganda.

It was while in the West Nile district, in the extreme south of the old Lado Enclave, and a few miles west of the Albert Nile, that Pitman had his last view of the steppe buzzard on passage. At 3.45 in the afternoon of 27th March 1928 a flock of more than 150 birds was encountered flying in a north-easterly direction : " The birds were moving in characteristic fashion, sometimes high, sometimes low, accompanied by much wheeling, an evolution which was repeated again and again, until at last they all disappeared from view."

It was left to the late Sir Frederick Jackson to record something of the habits of the steppe buzzard during its brief stay in tropical Africa. Writing of the species in his book,[1] in which it is termed the rufous buzzard, Sir Frederick wrote that during its visit between September and March it is widely distributed in Kenya and Uganda but is nowhere common in either territory. He found that it frequented wooded water-courses and the outer edge of forests and forest-glades, where it takes up a position on a branch of a large shady tree. In such positions, Sir Frederick observes, it will sit for an hour or more, calling at intervals, and then move on a few hundred yards. It is occasionally seen sailing round in circles high up in the air, and every now and again hanging absolutely stationary in the same spot, and without any apparent movement of the wings, like a kestrel, ready to drop directly its quarry exposes itself.

The steppe buzzard is credited with quite remarkable eyesight, in support of which Sir Frederick cites an instance where a bird was seen to leave the tree in which it was perched, fly direct for, and pick up, a green whip-snake about four feet long, and fly back with the reptile to the tree from which its attack had been launched. On measuring the distance it was found to have flown 623 yards, which, as Sir Frederick remarks, conveys some idea of the bird's keenness of sight. Snakes are hardly likely to

[1] *Birds of Kenya Colony and the Uganda Protectorate,* i, p. 202.

figure so prominently on the diet sheet of the steppe buzzard as they do on that of the short-toed eagle, but the above tale is proof that they do not come amiss when opportunity offers.

The usual food of this buzzard is said to be mole-rats, birds, small reptiles and rodents, and insects of various kinds, upon which it generally pounces from its look-out post. Like many other birds of prey, when the winged termites swarm the steppe buzzard is to the fore ; nor is the bird averse to lifting a chicken !

In South Africa it is said to live principally on large insects such as locusts and grasshoppers but there again it has been noted to feed upon lizards, small rodents and birds, among which young poultry are snatched up when the chance offers. Its food as observed in Russia will be mentioned later.

Very little has been published in Europe concerning the steppe buzzard's arrival in its breeding area or its nesting habits in eastern Europe and Siberia, and I am therefore greatly indebted to Madame E. Kozlova, who writes :

Buteo vulpinus first arrives in the Ukraine from late March to mid-April, according to whether the season is early or late, and the buzzards arrive in the northern portions of their range in eastern Europe and Siberia in the last part of April. Spring migration through the deserts of southern Turkestan continues during April and May.

In Russia the steppe buzzard is a bird of coniferous, mixed and broad-leaved woods, also of scattered birch and pine groves in the steppe. As noted already when discussing its range, the steppe buzzard has been found breeding in the forest zone of the Altai up to an altitude of 2200 m.

In different regions of the U.S.S.R. it feeds on small rodents, squirrels, *Microtus*, *Arvicola*, *Citellus*, *Silvymus*, *Mycromys minutus* ; young nestlings of *Lyrurus*, *Lagopus* and *Coturnix*, larks and thrushes. It also devours serpents, lizards and frogs, *Triton taeniatus*, beetles, locusts and other insects. In one case this buzzard has been observed hunting *on foot* after locusts (*Pachytilus* and *Calliptomus*).

BREEDING HABITS : In Witherby's *Handbook of British Birds* F. C. R. Jourdain wrote that the steppe buzzard has been " generally recorded as breeding in trees, but much uncertainty as to race in most references ". There is no ambiguity about the notes which have reached me from Russia. The race to which Madame Kozlova is referring is the typical subspecies, *Buteo vulpinus* of Gloger, and there appears to be no noticeable difference between its nest and that of *Buteo buteo*.

Nests have been found on fir and spruce trees, also on birches, oaks, willows, ash trees, etc., usually nearer to the forest rim. In the forest-steppe zone the buzzards nested by hundreds in small pine groves and in Central Kasachstan (near Karkaralinsk, north of Lake Balkash) a nest was once found in 1937 on a cliff. Small rodents were very abundant in that region in 1937 and so were the buzzards, which may have accounted for the unusual situation of the nest.[1]

The nest is usually placed from eight to twelve metres above ground level, more rarely from four to five.

From about mid-April to mid-May is the season when eggs have been recorded according to the various localities. Madame Kozlova gives the following instances as typical of the breeding season :

In the region of Minsk eggs have been recorded on 15th to 20th April ; in the region of Kiewkon on the Dnieper River 22nd April ; near Pskow 19th April ; eggs slightly incubated found near Tomsk, western Siberia, 17th May ; in the Barabinsky steppe, western Siberia, 11th May ; and in the southern Ural Mountains early May.

The full clutch normally consists of from two to three eggs, occasionally four, and once five has been recorded from Minussinsk. Incubation starts with the first egg and lasts for twenty-eight days. Downy young, just hatched, are recorded from the region of Minsk on 20th May ; from the forest-steppe zone near Minussinsk on 12th June and also in late June ; from the region of Tchkalow (formerly Orenburg) on 4th June. Both sexes take part in incubating but chiefly the female. The male brings the food for the incubating female and for the young but the female feeds the young herself.

According to I. Hortling the fledging period lasts from forty to forty-two days.

There are some additional notes in *The Handbook* regarding the breeding season in Finland, which is said to be from late April until the end of May, but whether Russian ornithologists consider Finnish buzzards to belong to the same population as those in western Siberia I am uncertain. Jourdain describes the eggs as similar in appearance to those of the common buzzard, spotted or blotched with yellowish- or reddish-brown on a white ground, but sometimes hardly marked at all. The eggs are remarkably small in comparison with those of *Buteo buteo buteo*, twenty-two eggs from the Dobrogea averaging $53 \cdot 13 \times 42 \cdot 77$ mm. Max. $57 \cdot 4 \times 43 \cdot 5$ and $54 \cdot 5 \times 44 \cdot 6$ mm. Min. $50 \cdot 5 \times 42 \cdot 4$ and $50 \cdot 8 \times 40 \cdot 1$ mm.

REFERENCES : Original Description. *Buteo vulpinus* Gloger, Abänd. Vög. Klima, 1833, p. 141 : South Africa (ex Lichtenstein MS in Berlin Museum).

[1] It will be remembered that Ticehurst and Cheesman found a buzzard's nest on a cliff on Jebel Kharma Zarnuqa in Arabia. It was built of sticks on a narrow ledge and contained three young on 29th February which they assigned to *Buteo vulpinus*, but as the old birds were not clearly identified, the record should not be accepted.

Genus *CIRCUS* Lacépède

PLATE 20   **MARSH HARRIER**

Circus aeruginosus aeruginosus (Linnaeus)

A Summer Visitor which breeds sparingly in England. It has been known to nest in Wales and was formerly widely distributed in Ireland but has ceased to breed since 1917. Now a Rare or Uncommon Visitor in all parts of Britain except for the few pairs which nest in East Anglia annually.

IDENTIFICATION : This is the largest of the harriers which occur on the British List. An adult bird measures in total length from nineteen to twenty-two inches ; the male is very slightly smaller. The wings are long but noticeably broader than in the hen-, pallid or Montagu's harriers, which all appear slimmer in build. An old male marsh harrier is very distinctly marked and therefore not difficult to recognize, especially when seen, as is usual, in flight. The body plumage is dark rust-brown and the crown and chin creamy-buff streaked with dark brown ; the crown in some examples is almost white. The underparts are chestnut with dark centres to the feathers. Some very old males have a very little white at the base of the tail, but this is not always present. The tail is silver grey. Most characteristic is the pattern on the wing : the greater and median coverts are mostly brown, as are the three or four innermost secondaries, but the majority of the secondaries are blue-grey, and when the wing is open this grey area extends as a broad oblique band right across the wing, contrasting with the broad black terminal portion of the primaries. The legs are bright yellow and the tarsus completely bare of feathers ; the thighs appear rufous.

The adult female is more uniform in colour than the male but like its consort it has a cream-coloured head and throat, the former less streaked than in the male. The wings and tail are brown ; the secondaries are *not* grey as in the male, so that in flight there is no pale grey band across the wing. The underparts are mostly dark brown, sometimes with a lighter patch on the breast.

Owing to the various stages of plumage through which this bird passes it is anything but easy to give a written description to enable the birds to be recognized by anyone unfamiliar with them. T. A. Coward, whose *Birds of the British Isles* is so generally used, stressed in his book that age and sex descriptions in most textbooks are misleading, as an examination of a series of skins will show, " for no two birds seem exactly alike ". He described the male as a large brown and grey bird with black wing-tips in marked contrast to the grey of the wing, the head paler than the back but not white, as would be imagined from reading descriptions taken from skins. The female he described as looking larger and much darker, her browner wings failing to show up the blacker primaries.

Immature birds exhibit a variety of plumage which may be very puzzling ; the plumage is mostly dark chocolate brown, in some examples including the crown, when the nape is cream streaked with brown. The amount of creamy-buff on the head, mantle, breast and shoulders is variable. Some examples exhibit a cream coloured crown and throat with the rest of the plumage dark chocolate brown, such as is illustrated by Thorburn in Lord Lilford's *Birds of the British Isles*, 2nd edition, Plate 3. After the first summer moult both sexes are like the adult female. The tails of the males begin to show a grey tinge and the pale crown is fairly heavily streaked. Not until the third summer does the marsh harrier assume fully adult plumage.

STATUS IN GREAT BRITAIN [1] AND LOCAL DISTRIBUTION : The status of the marsh harrier as a breeding bird in Great Britain has been very precarious for many years. For at least forty-five years prior to 1915 there are no records of successful breeding, though three attempts were made at intervals in Norfolk. In 1915 a pair bred at Hickling but neither they nor their offspring returned to nest. It was not until 1921 that a pair again bred successfully. After this there followed an interval of six years before a very small number of pairs—between one and four—settled down in 1927. Since then they have bred regularly, although not more than three pairs have been recorded as actually rearing young in any one season. Thus wrote Mr. Eric Hosking in 1943, adding that—at the time of writing— Norfolk is the only British county in which they are known to breed, with the possible exception of Suffolk, where instances may have occurred in recent years. It so happened that 1942 was an exceptionally unfortunate year for the marsh harrier ; owing to various causes only one chick appears to have been successfully reared in the whole country. The breeding season of 1943 saw an improvement and four pairs nested, one nest containing the exceptional number of eight eggs, which Mr. Hosking succeeded in photographing.

From then onwards the number of breeding pairs in Norfolk has varied slightly from year to year ; the average annual number of *successful* nests of the marsh harrier is three—and from this it will be seen that this bird is hanging on by a bare thread to its old haunts. Although the very restricted area in which it nests is known to many, nothing is gained by adding to the publicity—therefore no more will be said here.

When C. B. Ticehurst wrote his *History of the Birds of Suffolk,* published in 1932, he stated that he had been unable to find any reference which would suggest that the marsh harrier has bred in Suffolk during the last hundred years, though it certainly must have done so in the dim past when the Suffolk marshes were wetter and rougher. At the present day there are, as he observes, few places left in the country where this bird could

---

[1] Some of the information in this paragraph is taken from Mr. Eric Hosking's article in *British Birds*, xxxvii, but I am mainly indebted for all recent happenings to Major Anthony Buxton of Horsey Hall, Norfolk.

find sanctuary for nesting, only two or three suitable spots remaining, and these did not appear to have been utilized for the purpose up to the date when he published his book. Whether or not they have been used since is problematical, though Mr. Eric Hosking is " fairly certain ", so he tells me, that a pair of marsh harriers did breed in Suffolk not so very long ago.

The blame for the serious diminution in numbers of the marsh harrier during the last century cannot be placed to the account of either game-keepers or egg-stealers, but must be given mainly to the reclamation of the fen country. William Yarrell wrote in 1837 that the history of the harriers as British birds could not be correctly told without referring to the changes effected by the systematic drainage of the extensive fens of the eastern parts of England from Lincolnshire southwards, adding that, of the three species of harrier which once abounded in these peculiar districts, the marsh harrier was the first to succumb.

It is of interest to note that in his account of the disappearance of the bird from many counties which he cites, Yarrell states that there remained in his day only two districts in England—Devonshire and the eastern portion of Norfolk—where the birds bred *regularly*, though a nest was occasionally to be found, according to an authority whom he quotes, in the counties of Cornwall, Somerset, Dorset, Hampshire and Shropshire. In Wales, Suffolk, Cambridgeshire, Huntingdonshire, Lincolnshire and the counties from Yorkshire northward it had already become historical.

The haunt of the species in Devonshire prior to 1848 appears to have been Dartmoor,[1] a locality which can have changed but little in the inter-vening years. From my knowledge of the area it is not exactly the country with which I should have associated this species in the breeding season but it seems that it bred there in bygone days. It was by no means un-common on the moor during the winter months and in one severe winter no less than eight were reported to have been destroyed by a warrener in one week. To-day in this same wild area the marsh harrier is practically unknown.

Within recent years there have been reports of marsh harriers nesting in other southern areas of England but from my acquaintance with the localities these shy birds can only hope to rear a family successfully on very rare occasions, even if not shot or trapped.

Wales came dramatically into the picture in 1945 when a pair bred successfully in an unspecified county in North Wales, and the fact was duly recorded in *British Birds*[2] by A. W. Colling and E. B. Brown. The last known cases of nesting of the marsh harrier in the Principality were in Merionethshire in 1869 and 1877. The 1945 nest was discovered on 10th July in a large reed-bed bordering a lake. It contained four chicks whose ages ranged from about twelve to eighteen days.

[1] *The Birds of Devon*, by D'Urban and Mathew, 1895, p. 140.
[2] *British Birds*, xxxix, 1946, p. 233, in which a very full and excellent account is given of the breeding habits as observed at this nest.

PLATE 20

MARSH HARRIER

Circus aeruginosus aeruginosus (Linnaeus)

Left Figure	. .	Adult Male
Right Figure	. .	Adult Female

PLATE 20

MARSH HARRIER

Circus aeruginosus aeruginosus (Linnaeus)

Left figure . . . . . . Adult Male
Right figure . . . . . Adult Female

To Scotland the marsh harrier is an uncommon visitor and has never been known to breed. It is said [1] that Solway and East Lothian are the areas in which it has occurred most frequently in the past. Dumfriesshire is the county from which most records come and it occasionally occurs in Kirkcudbright. There are odd records from other parts of Scotland, including two apparently reliable records from Orkney, one in November, the other in April, and there is one record from Fair Isle in the spring of 1932. The Western Isles are naturally seldom visited, the whole of the western Highlands and islands being too precipitous for a bird of the harrier's habits. There was a report that one was killed on Scalpay off Skye at some time previous to 1904, but that is the only record which has found its way into the standard work on the birds of Scotland.

Ireland is a country much more suited to its habits but there the sad tale of destruction is complete. In Ussher and Warren's *Birds of Ireland* (1900) the authors quote Watters, who, writing in 1853, records that the marsh harrier was at that time " the most abundant of our larger birds of prey and widely distributed ". Ussher and Warren remark that since then it has been exterminated in most of its former haunts, though it maintains a precarious existence on the midland bogs and in parts of Galway and is preserved on one estate in Queen's County.

Thompson, who wrote fifty years before the first *Birds of Ireland* was published, and was the first and only author to treat Irish birds in detail, records that among the counties in which the marsh harrier bred in his day were Kerry, Cork, Tipperary, Monaghan, Tyrone, Down, Antrim and Londonderry. The slaughter of these beautiful birds went on unabated until in 1917 or thereabouts breeding had ceased in Ireland. We learn from Colonel C. F. Scroope (1954) that since the species ceased to breed in the country only about thirteen vagrants have been recorded, six of these being seen in October and November 1934 by Father P. G. Kennedy. As the authors observe in the new *Birds of Ireland*, the present status of this harrier is a sad contrast to that which prevailed a hundred years earlier.

As a casual visitor to Britain from the Continent the marsh harrier is recorded at irregular intervals, as the occurrences tabulated in the County Fauna reports or communicated to *British Birds* magazine bear witness.

In order that some indication of their relative numbers may be obtained the following list of sight records accepted by the Editors of *British Birds* during a period of ten years is given ; it is safe to assume that a number of others went unrecognized or unrecorded. This list does *not* include the small breeding population of Norfolk.

It is encouraging to note that in Lancashire Mr. R. A. H. Coombes was able to record that the marsh harrier's visits are becoming more frequent in the spring and summer to Leighton Moss, a locality where a visit was

[1] Baxter and Rintoul, *Birds of Scotland*, 1953, pp. 304-305.

formerly a rare event. There are other areas too where it may perhaps establish itself if given the chance to do so under the new bird protection laws.

Sight Records Published in British Birds *between* 1943 *and* 1953 *inclusive*

	Date when seen	*Locality*	*Observer*
1943	4th September	Northampton Sewage Farm	B. W. Tucker
	24th October	Near Poole Harbour, Dorset	J. R. M. Tennent
1944	No records published		
1945	6th May (♂ carrying nesting material)	" A reed-bed in South of England "	W. Macnae
	June	Dunwich, Suffolk	P. Pardoe
	25th August, joined 31st by a hen	Cuckmere Valley, Sussex	D. D. Harber
	9th September, joined 14th by a hen	Hornsea Mere, Yorkshire	J. Lord and G. H. Ainsworth
1946	26th January and past six months	A marsh in Kent	T. C. Gregory
	" Throughout spring and summer "	Leighton Moss, Lancashire	R. A. H. Coombes
	26th November	Thelwall Eye, Lancashire	A. R. Sumerfield
1947	27th October	Frampton-on-Severn, Gloucester	A. Whitaker
1948	" Throughout spring and summer "	Leighton Moss, Lancashire	R. A. H. Coombes
	15th August	Crawley, Sussex	I. J. Ferguson-Lees and J. A. Smith
1949	No records published		
1950	1st May	Poole Harbour, Dorset	T. Bispham
	3rd May	Mineworth Sewage Works, Warwickshire	M. J. Rogers and others
	7th May	Abberton Reservoir, Essex	G. A. Pyman
	14th October	Mouth of River Baumber, Hants	A. Moody and others
1951	16th August	"Seen over swampy ground", Surrey	H. E. Pounds
	August	Sussex	Editors *Sussex Bird Report*, 1951
	November	Sussex	,,
	" Throughout the winter " [1]	Scilly Isles	1951 *Report*, Cornwall Bird Watching Society
1952	No records published		
1953			

[1] In the *Report* for 1951 of the Cornwall Bird Watching and Preservation Society the Editors observe with regard to the marsh harrier wintering in the Scillies : " This is now becoming a regular feature."

DISTRIBUTION ABROAD: The marsh harrier occurs as a breeding bird over the greater part of Europe from the Baltic, central Sweden and Finland to the Mediterranean. In Russia it ranges to 58° in the Ural area, its range extending eastwards in western Siberia to the Yenisei and Altai and Tarbagatai. The bird is absent from the mountainous area of Switzerland, while in the south of Spain the Moroccan-Algerian subspecies, *C. aeruginosus harterti*, takes the place of the typical species. It is again the typical bird which is reported from the Balearic Islands and not, as one might expect, the south Spanish form.

Other islands in the Mediterranean from which *C. aeruginosus aeruginosus* is recorded are Corsica, Sardinia and Sicily, and it is this race which occurs in Asia Minor, Iraq and Persia.

The marsh harriers which breed in the northern part of the range occur there only in summer, after which the majority move south. Some of these birds remain to winter in southern Europe, where the local population is greatly augmented. Others pass on to winter in tropical Africa, mainly on the eastern side of that continent, while the population from Asia reaches India and Malay. Occasionally odd birds are recorded in winter from localities as far north as southern Norway, southern Sweden and the British Isles, but the greater number seek a more southern area until the spring.

There must be a considerable migration of this harrier across the Mediterranean, especially towards its eastern end, but what proportion, if any, of the south European birds move to Africa in winter is not really known. One assumes that the breeding birds of northern Africa also move south on the approach of winter, but there are large numbers reported from southern Spain at that season, some proportion of which may pass on.

On the African continent the marsh harrier reaches Tanganyika and the Transvaal on the east coast and Angola on the west. It has even been reported from clearings in the Ituri Forest. The grassy islands of Lake Chad were at one time much favoured by this harrier but south of Chad it probably does not cross the Great Equatorial Forest.

It does not breed in tropical Africa. As already indicated, there is a breeding subspecies *Circus aeruginosus harterti* in Morocco and Algeria and also in southern Spain. This race, when adult, is very dark, almost black, on the back and has more white on the lesser wing-coverts than the typical form, but it cannot be distinguished in the field. A closely allied species, *Circus ranivorus ranivorus*, is resident in South Africa and takes the place of *C. aeruginosus* in that area. Doctor Austin Roberts[1] considers the typical marsh harrier (*aequatorialis*) to be a subspecies of the South African bird.

HABITS: Of the four harriers which find a place on our British List the marsh harrier is the most ponderous and the least elegant in appearance,

[1] *The Birds of South Africa*, by Austin Roberts, p. 67.

but for all that some male examples are exceedingly handsome and wherever they may be encountered seldom fail to evoke one's admiration and excite one's interest. In these islands and the adjoining countries we must associate the marsh harrier almost entirely with high reed-beds, and only reed-beds of considerable extent, such as occur commonly in Holland and Sweden.

These form the ideal habitat for a bird which will all too readily desert its nest and even its young should the surroundings be disturbed. In such an environment as the extensive reed-beds of the Tåkern Lake in the Province of Östergötland, central Sweden, the marsh harrier is in its proper element. I have seen several on the wing at once when bird-watching on this lake with Count Nils Gyldenstolpe, for the birds took little notice of the boat as we moved noiselessly along under the shelter of exceptionally tall reeds. Close above their summits the marsh harriers beat steadily to and fro, with strong purposeful flight, their bright eyes ever searching the ground beneath for any suspicious movement in the swamp. The month was August and the young harriers must already have been abroad, but those which we saw so meticulously quartering the marsh were all old birds and, if I recollect rightly, mostly males. Every now and again a bird would arrest its flight and drop out of sight in the swamp with a corkscrew turn of the wings as if struck by a charge of shot. A frog may have been the cause of the sudden plunge or perhaps an immature coot. These harriers must be the terror of every marsh bird for miles around and in the nesting season they are constantly mobbed by redshanks and lapwings whose young, together with those of coots, moorhens and ducks, they so often destroy.

Game chicks and poultry chicks are preyed upon whenever the chance occurs and full grown chickens—especially in Spain and North Africa, where fowls seldom attain the size or weight of our own birds—are often carried off. The list of prey of this omnivorous feeder, if given in detail, would fill a page. Mr. T. C. Gregory found it feeding on the water-rail and the green woodpecker, to instance two extremes in its menu, but it is the opinion of those naturalists who have studied the bird in Andalusia that small snakes, frogs and wounded birds such as ducks, as well as eggs and nestlings, form the main part of the marsh harrier's diet. Not for nothing has it earned its name. Howard Irby, who detested it in southern Spain, observes what a pest it is to the shooting man, as slowly hunting along in front of the line it puts up every duck and snipe in its course, making them unsettled and wild. Little bustards are often flushed by the marsh harrier where the former are common, but harriers do not attack birds in flight, as do goshawks and sparrow-hawks, and all their prey is captured on the ground. These harriers will take quite large birds such as coots and gallinules but Meinertzhagen has seen one defeated by a little green heron (*Butorides*) which refused to be frightened into flying and struck a threatening attitude, with the intention to spike the hawk with its sharp bill. In its rush the harrier fell into the water with outstretched wings and tail and the two faced each other for half a minute before the hawk pulled itself together and left the heron in peace.

Coots are a never-ending source of fun to the marsh harrier and the noise which a party of them can make with a harrier in pursuit must be heard to be believed. In places where duck are shot in great numbers— as in India—these harriers reap a fine harvest, pouncing on the wounded birds, but unless injured in some way the hawks leave them alone. A tale is told of three marsh harriers attacking a little grebe on a lake in Egypt by constantly pouncing upon it when it surfaced, until, when finally exhausted, the unfortunate bird was killed. The grebe would be an easy prey and unable to put up much resistance but not all birds are so easily bullied. Captain Philip Munn, who was resident in Majorca and was an authority on the birds of that group of islands, has recorded that whenever a marsh harrier approached a colony of nesting stilts, one of the latter invariably arose to drive the marauder away.

Howard Irby, with long experience of the marsh harrier in Andalusia, labelled the bird as " cowardly in its habits, a terror to poultry and a continual source of annoyance to sportsmen ". After the passage of over sixty years it is equally difficult to find much in its favour.

In Morocco, where I have had opportunities of studying the bird myself in winter, it is exceedingly common. The early months of 1951 were exceptionally wet in northern Africa and vast areas between Tangier and Casablanca were turned into shallow lakes. In addition there are the brackish lagoons north of Port Lyautey which normally teem with water birds and, owing to the virulent mosquitoes which swarm there, are left severely alone by most ornithologists. The whole of the area specified is a paradise for harriers but it was the marsh harriers that had gathered in such numbers in this exceptional year and in February and March they seemed to exhibit a bewildering variety of plumages. We asked ourselves the question, were these all local birds, *Circus aeruginosus harterti* ? or were they migrants from further north in Europe which, attracted by the unusual conditions, had arrested their journey to tropical Africa ? The riddle was never solved, but it may be mentioned that a marsh harrier which had been ringed as young at Horsey, Norfolk, on 15th July 1935, was recovered in Morocco, 120 km. east of Casablanca, on 26th April 1937, which points to *some* north European birds at any rate remaining in, or passing through, Morocco during the months when they are not breeding. Many more, in my own opinion, winter in the south of Spain.

MIGRATIONS : The record noted above is a definite indication of the direction taken by the very few young of this species which are bred in England. Some may not proceed farther south than southern Spain. It is known that young marsh harriers bred and ringed in Sweden have been shot when migrating through western Germany, Holland, France and Spain. The late Professor Lönnberg, who recorded the fact,[1] remarked that one bird was shot in Spain in November of the year in which it was ringed, while another was recovered in eastern Spain in the middle of June when it was just about a year old, proving that young birds, not yet mature, may remain in the south even during the summer.

In Andalusia marsh harriers are especially numerous in winter. Irby wrote of vast numbers to be seen at that season over all wet ground, which suggests that many winter there from farther north. The typical species is said by Philip Munn to be a common resident in the marshy parts of Majorca and to a lesser extent in the other islands of the Balearic group, but he makes no mention of the resident birds having their numbers augmented by migrants in winter.

That there is considerable migration in the Mediterranean area seems to be evident. Favier observed years ago that it was both resident and migratory in the vicinity of Tangier, and farther east in Tunisia the marsh harrier is abundant as a regular migrant in all marshy districts, being especially noticeable during the spring passage.[2] Its abundance in Algeria on migration has also been noted. Jourdain has recorded it as a common winter visitor to Corsica, a few pairs remaining to breed in the swamps, while in Malta Colonel W. A. Payn was greatly impressed by the passage of all four species of harriers through that island in April, great numbers being killed and eaten by the Maltese.

It seems fairly evident that marsh harriers do not winter in any great numbers on the Guinea Coast, for much of that huge area, the bird-life of which I dealt with in my eight-volume work,[3] is too dry to attract marsh-loving birds like *Circus aeruginosus*, or else too heavily covered with " bush ", for harriers avoid forest and mountainous areas at all times. The few records in West Africa which I was able to collect were almost entirely confined to the Lake Chad area—one of the few really suitable localities— and to the Tibati plateau in northern Cameroon. The bird may well be present too in winter in the great inundation zone of the Niger around Mopti, but of that I have no definite information.

Eastern Africa is certainly frequented to a much greater extent. Meinertzhagen has stated that to Egypt [4] it is mainly a winter visitor in large numbers, arriving towards the end of August and remaining till the end of April ; from this area the birds spread over Africa south to the Transvaal.

A few marsh harriers remain in Egypt throughout the year, but as no specimens have been critically examined they may possibly belong to some other race. Mummified marsh harriers are among the birds which

[1] Introduction to his *Birds of Sweden*, p. xii.
[2] Whitaker, *Birds of Tunisia*, ii, p. 92.
[3] *The Birds of Tropical West Africa*, 1930-51, vols i-viii.
[4] Nicoll's *Birds of Egypt*, ii, p. 399.

have been discovered in Egypt.[1] The remains, most of which were found in Lower Egypt, date apparently from the Twentieth Dynasty, approximately 1000 years B.C.

In Arabia the marsh harrier is found chiefly in the south-west from October until April. In Colonel Meinertzhagen's new book on the birds of Arabia he draws attention to the probability that marsh harriers when migrating in spring keep to their own sex, and gives three instances when he found this to be the case. The first cases came under notice at Jedda, where on 30th April about fifty birds, all of which were females, passed north in less than ten minutes. Next he instances a party of sixty-six males which arrived in Afghanistan in the evening of 24th April and roosted on ploughed land, resuming passage at dawn next day. In Syria he noticed the same daylight passage on 28th April, all of the birds being males.

Many of these harriers on their journey south pass through north-western Abyssinia in September and many remain until May in suitable localities, where reed-beds fringe lakes. All have gone by June. The European birds visit both Kenya and Uganda in winter. In the former territory they confine themselves mostly to the Rift Valley and adjoining plateau, but in Uganda, Sir Frederick Jackson tells us, they are more widely dispersed. Most of these birds are in immature dress but all varieties of plumage may be encountered.

It is of interest to remark that in the countries specified the European marsh harrier is mostly a rat-hunter and is less dependent on marshy ground for its food supply than is the tropical marsh harrier *Circus ranivorus aequatorialis*.[2] In Uganda it quarters the grassy hillsides quite as much as it does the marshes, while at Naivasha it may frequently be seen quartering the plains away from the lake. An example obtained had its stomach full of rats and mice.

It seems from van Someren's records that the adult European birds take their departure from Kenya in April, but that some of the immature birds remain until the third week of May before setting off for their breeding areas in Europe.

A word may here be said about its roosting habits. Marsh harriers— and other harriers as well—never roost in trees but always on the ground, and in places where they are seen commonly the birds have been noted coming in singly from long distances to roost in long grass. Major Cheesman found a roost in Abyssinia when camped beside a grassy plain, and counted twenty birds as they assembled, some arriving just as darkness was falling. He formed the opinion that it was the habit of most harriers to

[1] Lortet and Gaillard: *La Faune Mommifiée de l'Ancienne Egypte*, p. 113, and *Birds of Egypt*, p. 74.

[2] I follow Doctor Austin Roberts (*Birds of South Africa*, p. 67) and Professor Stresemann in considering the tropical *aequatorialis* a subspecies of the South African *Circus ranivorus*. W. L. Sclater, on the other hand, placed *ranivorus* as a subspecies of *aeruginosus*.

come long distances to roost together, for they had not been hunting in the vicinity during the day. Both marsh and pale harriers had gathered together on the occasion cited, arriving one by one, and it may be that this is the normal way for them to spend the night. The roosting habits of the larger birds of prey are not too well known, and in our own islands the numbers are never large enough to enable a true picture to be obtained.

BREEDING HABITS : In the last nesting place of the marsh harrier in these islands the nest is constructed where tall reeds and rank vegetation accord protection from observation. It is recorded that in the south of Spain the marsh harrier has been known to breed in a recently reclaimed cornfield.[1] That is a situation in which we cannot expect to find a nest in Britain, for it is difficult enough for the bird to find sufficient seclusion for its needs even in the Broads of Norfolk. It is indeed only the strict protection afforded it by such landowners as the late Lord Desborough, whose head keeper, the late Mr. Jim Vincent, did so much to encourage the rarer marsh birds to nest on the estate, and Major Anthony Buxton, the owner of Horsey Mere and surrounding marshes, which has enabled the marsh harrier to survive in this, its last stronghold in Britain. The breeding habits of this harrier are naturally more easily studied in Holland, and in strictly preserved localities such as the Naadermeer several may be seen on the wing together.

Marsh harriers need a much larger area of reed and sedge than do Montagu's harriers and do most of their hunting over thick cover such as a tall reed-bed affords. Since 1931, when he first went to live at Horsey, Major Buxton has kept close records of the harriers which have bred on his and the adjoining Broadland property and has most kindly put all his information at my disposal. He tells me that breeding marsh harriers normally arrive in the last week of March or first week of April and usually begin to nest between 15th and 25th April. Nesting operations also begin in Holland in April and according to most accounts laying begins in the last two weeks of that month, though I should have considered the first fortnight of May a more likely period in which to find eggs in Britain. On one occasion in Norfolk the late Jim Vincent found the first nest on 19th April, when only the preliminary pieces of sedge had been placed in position. This nest was completed and ready for eggs on 6th May.

Before describing the nests which this harrier builds mention must be made of its interesting courting display, which has been described by both Buxton and Hosking in their several writings but which I have never seen for myself. A pair which Major Buxton had under close observation at his home enabled him to give the following account [2] :

However heavy in flight a marsh harrier may be at ordinary times the cock when on the court becomes a real aerial acrobat. Appearing as a speck in the sky, he

---

[1] Witherby, *Handbook of British Birds*, iii, p. 58.
[2] *Trans. Norfolk and Norwich Nat. Soc.*, xiii, pp. 318-324.

descends in a series of great swoops with closed wings, each swoop being followed by a check and an upward jerk with a few strong beats of the pinions. At each check and upward jerk he gives out a loud scream not unlike that of a pee-wit, but with the accent on the second instead of the first syllable. As he nears the ground the hen joins him and after a second or two together the cock alights on his own particular nest . . . at a considerable distance from the hen's nest. After remaining a moment or two on the nest the cock rises to give place to the hen, but immediately rejoins her on the nest, where the two birds remain for perhaps a minute. Then the cock rises and flies to a bare piece of ground, followed by the hen, who then receives the prey he has carried all the time in his claw. This procedure was perfectly regular until incubation began ; then it ceased, but on fine days, when presumably the cock was feeling above himself, he would sometimes resort to his screaming and acrobatics, even after the young had flown. Owing to high sedge, it was impossible to see the birds on the cock's nest but the above evidence points in my opinion to its use in day time for pairing purposes.

It was distressing to learn that after the first three eggs out of seven had successfully hatched the cock disappeared and was never heard of again. Against all the rules of harrier conduct, as Major Buxton wrote, the hen had to go off on the hunt, instead of, as would normally happen, leaving that part of the business to the cock. None of the other eggs was successfully hatched but to the credit of the hen she reared the three chicks unaided and, as we are told, " a more cheery, healthy family it would be difficult to find ".

A number of years after the above description had appeared in print Mr. Eric Hosking and the late Jim Vincent saw a remarkable display flight which took place as late as 5th July : " The cock began by circling higher and higher, then dropped like a stone to within a few feet of the ground, rose again and with very slow flapping wings wheeled round in circles, gaining height all the time. He continued this ascent until he became a mere speck in the sky,[1] then, closing his wings, he just fell down through the air, spiralling in quite small circles until it appeared he would crash into the marsh before he straightened out. He repeated this performance." The watchers assumed that one of the two hens which were in the vicinity was perched within sight of this display, and this proved to be the case, as later a hen was seen to rise to meet the cock. Then, from another direction, appeared a second hen, who also flew towards the cock.

It was while engaged in watching this trio that Hosking and Vincent had observed what appeared to be forced polygamy in the case of the male marsh harrier. " Forced " because had a second cock been present it is unlikely that the male bird under observation would have had it all his own way and successfully mated with two hens. The drama was enacted under their eyes and left no room for doubt. " We saw the cock fly in,

[1] In a letter to me of recent date Major Buxton states that it is not generally known that both marsh and Montagu's harriers, but particularly marsh harriers, will rise on a fine day sometimes clean out of sight of the human eye.

circle over the nest, and a moment afterwards the hen flew up to receive food from her mate which she immediately took back to her nest. The cock continued hunting and we watched him quartering the ground in the manner characteristic of this harrier. He dropped down to the ground to rise a minute or so later with food dangling from his talons. With this he flew to a spot on another marsh about 300 yards from the nest under observation and after circling he was met by a second hen which received the food from him." For some time Mr. Hosking had suspected that the two hens were both mated to this cock, but the above incident was the first definite proof he had, and provided what appears to be the first known case of polygamy in a cock marsh harrier. The second nest was located on the day following the incident described.

Some years later a clear case of polygamy came to the notice of Major Buxton when a particular cock marsh harrier had two nests and two hens two years running, 1947-48, and in one year this cock was suspected of having three wives.[1]

It is well known by those who have made a close study of this species that the cock bird also builds a nest for himself in addition to the nest built by his hen, for she apparently does all the work on the one which is eventually to hold her eggs. To what use the second or " cock " nest may be put has already been suggested.

The nest built by the hen marsh harrier can be a bulky affair and when built among very tall reeds, as it usually is in the south of Spain, is of considerable dimensions. The foundation of the nest is sedge broken down by the bird, reed stems and roots of aquatic plants, with occasionally branches of alder and sallow woven into the structure. It is lined with finer material, chiefly grasses growing nearby and the blades of water plants from the immediate neighbourhood.

In the south of Spain the marsh harriers make use of the nests of the purple heron—at any rate as a foundation—which are built in the dense masses of bullrush and reeds in the extensive lagunas. These reed-beds are as much as eight or nine feet in height and a nest built amongst them is fairly safe, at any rate from ground-marauding animals, if not from snakes. The bulky platform is of course raised well above water-level, or above that of the wet marsh.

One of my earliest ornithological friends, who had already retired from the Rifle Brigade when I was still a youth, was Colonel Willoughby Verner, whose book *My Life among the Wild Birds in Spain* is filled with many interesting anecdotes of Spanish bird-life. Verner wrote that the marsh harriers were his daily companions at all times of the year when in the low-lying country. On one occasion when riding his horse near a marsh he watched a marsh harrier disappear into the bullrushes and waded in : " The

---

[1] *Trans. Norfolk and Norwich Nat. Soc.* for year 1947, vol. xvi, part iv, p. 302, and for year 1948, part v, p. 356.

water was three feet deep and the reeds so dense that it was difficult to force one's way through them. Suddenly I came upon a nest with four young birds in the white down stage with their primaries just budding. The instant they saw me they sprang up and showed fight, assuming various attitudes of defiance. It was a novel and interesting sight to see these little savages in their home amid the waters. . . . Owing to their weight the nest had got flattened down and was more like a raft on the surface than anything else. In it was a half-eaten water vole and the remains of some snakes and frogs."

The first nest of the marsh harrier to be found in Wales for many years was described [1] as a bulky structure about twenty-four inches wide, resting on the reeds at water-level and built up to a height of eighteen inches. It consisted mainly of reed stems mixed with fairly large twigs at the base, with a saucer-shaped hollow about twelve inches wide lined with finer material at the top. A thick growth of reeds (*Phragmites communis*) six to eight feet tall surrounded it on all sides.

Earlier in this account mention was made of the nest of a marsh harrier in Norfolk which had been finished on 6th May. This nest was kept under observation by Eric Hosking. On 13th May it contained three eggs and on 20th May the full clutch of five had been laid. Throughout the period of incubation material was being constantly added to the nest, which eventually measured eighteen inches in diameter. The first egg hatched on 7th June, the second on the 9th, the third on the 12th, the fourth on the 14th and the fifth on the 17th, there being eight days' difference between the eldest and the youngest chick. A series of disasters due to various causes followed and the parents refused henceforth to feed or brood the young. In fact they took no further part in rearing their family, other than to drop food in the nest, after which they left immediately. The nights were bitterly cold and one by one the young ones perished until only one was left, despite the fact that Mr. Hosking and his wife had fed the family by hand. The cold of the nights was too much for them. One bird, however, survived, to which the cock bird continued to bring food, which was then " prepared " by one of the human foster-parents, who recounts the following anecdote :

No doubt owing to the neglect on the part of the adults the chick came to rely on us for food . . . and it certainly paid more attention to us than it did to its parents. One incident will remain in my memory for a long time. It was on 9th July. I visited the nest as usual to feed the chick, but there was no trace of it on or near the nest, so I called to it and received a reply immediately. Then the chick came running towards me from a point quite twelve yards from the nest along a track in the sedge, and as I was kneeling down by the nest cutting up the food, it jumped up on my shoulder, then down on to my knee, where I was able to feed it.

---

[1] A. W. Colling and E. B. Brown, *British Birds*, xxxix, pp. 233-240 : Plates 27-30.

At forty-five days old this chick took its first flight of about five yards and three weeks later Jim Vincent reported that he had seen it flying strongly over the marsh. A happy ending to a very nice tale.

While Mr. and Mrs. Hosking were engaged in bringing up this chick many observations were made on the parents, who still remained in the vicinity, their presence being made known by the mobbing redshanks and lapwings, which showed much hostility to the harriers, following and mobbing them right to the nest. Excellent views of the food-pass of the cock to the hen were also witnessed : " The cock first called over the nest, but then flew towards some bushes where apparently the hen was perched. As she flew up to meet him she turned over on her back and actually took the prey from his talons." Usually, as Mr. Hosking observes, the food is dropped by the cock and caught by the hen.

It is much more rarely that the business is reversed but both Hosking and Vincent were to witness the act on two different occasions towards the end of June : " We first noticed the birds circling at a great height and saw the cock pass food to the hen in the normal way. Both birds then descended, not in a direct line but by wheeling round in great circles until they were about fifty feet from the ground. The cock remained at a higher altitude than the hen, but when immediately above the nest, the hen swung up again, rose above the cock, called, and the cock turned right over on his back and took the food from the hen."

Although the following is not, Mr. Hosking assures us, an entirely accurate list, the food brought to the nest in twenty-eight days, i.e. from 22nd June to 20th July, consisted of twenty-nine young pheasants, twenty-one young common partridges, eight young red-legged partridges, seven fledged meadow pipits, two young moorhens, one young mallard, one young lapwing, one young rat, fifteen rabbits or parts of rabbits, five adult water voles, seven adult field voles, seven leverets and two unidentified Passerines.

As a matter of interest it was noted that these harriers usually carry the food in the talons of their left foot. Occasionally both the cock and the hen marsh harrier will carry food in their bills, sometimes even when flying at a considerable height.

Marsh harriers are single-brooded, and when we realize what tremendous labour is involved in the bringing up of a family, the fact is not surprising.

H. Weiss [1] has pointed out that female marsh harriers will breed when one year old, but that the males are not sexually mature until two years of

[1] In my account of the marsh harrier, especially as regards its breeding biology, the excellent work by H. Weiss, *Life of the Harrier in Denmark* (1923), has not been overlooked, though reference herein is mostly to British authors and their investigations, and especially to Major Anthony Buxton of Horsey, to whom I am indebted for much information under this heading sent me in a letter dated October 1954.

age.   He also indicates that older birds tend to settle down to nesting earlier in the season than do those breeding for the first time.

The number of eggs in the clutch has been the subject of some controversy.   Usually four to five is the full complement but much larger clutches are on record.   In Mr. Hosking's and Mr. Newberry's *Birds of the Day*, in which incidentally numerous photographs appear of the chick whose adventures are recounted above, there is a photograph of a nest containing eight eggs which is acknowledged to be most exceptional.   In *The Handbook of British Birds* it is stated that c/6 is scarce but that statement was challenged by Fr. Haverschmidt [1] from his experience in Holland.   Of fifteen nests which he examined over a period of years three contained c/6, four c/5 and seven c/4.   There was a very low mortality among the chicks.   Of the three c/6 the number of young fledged from each was six, four and four respectively, and in the case where all six young successfully grew to maturity the nest was in the middle of a colony of black-headed gulls and the nestling harriers were fed to a large extent on young gulls that were just able to fly.

In the Horsey-Hickling area, Major Buxton tells me, the average number of eggs laid is five and he knew of a clutch of seven, all of which hatched and the young flew, but he emphasizes the point that if anything goes wrong when marsh harriers are in the nest, the largest of the nestlings often kills and *eats* the smallest.   As he puts it in his letter to me, " they will not wait for lunch " !

There are cases on record where the male bird has been flushed from the eggs but for the most part the hen does the incubating—sometimes entirely so.   The incubation period, which begins with the first or second egg, may extend to thirty-eight days but Jourdain [2] considered thirty-six days for each egg to be the average.   The young remain in, or in the vicinity of, the nest for thirty-five to forty days but are not fledged until about three weeks later.   They are fed by the parents by dropping prey near them for some time after they can fly, as the various authorities who have studied the nesting habits of this very shy bird have proved on numerous occasions.

The eggs are white without gloss and according to the measurements of Jourdain and Rey, 130 eggs average 50×38.75 mm.   Max. 55×41.3 and 54.5×42.5 mm.   Min. 47×37.9 and 48×35 mm.

Eggs of harriers are apparently unpalatable to predators, as Major Buxton assures me that their eggs are never taken by crows or magpies, to which they must be very visible when the hen bird is away for any purpose. He is unable to recall a single instance of the eggs being taken by these usually egg-robbing species.   This also applies to the eggs of Montagu's harrier.

[1] *British Birds*, xlvi, 1953, pp. 258-259.
[2] *Handbook of British Birds*, 2nd ed., iii, p. 58.

In a contribution to *British Birds*[1] by Caroline and Desmond Nethersole-Thompson the statement appears on the authority of Jim Vincent that the female marsh harrier ejects egg shells over the edge of the nest or carries them for a distance of twenty to a hundred yards before dropping them, and that addled eggs are not ejected. This last statement is contrary to the experience of Fr. Haverschmidt in Holland, who, in all cases which he was able to study, found that the addled eggs vanished after some time, except in a single instance where an addled egg remained in the nest until after the young had left. The naturalist cited has also drawn attention to the fact that the incubating hen marsh harrier, when hungry, often sits on the nest calling loudly while awaiting the arrival of the male with food, and states that he has discovered several nests in this way by locating the calling female.

Nestling marsh harriers from a very early age are conscious of the maxim : survival of the fittest, and if Major Buxton's description of what occurs in the nursery is anything like general, it is surprising that the weakest of the brood ever survives. After describing the only brood of the year in which the hen was able to keep some sort of discipline in the family, doling out food evenly and fairly, and in which there was consequently very little squabbling, he continues :

The behaviour at the other two nests was appalling and there was a row between the young at every meal. The strongest or most hungry member of the brood would, on spotting its parent in the air, secure a central position in the nest and, when the parent arrived, seize the food. It would hold the prey until it choked or became absent-minded, when one of its brethren would waddle across the nest with an air of complete abstraction, and then suddenly shoot out a claw and seize the food : the same process would continue with the next young bird. As soon as they could walk about, the young made seats in the rushes and tunnels leading away from the nest : the bird securing the prey would spread its wings and hold the entrances to these tunnels in order to prevent the others getting out, while it ate its fill.

In the early stages the young marsh harriers are forced to learn to fly by a process of starvation, as described in my account of Montagu's harrier, but later in their training both Montagu's and marsh harrier parents encourage their offspring to fly by displaying the food in their claws and making them fly all over the place after them, eventually teaching the young birds to take a pass in the air.

REFERENCES : Original Description. *Falco aeruginosus* Linnaeus, Syst. Nat., 10th ed., 1758, p. 91 : Europe. Restricted type locality Sweden.

[1] *British Birds*, xxxv, 1942, p. 219.

MONTAGU'S HARRIER

PLATE 21 ♂

Circus pygargus (Linnaeus)

PLATE 22 ♀

A Summer Visitor in small numbers breeding locally in England and Wales; an Uncommon Visitor to Scotland which may once have bred in the Solway area. To Ireland a Rare Vagrant. With encouragement this harrier would remain to breed more often than it does.

IDENTIFICATION : The distinctions between this bird and the hen-harrier, with which it is easily confused by anyone unfamiliar with both, have been given under the latter species (see p. 202-3). The main points to remember are that the male Montagu's has a narrow black bar across the wing, chestnut streaks on the flanks and a narrower area of white at the base of the tail. In build Montagu's harrier is smaller in size and more elegant in form than the hen-harrier. The females of both are unfortunately very much alike, the narrower white band at the base of the tail in Montagu's not always being easy to see, and even if clearly observed it is but a comparative difference.

Comparison with the pallid harrier (*C. macrourus*) is easier. In size these two are much alike, but whereas the male Montagu's has a grey throat and breast, and striped belly and flanks, these parts in the pallid harrier are pure white. Moreover, the pallid harrier has no black bar across the grey secondaries.

The following technical description of Montagu's harrier is taken from my two-volume work on the birds of West and Equatorial Africa.

Adult male : Upper parts slate-grey, darkest on mantle, palest on crown and wing-coverts. Primaries black with pale tips; secondaries grey crossed with a black bar, white on basal part of inner web. Upper tail-coverts white with broad subterminal grey bands, tips white; middle pair of tail feathers uniform grey, remainder grey on outer web, white on inner, barred with dark grey. Breast grey, belly and thighs white, streaked with rufous-chestnut; axillaries rufous-chestnut with white margins and spots towards base. Eye yellow, bill black, greenish at base of lower mandible. Cere, legs and feet yellow.

The female is similar to the female of *C. macrourus* in most plumages (see p. 221) but as there stated it can be distinguished in the hand by the wing formula.

There has always been great difficulty in distinguishing the female of this harrier from the female of the pallid harrier (*C. macrourus*) even when handled, and it may therefore be borne in mind that [1] in

Montagu's harrier the tips of the primary coverts are well short of, or do not extend beyond, the notch on the outer web of the second primary, while in the

Pallid harrier, the tips of the primary coverts are just equal to, or extend beyond, the notch on the outer web of the second primary.

[1] After Grant and Praed, *The African Handbook of Birds*.

In life the female and young of these two harriers are practically indistinguishable.

It has been noted already that the juvenile Montagu's differs from the adult female and from the juvenile of the hen-harrier by having uniform rufous-buff underparts without any markings.

In addition to the normal plumage of the adults already described, Montagu's harrier occasionally has a melanistic phase in which the whole body plumage of the male is sooty black with a shade of grey of varying degree on the back and wings. The dark chocolate female exhibits some barring on the tail. This variety occurs with relative frequency in Great Britain but for some unexplained reason is unknown in Spain, so Doctor Blair informs me. This phase of plumage has not been depicted by Mr. Lodge but a coloured illustration of both sexes will be found in *The Handbook of British Birds*, vol. iii, Plate 68.

LOCAL DISTRIBUTION : Compared with the other two breeding harriers on the British List, Montagu's harrier is much more widely spread, though its nesting places are now entirely restricted to England and Wales. It is a true summer visitor, departing again after it has reared its young, which, owing to ceaseless persecution in most of its haunts, it does with difficulty. Like the marsh harrier it nests more or less regularly in Norfolk, where it receives close protection on its actual breeding ground, but once it strays over the boundary it is liable to be shot or trapped. The list of the number of young reared during the last five years in the protected area where it breeds shows that it has an even more precarious hold than the marsh harrier, and being a more confiding bird is even more likely to be shot than that shyer species.

In Suffolk, as Claud Ticehurst and others admitted some twenty-five years ago, a few pairs nested, or attempted to nest, fairly regularly, but were just as regularly shot, and it is a wonder the birds persisted in their hopeless attempts. At the present day there is a slight improvement in the outlook and further attempts to breed in Suffolk may have more chance of succeeding, thanks in no small measure to the Royal Society for the Protection of Birds.

Montagu's harrier is also known to breed in the counties of Cambridge, Hants, Devon and Cornwall and in South Wales. Occasional nesting has taken place in addition in Dorset, Wiltshire, the Isle of Wight, Sussex, Surrey, Worcester, Yorkshire and Lincolnshire (first record 1951) and Northumberland.

The first record of Montagu's harrier breeding in North Wales since 1900 was made public in 1945,[1] when in June of that year a nest was found containing three young and an infertile egg. In 1948[2] a nest with five young was found in the same area, while in 1949 there were three nests with eggs

[1] *British Birds*, xxxix, p. 241 : A. W. Colling and E. B. Brown.
[2] *British Birds*, xliii, p. 158 : E. K. Allin.

but only one reached the hatching stage. One of the nestlings from the nest was ringed on 1st June and recovered on 27th September at St. Jean Pied de Port, Basses Pyrénées.

The status of this harrier in Scotland is unfortunately only that of an uncommon visitor and records of its occurrence are few and far between. There is a possibility that it may have attempted to breed once in Kirkcudbrightshire as long ago as 1881, but no better evidence was forthcoming than that one was shot in June with a brooding spot.

As a correspondent to the *Scottish Naturalist*[1] pointed out when recording a specimen killed near Perth in April 1951, there were then about eight examples of Montagu's harriers known from south Scotland, including the one killed in April 1925 at Loch Ken, Kirkcudbrightshire, and the first recorded specimen from East Lothian killed in April 1947. Miss Baxter and Miss Rintoul in their standard work mention examples procured in Lanarkshire and Roxburgh and another from Arbroath in Angus—all localities, be it noted, in low-lying country. They further draw attention to the fact that Montagu's harrier has occurred in Orkney—as a vagrant— and was recognized on Fair Isle[2] by George Stout in May 1937.

As for its status in Ireland at the present day, 1954, the authors of the new work on that country include it as a rare vagrant, remarking that the species may have bred within or near the boundaries of Wicklow in 1899, for three immature birds were shot there in August and September of that year. That is the only evidence they can produce. In all Ireland only thirteen or fourteen specimens have been obtained in addition to a few sight records.

Some twenty years ago (in 1935) the late Harry Witherby undertook a census of the numbers of Montagu's harriers breeding in Britain, though in point of fact his census was perforce restricted to Yorkshire, eastern England, southern England and South Wales. Besides birds which were destroyed before starting to breed, seventeen or eighteen pairs nested, and though all of these did not successfully rear young it was estimated that between thirty and forty young ones flew. Nine years later—in 1944— W. B. Alexander and David Lack gave it as their opinion that although sometimes stated to have greatly increased, there was no real evidence that this species was ever much commoner than it was in the year cited. It is believed to-day, 1954, to be holding its own in some of its old breeding haunts and to have slightly increased in Cornwall and in Wales.

DISTRIBUTION ABROAD: Montagu's harrier is a summer resident in the whole of the western Palæarctic Region, ranging in Europe from the Mediterranean north to southern Sweden, the Baltic States and Russia (Kostroma and Ufa Governments). Eastwards it extends right across Europe to the Kirghiz Steppes, Turkestan and the Altai and Tarbagatai regions.

[1] *Scottish Naturalist*, lxiii, 1951, p. 132 : J. M. D. Mackenzie.
[2] *British Birds*, xxxviii, p. 230 : George Waterston.

There is, or used to be, a colony of these harriers in Morocco, though I confess I should like to have this substantiated to-day. Irby was the first to mention it, in his *Ornithology of the Straits of Gibraltar*, but there appears to be room for doubt about this " colony " at Lixus. Jourdain and Congreve, however, clinched the matter of its nesting south of the Mediterranean when they found half a dozen pairs breeding near Rabat and others near Kenitrea.

Montagu's harrier winters in Africa (ranging as far south as Cape Province), India and Ceylon and is reported to occur in the non-breeding season in China. According to Meinertzhagen, some remain during the winter as far north as Palestine,[1] and yet it is said to be only a passage migrant in Arabia. Even more remarkable is N. F. Chasen's statement that he saw it " several times in winter " in Macedonia,[2] while the single adult male bird recorded from the Camargue[3] on 31st December by Ludlow Griscom appears to be a unique record for the area. To me these winter records so far north of its normal winter quarters appear to require confirmation. In the Mediterranean it occurs during migration on most of the islands but more commonly from Malta to Cyprus than in the western half of that sea. As a vagrant it has reached the Canary Islands,[4] the most westerly place in the Palæarctic Region from which it has been recorded. It has also been found once in the Cape Verde Islands.[5] Its winter range in Africa will be discussed under the next heading.

MIGRATIONS : To the British Isles, on the extreme western edge of its range in northern Europe, Montagu's harrier is a summer visitor, and because of this only a very few of the birds which regularly wend their way north through the Iberian Peninsula and France in the spring reach our inhospitable shores. It says much for the persistence of this harrier that it returns year after year to the same restricted areas in which to attempt to rear its young, despite the reception which it has received in the past in all game-rearing counties.

It is not an early migrant and normally does not put in its appearance before the second half of April or more usually the beginning of May. Major Buxton informs me that the earliest date of which he has record of its arrival at Horsey is 9th April and that is, of course, quite exceptional. Claud Ticehurst in Suffolk considered the second week in May to be the more normal time to note its arrival, while the end of April was the earliest according to his county records. In certain years, in the southern counties, its arrival in the early half of April has also been noted; two such figure in the B.O.C. Migration Reports as arriving in Surrey on 8th April, while

[1] Meinertzhagen, *Birds of Arabia*, p. 365.
[2] N. F. Chasen, *Ibis*, 1921, p. 217.
[3] L. Griscom, *Ibis*, 1921, p. 596.
[4] Bannerman, *Ibis*, 1919, p. 482 : Tenerife.
[5] R. C. Murphy, *Birds of the Cape Verde Archipelago*.

PLATE 21

MONTAGU'S HARRIER (Adult Male)
Circus pygargus (Linnaeus)

PLATE 21

MONTAGU'S HARRIER (Adult Male)

Circus pygargus Linnaeus

J. Walpole-Bond considers arrivals in Sussex before mid-April to be not exceptionally rare. Be that as it may, the latter part of April or the first week of May is the more *normal* date to look for its advent in these islands. The pair recorded from East Lothian,[1] one of which was killed in April 1947, must have been exceptionally early arrivals, for they were reported to have been in the vicinity " for some weeks " !

As this harrier is only a vagrant to Norway and does not breed in Scotland there is no regular migration up or down the east coast of Britain and the few birds which reach our shores come to stay for the short summer months, for they leave again just as soon as their young are able to fend for themselves. Major Buxton tells me that the Norfolk pairs leave the district in August, generally about the middle of the month.

The ringing of nestlings in Britain goes to prove that a southerly direction is taken and sometimes within the space of two months from the ringing date the unfortunate birds fall victim to some gunner in France. One bird indeed reached the Basses Pyrénées and another Portugal, but as yet there have been no returns from south of the Mediterranean of nestlings ringed in this country, for tropical Africa must surely be their ultimate destination. The following is a short list of returns up to 1952.

Ringed		*Recovered*	
Hickling, Norfolk	. 24.6.30	Lagarde, central France	. 21.9.30
North Yorkshire .	. 6.7.47	Fafe, Portugal	. -.10.47
North Wales	. 9.7.49	St. Jean Pied de Port .	. 27.9.49
New Forest .	. 7.8.49	Champagne les Marais, Vendée	22.9.49
Dartmoor	. 3.7.50	Meymac, Corrée, France	. 8.9.50
North Wales	. 15.7.51	Bressuire, Deux Sèvres	. 15.9.51
East Dorset [2]	. 2.7.50	Montreuil, Pas de Calais	. 20.5.52

Two other recoveries are of interest to us :

(*a*) Ringed Texel Island 28.6.28, recovered Suffolk -.6.29.

(*b*) Ringed Texel Island 28.6.28, recovered Suffolk 21.9.30.

While Montagu's harrier is only second in point of numbers to the marsh harrier during the summer months on the marismas of southern Spain, it does not, unlike its larger relative, remain during the winter, and it certainly does not winter in France, the inference being that all the breeding population of western Europe must somewhere cross the Mediterranean in early autumn. And yet how many are ever seen on their way *south* ? Even Favier, who chronicled the passage of birds across the Straits of Gibraltar so meticulously, failed to note the autumn passage. Jourdain has recorded a specimen taken in Corsica many years ago on 17th November, but almost every other record I have been able to consult

[1] *Scottish Naturalist*, lxi, 1949, p. 122. This bird was examined by the Editors but the exact date of its death is not recorded.

[2] Recovered two years after ringing.

refers to the spring passage.   As an instance of the distance which a migrant will cover may be cited a Montagu's harrier ringed in southern Sweden which was recovered in the Yola district on the Niger River.   If this bird proceeded due south it would cross the Mediterranean in the neighbourhood of Corsica and Sardinia or perhaps a little further east, passing down the coast of Italy and via Sicily to Tunisia, whence it must have continued almost due south across the whole length of the Sahara to reach its destination in Nigeria, where it was recovered only slightly west of its starting point.   The above hypothetical route is a perfectly possible one for the bird to have followed.

It has already been stated that this harrier spreads over a very wide area in Africa during the winter months.   I gave some indication of its immense travels in my volumes on the birds of West and Equatorial Africa, where it was pointed out that the eastern half of the continent was resorted to much more than the west.   Unlike the marsh harrier the species under review is more addicted to comparatively dry grasslands and consequently is less dependent on swampy ground, though it may often be found there also.   It does not favour desert conditions and doubtless crosses the Sahara and similar dry areas without undue delay.

There has always been speculation about the route which Montagu's harrier takes on its journey south through north-east Africa to reach the open grassy plains of Uganda and Kenya.   Sir Frederick Jackson has told us that it is abundant in Uganda on migration, particularly on arrival at the Albert Lake in November.   It was in that area too that Sir Geoffrey Archer encountered considerable numbers on the open grassy flats at Butiaba between 8th November and 7th December.   W. L. Sclater when editing Sir Frederick's volumes (1938) wrote that the great river certainly suggests itself as the most suitable route, but that now seems to be unlikely in view of the fact that Montagu's harrier has not been recorded from the Sudan or from the Nile Valley for very many years.[1]   It would appear more likely that to reach Uganda the harriers must follow a route far to the west of the Nile, and it will be remembered that it was in the Western Basin of Darfur that Admiral Lynes[2] found it to be a common migrant in autumn on passage southwards, remarking that its journey came considerably later than those of the other harriers—not until nearly the end of October. Grasshoppers and field crickets were then extremely abundant and formed the staple food of this and several other species.

The birds which enter Kenya probably do so via Eritrea, Abyssinia and Somaliland.   Thus the Nile Valley would be avoided and this may account for the paucity of Sudanese records.   Von Heuglin, the German traveller and ornithologist, recorded it many years ago from various localities in Eritrea and Abyssinia, even meeting with it in the latter

[1] Grant and Praed, *Birds of East and North-Eastern Africa*, i, pp. 214-215.
[2] *Ibis*, 1925, pp. 410-411.

country at 13,000 feet.   Incidentally, he also found it in the Sudan and it is probable that a proportion of the migrants still come that way, for the Sudan is a vast area and observers of bird habits in that field are few and far between.

We know from Sir Geoffrey Archer that this harrier passes through British Somaliland on its way south during the second half of September and that it returns again through that territory on its northward journey in the middle of April, the migration being at its height about the 18th to 21st of that month.   Archer found that the above dates clearly indicated the time of passage through Somaliland, which is quite constant.   Montagu's harrier does not appear to remain in Equatorial or East Central Africa for long but continues its way southward, and though nowhere very common it is widely spread in South Africa from the Cape Division of the Colony to the Mashonaland area of Southern Rhodesia.   As the late Doctor Austin Roberts wrote in his *Birds of South Africa*, Montagu's harrier appears only in midsummer and does not breed.   It occurs more in the open plains and savannas than the other harriers and seldom in the marshes.

Considerably more time is spent in its winter quarters—which, be it remembered, embrace India, Ceylon and China as well as the African continent—than on its briefer stay in its breeding area, and it is not until April is well on the way that the *bulk of the migrants* cross the Mediterranean to reach its numerous islands and the shores of Europe beyond. Montagu's harrier has been seen by C. G. Bird coming up the inhospitable coast of Rio de Oro and passing through that desolate country on 16th and 23rd April, and though he was not himself sure whether the birds he saw were Montagu's or pallid harriers, I have little doubt from the dates involved that they were the former, for *Circus macrourus* is unlikely to take that direction, and secondly it should have left West Africa before that date.

The earliest recorded dates when Montagu's harrier has arrived at stated points on the Mediterranean area have been noted by several observers, and if we compare the first arrivals at the two extreme ends of the Mediterranean and again in the middle of this area we find that the dates agree very closely, as the following list shows :

Tangier	1937	25th March	Colonel W. A. Payn
	1951	22nd to 26th March	D. A. and W. M. Bannerman
Malta	1942	2nd April	John Gibb
	1943	1st April	,, ,,
	1944	9th April	,, ,,
	1945	22nd March	,, ,,
Cyprus	1938	28th March	Colonel W. A. Payn

In the case of Malta, through which there is a considerable spring passage but practically none in autumn, Mr. Gibb found that a second wave of harriers, amongst which Montagu's figured, occurred in the years mentioned on April 21st, 28th, 26th and 6th respectively.

I will close this section of my essay with a note from my diary describing the remarkable migration of birds which my wife and I witnessed at Tangier in 1951.[1]   The greater part of that account dealt with the passage of black kites over the Straits of Gibraltar (for which see my essay on that bird), but after describing how we had been awakened in the early morning of 23rd March by the roar of the wind, and the cries of bee-eaters passing overhead, I refer to the migration in more general terms, as the following passage indicates :

" When we drove down to the sea on the Atlantic side of Cape Spartel to obtain a view of the kites coming over the low ground from the International Bridge, we became aware for the first time of the large migration of Montagu's harriers which was following the shore-line and the maritime plain.   Some of the harriers we watched beating in from over the sea, over which they must surely have been blown by the fierce levanter farther down the coast.   All these harriers were flying due north and coming along singly or in pairs.   The terrific easterly gale made it difficult enough for ourselves to stand against it, and many of the harriers—but no kites— settled on the shore, particularly in a sandy inlet where they could, at ground level, obtain a little shelter and rest before passing over the rising ground between Cape Spartel and Tangier.   It was noticed that none attempted to pass the lighthouse to seaward, which would have entailed meeting the full force of the gale on the Mediterranean side.

" Skimming low over the ground and constantly seeming to be blown backwards as they followed their erratic course, the harriers gained height as with the much more numerous black kites they passed low over the woods which impeded their course and then rose high over the town of Tangier.   Having gained a considerable height they headed across the Straits in the direction of the Spanish coast.   How many hundreds passed in this seemingly unending stream—for there were many other birds braving the crossing in addition to the kites and harriers—it is impossible to guess.   Their course—if they could maintain position by travelling high—would have brought them, we surmised, to the Spanish coast somewhere between Tarifa and Cape Trafalgar, but with the wind that was blowing it seemed to us, standing on the heights above Tangier town, that the birds, especially the smaller ones, would be lucky if they made the land anywhere."

As we wrote in our account of this migration published in the *Ibis*, the 23rd of March was a memorable day of migration, and the sight of the Montagu's harriers battling their way across the Straits in the face of the gale was a sight we shall never forget.

[1] The full account of this migration was published in the *Ibis*, 1952, pp. 678-682.

HABITS : One of the chief differences between Montagu's harrier and the marsh harrier lies in the fact that the high reed-beds which are so necessary for the marsh harrier are not essential in the habitat of Montagu's. Time and again I have watched it quartering the plains and bare slopes of hillsides far from any marshland, but that has been in its winter quarters, where it must often occur in an environment far removed from anything we can offer in these islands. In England it may be seen—and indeed it nests—in widely differing situations. In eastern Norfolk we think of it breeding in the same haunts as the marsh harrier selects among the tall reed-beds of Horsey or Hickling, making its nest on the ground in the rank marshland vegetation with high growth around it to shield it from view. That is certainly one type of habitat, not only in this country but also abroad, but it is just as likely to make its nest, as Howard Saunders wrote many years ago, in the middle of a small clearing in gorse or heather or in a field of grain. A nest discovered in North Wales in 1945 was on firm ground among rushes in an area of common land ; it will be referred to again later in this account.

In its habits this harrier is by choice gregarious. It migrates in company with others of its kind, though not in close flocks but in couples and singly in sight of others as already described. Often on these long journeys it is accompanied by other species, kites and snake-eagles and smaller birds as well. Under a previous heading I wrote of watching them making their way to Spain, setting out over the sea from the African coast when the sky seemed to be full of them.

In his famous work, with the same title as mine, Lord Lilford has described their arrival in Spain on an April day at the very point for which our birds appeared to be making. It must have been in the neighbourhood of eighty years ago that he was engaged in a great-bustard drive on the Guadalquivir marismas when seventy of these harriers passed within range of his gun and many others at varying distances beyond, " passing steadily to the northward, evidently on migration ". Without exception they flew within a few feet of the ground, without pausing to hunt or reconnoitre the territory, all bound for some special breeding place already determined. In those days, as he tells us, it nested abundantly in the great marshes and cornlands below Seville, but whether it does so to-day I must leave to others to discover.

As such numbers can never appear in Britain we have no opportunity of seeing a " colony " of these harriers on their nesting ground such as Colonel Howard Irby appears to have discovered in Morocco, where on a salt marsh he watched through his telescope fifteen or twenty pairs apparently on their breeding site—the hen birds sitting dotted about the marsh—from his vantage point on the opposite side of a river.

Lord Lilford himself never knew of more than three or four nests in close proximity, placed upon ground in small open spots amongst low vegetation in the dry marshes, or amongst the standing corn. In Andalusia he never found a Montagu's nest in the reed-beds that are so dear to the marsh harrier. His observation that this bird is easily attracted by an imitation of the call of the quail interested me particularly, for it is by this same call that the Maltese gunners attract the harriers which pass through that island on migration, and no doubt the quail falls an easy prey to such quick-sighted ground-feeding birds, just as the poor bird falls an easy victim to the Maltese gunners. Lilford remarks that he never remembers having seen a Montagu's harrier in pursuit of any flying fowl, and described its diet in Andalusia as consisting chiefly of frogs, lizards, various insects, worms, small rodents and the eggs of ground-breeding birds, for like all the rest of its clan Montagu's is a noted egg-stealer.

There can be no two opinions as to the menace which this harrier is to game chicks in country where partridges are really plentiful. Not many sporting landowners or their keepers can view with equanimity eight partridge chicks being served to the young between 10 a.m. and 5 p.m., as was recorded by Miss Frances Pitt when keeping a nest under observation at Horsey. Only a true naturalist could have written of the incident as did the owner of the land : " These birds gave pleasure to a number of people besides myself and despite some strange experiences and unwonted publicity, they passed a happy summer, enjoyed grand sport (which I should be the last to grudge) and reared a healthy family." [1]

It is not everywhere that game chicks fill so important a part of the menu. In Cornwall Colonel Ryves found that it subsisted largely on vipers, frogs, lizards, mice and small birds, skylarks and meadow pipits especially falling victim. Insects, eggs and earthworms are always devoured and eggs especially are taken whenever opportunity occurs. He quoted Mr. B. Vesey-FitzGerald, one-time Editor of *The Field*, as stating that Montagu's harrier is not a menace to game birds, but that remark certainly requires qualification. As long ago as 1890, when pleading for the protection of this bird by landowners, Lord Lilford was careful to observe : " As no good cause is promoted by over-statement, I will not attempt to deny that all harriers are egg-stealers, but I would at the same time remind game preservers and our unfortunate British agriculturalists, that these birds are very active and sharp-eyed enemies to field mice, moles and voles." That is undoubtedly the most sensible advice and loses nothing by repetition after many years.

The food of Montagu's harrier as exemplified by examination of some pellets taken from a pair feeding flying young in Yorkshire in August formed the subject of a note in *British Birds* by the late Claud Ticehurst. Examination of these pellets revealed the following : snake scales, grouse chick, juvenile Passerine bird, vole fur, short-tailed field vole, feathers of a

[1] *Fisherman Naturalist*, by Major Anthony Buxton, D.S.O., p. 134.

small Passerine, juvenile golden plover, and fragments of a meadow pipit and of the wing of a song thrush. Doctor Ticehurst adds that it would appear that unlike the barn owl Montagu's harrier not only plumes off most of the diagnostic feathers of its prey, but also does not swallow the heads of birds and but few bones. It was possible, he found, to recover the gizzard of the prey from the pellet, together with its content, grit and various seeds.

Of the four harriers, this and the pallid harrier are the most peerless fliers. The grace which Montagu's harrier exhibits in the air is second to none and as this gracefulness is enhanced by the beauty of an adult cock's plumage, and not least by its slim body and long black primaries, it is quite one of the most attractive birds on the British List. Major Buxton suggests that an old cock Montagu's takes at least three years to attain a complete grey livery, four or five years to acquire a yellow eye, and longer still to reach that paleness of colour which gives real distinction. Colonel Montagu, the well-known ornithologist, was honoured indeed to have his name linked with such an outstanding bird, but it was he who first distinguished between this and the hen-harrier which it so closely resembles, and such meritorious work brought a quick reward in those halcyon days of ornithology, an opportunity of which William Yarrell was not slow to take advantage.

My own experience of this and our other harriers has generally been outside the breeding season, but it is no doubt during nesting time that their skill in the air is seen to best advantage. Under the next heading some account of the serious business of the " pass " will be given, but harriers will at times break off from their more arduous duties and indulge in aerial manœuvres for the pure fun of it. Thus in a passage in Major Buxton's *Fisherman Naturalist* we have such a display described :

The finest exhibition of aerobatics was given by this pair one morning, when, after a number of kills had been brought in, work was interrupted and they gave themselves up for half an hour to sheer enjoyment of the art of flying. Their antics were centred on the manœuvres of the " pass ", but no food was in their claws ; it was all pure fun. Screaming and chattering they swept past each other in the air at every angle, sometimes on their sides, sometimes on their backs, and as they met their claws went through the motions of the " pass ". Then the game ended and serious work was resumed.

There are times when Montagu's harrier will ascend to a great height. Colonel Ryves has described it thus :

For ease and elegance in soaring it is certainly not second to the buzzard, and excels it in the rapidity with which it can rise to great altitudes. The wings are canted upwards with the primaries expanded, the tilt appearing to be more pronounced in the male. When quartering the ground the action is leisurely, and the bird swerves from side to side ; this action because of its buoyancy does not detract one whit from grace of movement. . . . In rapid aerial descent or in direct and fast forward movement, the wings are curved like a crescent and the tail is tightly closed.   But at the moment of a sudden change of direction the tail is fanned.

The various cries used by Montagu's harrier to express alarm and anger or again to give warning of food are discussed by A. W. Colling and E. B. Brown when describing the pair which they discovered breeding in North Wales.   The female's alarm call is described as *ick-ick-ick*, averaging from seven to ten syllables and uttered on the approach to the nest of humans or sometimes when being mobbed by lapwings or curlews.   The male's alarm cry is louder and slower and is expressed by *yeck-yeck-yeck*. On approaching the nest with food the male was heard to make a soft mewing sound to call the female up, and as she rose to receive the prey the female responded with a thin long-drawn whining which may be interpreted as *psee—, psee—*.   The " food calls " of the young when able to fly are uttered in excited chorus and are shriller and more hurried than that of the female, while youngsters of two or three weeks old utter an angry twittering sound when handled.

The calls of birds are seldom interpreted in the same way by two observers but in general they agree in the end.   Colonel Ryves writes the alarm and anger cry of this harrier as *kek-kek-kek-kek-kek-kek-kek*, high-pitched and far-reaching.   The food call as given in *The Handbook* on the authority of Schuster would appear to need some amending and is difficult to identify with any bird note, but it must have sounded like that to his ears.

BREEDING HABITS :   In one of his books Anthony Buxton has expressed the view that more is probably known by British naturalists about Montagu's harrier than about either of the other two, by which he means the marsh and the hen-harrier, for the pallid harrier is but a rare stranger within our gates from beyond the Iron Curtain.   For this state of affairs naturalists of our day owe a deep debt to several distinguished men whose names should be put permanently on record in this book, for it was through the action and foresight of Lord Grey of Fallodon, Mr. Edwin Montagu, Lord Lucas, Lord Desborough and his head keeper Mr. Jim Vincent, and not least of Major Anthony Buxton of Horsey Hall—the only one now surviving—that the marsh and Montagu's harriers which breed in east Norfolk were saved from certain extinction.   Their combined efforts have enabled the leading ornithologists of our time to study the harriers on their breeding ground and so increase our knowledge of their habits.   They have also enabled countless visitors to Broadland to enjoy a spectacle which would otherwise have been denied them.   We should never forget what we owe to these men.

In an earlier paragraph I have quoted Major Buxton's opinion that Montagu's harrier normally arrives on its breeding grounds in east

Norfolk in the last half of April or beginning of May, and from then on he has been able to watch the behaviour and early courtship of the pairs which breed on his estate. Of that he has given us the following picture :

Montagu's are delightful to watch at the moment when they are settling the important question of where they are going to nest. They float perpetually about over the chosen area, obviously trying to decide exactly where the nest shall be, but behaving all the time as if they had nothing whatever to do and all the day in which to do it. Now and then the cock goes off but soon returns, generally with some very small object which he passes to the hen in the air in the approved style. I have never been able to discover what these small objects passed by harriers at courting times are : they may be the heads of small birds or they may be love tokens and nothing to do with food at all. There is at these times much aerial flirtation, the cock swaggering with slow majestic wing-beats and sidling up to the hen in the air and she pushing him away with her foot, but taking care not to push too hard or to fly too far. Then comes the decision—the nest shall be here—and much carrying of single bits of material by both birds, but never a proper bundle, as though they thought it all such fun that it would be a pity to finish the job too quickly.

Although at the most four pairs may nest in this territory at no great distance from one another, there seems to be no animosity shown on the part of these harriers to their nearest neighbours and even when, as occurred on the territory in North Wales, a second male which had no mate of his own appeared on the scene, he was often to be observed flying about with the attached male and was evidently tolerated by both male and female of the nesting pair even in the vicinity of the nest. Although in this case the triangle appears to have been perfectly innocent, there have been a number of cases of proved and shameless bigamy in this species. Mr. Geoffrey Dent has given an account [1] of two hens which nested within seventy yards of one another and were obviously both paired to the same cock, who fed them alternately while brooding. For a day or two one of the hens had a tendency to come off her nest out of turn in response to the cock's call to her rival, but after a week all settled down amicably and the hens were fed in turn, only the one who was called off rising to take the " pass ". The only trouble occurred when one hen flew over the nest of the other. Then a fierce battle not unnaturally took place. After passing his kill, the cock would settle on one of a row of posts close to the nest of whichever hen he had fed until she had finished her meal and returned to her eggs. The cock brought five kills in the hour, two to one nest, three to the other. One hen reared four young, the other three, out of five eggs. Mr. Dent observed that neither of the hens hunted much until their young were well grown and both broods were reared almost entirely by the efforts of the one cock bird.

[1] *British Birds*, xxxiii, p. 51.

The above case took place in Norfolk in the summer of 1938. Four years later Mr. Eric Hosking had much the same experience when in 1942 two hens and a cock arrived late in the season in the Hickling area.[1] The cock mated with both hens, who built their nests not more than 300 yards apart and were fed alternately by the cock. Both hens reared young. Mr. P. A. Hens had drawn attention to polygamy in this harrier in Holland even before the two instances recorded took place in England.[2]

The building of the nest is largely done by the hen. When in marshland it is built mainly of sedge and rushes and lined with finer material. The nest of the Welsh pair to which allusion has been made was on firm ground among rushes and consisted of a thin flattened layer of *Juncus* stems lining a space about twelve inches in diameter. In Cornwall we hear of nests built of dried grasses only, neat structures in a trodden-down clump of marsh herbage, well concealed by the standing jungle. Round one nest the birds had prepared quite a large " playground ", while in another about three miles distant there was practically none.

The only nest ever taken by Henry Seebohm was in a cornfield in Germany. There was no hole or scraping in the ground ; the rye had only been trampled down, and a slight but rather neat nest made of cornstalks, lined with a little dry straw. The nest was rather more than nine inches in diameter and about two and a half inches deep in the middle. This type of nest is likely to be confined to breeding areas beyond the British Isles.

It has been remarked by Colonel Ryves[3] when watching this harrier in Cornwall that he has seen materials carried by the female to the nest off and on throughout the period of incubation and brooding the chicks, and even a male has been observed to pick up a strand of grass and drop to the nest with it, after passing a kill to his sitting mate.

Eggs are laid at the end of May or early June in Britain but are said to be laid two or three weeks earlier in the Mediterranean region (Jourdain). In the Horsey-Hickling area in this country the normal date of egg laying is the latter part of May, Major Buxton assures me. The number in a clutch varies. Four to five is the normal laying but clutches of eight and ten have been recorded. A photograph of a nest with its ten eggs appeared in *British Birds*,[4] together with a forcible letter from Lord Desborough's head keeper, for this clutch was stolen before the eggs were hatched, a mean action for which no words are too strong. The history of this unique clutch is as follows (I quote from Jim Vincent's narrative) : A pair of Montagu's harriers arrived on 23rd April 1930 at Hickling, Norfolk,

[1] *British Birds*, xxxvii, p. 3.
[2] " Avif. d. Nederl." in *Beiträge z. Fortpflf.-Biol. d. Vögel*, iii, p. 22.
[3] *Bird Life in Cornwall*, p. 134.
[4] Vol. xxiv, p. 81.

PLATE 22

MONTAGU'S HARRIER (Adult Female)
Circus pygargus (Linnaeus)

and had two eggs in the nest on 11th May. On the 14th there were three eggs, on the 17th four, on the 19th five, on the 22nd seven, on the 24th eight, on the 27th nine, and on the 30th ten. Mr. Vincent added that he felt certain this remarkable clutch of eggs was the product of one bird, both because of the intervals of laying and because the female would not tolerate another female near the nest, nor would the cock if the female was away eating the food he had brought, for, as Vincent had remarked, he always saw her back to the nest and guarded her.

On what grounds F. C. R. Jourdain suggests in *The Handbook* that this particular clutch was the product of two females it is difficult to conjecture. Vincent is not likely to have allowed a second female Montagu's to have escaped his notice day after day. He was too practised an observer for that. It is known from long observation at other nests that eggs are laid at intervals of thirty-six hours to three days[1] and that the female begins to sit from the day the first egg is laid. On very rare occasions a cock has been put off the eggs.

The eggs may be rounded or ovate, as is well shown in Seebohm's *Eggs of British Birds,*[2] and as that authority pointed out, may readily be distinguished from the eggs of other British harriers by their decidedly smaller size. The egg is unglossed and fine-grained and is unspotted pale bluish- or greenish-white; very rarely an egg bears some small rust-coloured spots and streaks. Measurements (after Jourdain) of 100 eggs average $41 \cdot 54 \times 32 \cdot 67$ mm. Max. $46 \cdot 5 \times 32 \cdot 5$ and $42 \cdot 5 \times 37 \cdot 5$ mm. Min. $37 \times 30 \cdot 2$ and $41 \cdot 5 \times 29 \cdot 6$ mm.

The incubation period varies from twenty-seven to thirty days, twenty-eight to twenty-nine being the usual time for each egg. The first chick to be hatched keeps its advantage in age and size and flies before the second chick to be hatched is ready to do so—and so on through the brood.

Once the female has begun to sit she is a very tight sitter and will only rise from the eggs on the close approach of a human being. The only time when she regularly leaves her nest is to take the food which has been brought by her mate and in this action the members of the genus *Circus* are practically unique. While the hen is sitting the male does all the hunting and feeds her entirely. Many accounts have been published of the astonishing procedure commonly known as the " pass ", which appears to differ but slightly between individuals. Major Buxton's account[3]—he must have

---

[1] At Horsey eggs are normally laid every other day and naturally hatch in that order. Four is the usual clutch in that area.

[2] Plate 5, figs. 1 and 3.

[3] The quotations from Major Buxton's writings are from the journals of the Norfolk Naturalists Society and from his book *Fisherman Naturalist*, Chapter ix (Collins, 1946), with grateful acknowledgment to the author for his permission to quote from any of his publications.

witnessed the action times without number on his Norfolk estate—refers to a particular pair which he had under observation :

The cock would come over, making his particular call, on hearing which up would come the hen from the nest, often with a scream to meet him in the air. In a high wind he would frequently manœuvre for a considerable period in order to get their respective positions exactly correct. Then out would shoot his claw, holding the prey with every leg muscle stiff, and finally dropping the prey to be caught by the hen in the air . . . never did we see her miss a catch. Sometimes she would tilt up so as to be almost on her back in the air—and indeed the film record in one case shows that she turned a complete somersault ; but often she would scarcely tilt at all and, without apparently even looking at the cock, lazily put out a hand, back uppermost, and take the prey in her claws as it dropped in front of her nose.

At times the " pass " is made from foot to foot and the prey not dropped at all, the female rising to meet her mate and take the prey from his claws. In a pair under observation in North Wales food exchanges occurred mostly by dropping but sometimes, as described, the prey was passed from foot to foot. When bringing prey the male generally approached the nesting area flying only ten to twenty feet above ground level, but once he appeared at a very great height and dived steeply with half-closed wings. As he dived the female rose to meet him and the prey was exchanged from foot to foot fairly high in the air. A somewhat similar performance was witnessed by an Air Force officer in Cornwall [1] :

The male arrived carrying food over the nesting area and then proceeded to soar in circles to a considerable height, still carrying the food. He then dived down almost vertically, with half-closed wings, making a spiral turn as he did so. At the bottom of the dive he " zoomed " up steeply and looped right over on to his back, whence by a half roll off the top of the loop (as we should describe it in the R.A.F.) he resumed normal flight. The female then came off the nest, which contained three eggs, and the " pass " took place.

Major Buxton estimated that one cock bird which he watched brought in on an average about sixteen kills for his family of five between 10.30 a.m. and 5.20 p.m. and within that time he occasionally reached the total of twenty-five. Not much hunting was done very early or very late and twenty kills per day was about the average. The kills were nearly all very small stuff, consisting mainly of larks and meadow pipits, varied by a few young partridges, mice and other things. After the hen had ceased to brood the prey was usually passed to her several hundred yards from the nest, and when she had finished the plucking the cock escorted her back and hung in the air over her until he saw that she was happily engaged in doling out the food to the young, when he would waft himself away with a series of long planes back to his hunting ground.

In very hot weather, when the young were still in down, their mother

[1] *British Birds*, xxxviii : Group-Captain J. G. Davis.

spread her wings and tail over them to act as a parasol, and when all the family except the youngest had begun to grow feathers, she made a sort of shelter in the rushes for them, by plucking the grass and opening out a hollow from the edge of the nest, into which she carried what appeared to be a cushion of grass.

Mr. J. C. Harrison, the well-known bird artist, has described how on one occasion during a storm the mother bird came to the nest and spread her wing over one youngster to shelter it from the downpour, while the remainder of the family, not so fortunate, stood motionless and upright to allow the rain to run down their feathers. When it ceased raining and the parent bird had left, they fully expanded their wings on the nest to sun themselves, much as I have seen the griffon vultures do after a wetting in Andalusia.

I will end this essay with Major Buxton's description of how the young birds are taught to fly, and cannot improve on his own words [1] :

The method of inducing young harriers to leave the nest is similar to that enjoyed by other hawks, including honey buzzards. The particular bird ripe for departure is starved when it can just begin to use its wings in flight. At a certain nest at which four young were hatched there was a week between the hatching of egg number one and egg number four, and the young birds maintained the respective intervals throughout their stay in the nest, the younger never catching up the older. When the correct moment arrived the oldest was starved, while the others were well fed : the oldest got more and more impatient and fluttered further and further from the nest, always returning to the nest when food was brought in but just too late to get any. The cock fed the three in the nest, while the hen sat at a distance watching. At last in desperation the starved first-born took a flight of about fifty yards, when the hen instantly flew to it in the reeds and rewarded it with food. From then onwards it was always fed away from the nest and the same process was followed with all the brood. As their flying powers improve they are taught to follow their parents carrying food in the air and finally to catch it like their parents at the " pass ". By the end of about a fortnight they are quite expert at the game, and Montagu's usually depart for the south some time in August, about a month after they have left the nest.

Those who have read this essay from its beginning will realize what immense distances these young harriers have to travel so soon after quitting their nursery and will have learned how many are the hazards which they have to overcome ere they reach their journey's end.

REFERENCES : Original Description. *Falco pygargus* Linnaeus, Syst. Nat., 10th ed., 1758, p. 89 : Europe. Restricted type locality England.

[1] *Fisherman Naturalist*, pp. 134-135.

PLATE 23

HEN-HARRIER

Circus cyaneus cyaneus (Linnaeus)

Partly Resident and Breeding in island groups of North Britain.   One or two pairs may nest occasionally on the mainland. Has recently bred again in Ireland. Very rarely recorded as having bred in England or Wales and has now apparently ceased to do so. It is an Uncommon Visitor in autumn and winter, but few manage to survive the local gunner or gamekeeper, and the country of origin of these visitors is not clear, though Norway is suspected.

IDENTIFICATION : This is a smaller bird than the last species dealt with and the sexes are more dissimilar than they are in that bird.   The male hen-harrier when it has reached maturity is, in fact, very striking.   The whole of the upperparts except the rump is pale slate-grey ; the rump is white.   Thus the head, wings and tail all appear uniform grey.   The throat and breast are bluish-grey and the rest of the underparts, including the axillaries and under wing-coverts, is pure white.   There is also a narrow white tip to the grey tail feathers.   The cere, legs and feet are yellow, the tarsus bare of feathers.   The bill and claws are black and the iris bright orange-yellow.

The distinctions between the male hen-harrier and the male Montagu's harrier will be mentioned after describing the hen.   For distinction of the male pallid harrier (also a grey bird) from the other two, see under that species.   It is well to remember, if the bird can be handled, that in the hen-harrier the outer webs of the primaries from the second to the fifth inclusive are emarginated.

The adult female hen-harrier, which is about twenty inches in total length, is very different in appearance, being proportionately larger than her consort and for the most part brown in colour.   The crown is much paler than the mantle and is streaked with dark brown, as is the distinct facial ruff.   The wings are dark brown and the tail light brown, crossed with five broad dark brown bands, including the penultimate.   The upper tail-coverts are white and this character shows in flight.   The throat and breast are buffish-brown, streaked with dark brown, the barring on the flanks more inclined to rufous in some examples.

Immature birds are very similar in appearance to the adult female and are similarly streaked on the underparts.

The following distinctions between the hen-harrier and Montagu's harrier should be borne in mind [1] :

HEN-HARRIER :

In form   Larger, squatter, stronger body.
           Shorter, broader, blunter wings.
           Shorter, broader tail.

In colour Tips only of primaries black.
(Adult male) No black band on secondaries, which are grey.
           A broad area of pure white on rump.
           No streaks on flanks.

[1] Partly after Hesse, *Orn. Monatsb.*, 1916, pp. 1-3.

PLATE 23

HEN-HARRIER

Circus cyaneus cyaneus (Linnaeus)

Upper Figure . . Adult Male
Lower Figure . . Adult Female

PLATE 23

HEN-HARRIER

Circus cyaneus cyaneus (Linnaeus)

Upper Figure . . .	Adult Male
Lower Figure . . .	Adult Female

Montagu's Harrier :

In form   Smaller, more graceful and slender body.
Longer, narrower and more pointed wings.
Longer, narrower tail.

In colour   In addition to black tips to primaries characteristic narrow
(Adult male)   black bar across secondaries.
Rump grey or greyish-white.   Never a broad area of white
as in hen-harrier.
Pinkish-chestnut streaks on flanks.

The females of these two harriers are very much alike but in the female Montagu's the white area at the base of the tail is generally narrower than in the hen-harrier and less pure white.

The immature hen-harrier closely resembles the adult female and has brown streaks on the breast.   The immature Montagu's harrier is unique among the harriers in having the underparts uniform rufous-buff.

Major Anthony Buxton, from familiarity with them on his own estate, summed up the characters and appearance of the three harriers many years ago in the following sentence : " An old cock hen-harrier is a great bird, but it just misses that perfect finish of a cock Montagu given by the pink streaks on the latter's breast and the thin black line down his secondaries. His likeness to the Montagu leads to the expectation of an equal gracefulness in flight, but he falls short in this respect of his smaller cousin, and yet in the opposite direction he misses that look of an out and out ruffian which is so characteristic of a marsh harrier."

Local Distribution :   As a breeding bird to-day (1954) in Britain the hen-harrier has been driven to its last retreat : the Orkney Islands and the Outer Hebrides.   In the latter group it is represented by only a very few pairs.   Its main stronghold to-day is the island of Mainland in the Orkneys, and there its nests are guarded during the breeding season against the unscrupulous egg-dealer.   The last *published* report of its status appeared over twelve years ago after Doctor David Lack's visit.   He then wrote[1] : " A number of pairs on Mainland and about two pairs on each of Hoy and Rousay.   In former times common, and Buckley and Harvie-Brown (1891) could still describe it as such.   Later it came very near indeed to extinction.   Latterly it has picked up, thanks to the untiring efforts of G. T. Arthur and his fellow workers, but care cannot be relaxed.   Although its numbers have gone on increasing there is reason to believe that it is not as numerous as is sometimes reported and though in no danger of extirpation great care must still be exercised in the breeding season."

Reviewing the status of the species in the 3rd edition of *The Handbook of British Birds* (1938) the late Harry Witherby wrote that in England and Wales it had nested in the last thirty years in Cornwall, Hants, Surrey

[1] *Ibis*, 1943, p. 8.

(1932), Anglesey (1924, 1925, 1926) and Caernarvon, and possibly in Devon. It attempted to nest in Perthshire (1922) and probably bred on the Cumberland-Dumfries borders in 1925 and bred in Inverness (1936). Otherwise he classed it—apart from its breeding places in the northern isles—as only a winter visitor and spring migrant.

Doctor Eagle Clarke in his *Manual of British Birds*, 3rd ed. (1927), includes Norfolk and Northumberland (1899) as counties in which the hen-harrier has bred " during the past quarter of a century ", but I can find no confirmation of the Northumberland record in George Bolam's *Birds of Northumberland and the Eastern Borders* (1912), so Mr. Witherby may have omitted the record with intent. Eagle Clarke included the island of Arran as a possible breeding place but it appears that they became extinct there in 1912, unless happily a pair should return from time to time.

The breeding history of the hen-harrier in the past in Scotland is told in detail by Miss Baxter and Miss Rintoul in *The Birds of Scotland* (1953) and deplorable reading it is, a tale of ruthless destruction by gamekeepers and others, certainly without justification.

Of recent years a pair are believed to have bred in 1925 on the borders of Cumberland and Dumfries[1] but from the Solway area the hen-harrier was exterminated as a breeding species about 1850. Another pair attempted to breed in Perthshire in 1922 but both birds were destroyed, though in this county Miss Baxter and Miss Rintoul had subsequent records of nesting and there appears to be some hope that in Perthshire it may re-establish itself. In 1936 a pair bred in Inverness-shire and according to the authors cited the birds continue to nest in the Cairngorms. I have had one or two other localities reported to me on the Scottish mainland where the hen-harrier is said to breed or to attempt to do so.

In the Shetland Isles the hen-harrier once nested on the island of Yell, according to Saxby, and in the winters of 1869-70 and 1870-71 it was much more numerous than it had been for some years previously, but it was even then only a rare visitor to Unst. There is no record of breeding in the Shetland group of islands since Saxby's day. Venables states it is now a rare autumn migrant and winter visitor only.[2]

In Skye there were five nests at Dunvegan in 1873 but in 1883 the bird nested there for the last time. In the Outer Hebrides it bred on South Uist in 1920, where it was reported to be fairly common, and was nesting there in 1931, in which year it was also breeding on North Uist. Since those days a decided decrease has taken place in the Outer Hebrides in the number of breeding pairs.

To the Scottish mainland to-day the hen-harrier is an occasional visitor but there seems to be some doubt whether these birds are genuine overseas migrants or whether—as I believe—our own breeding stock

---

[1] *Handbook of British Birds*, p. 68 : " H.F.W."
[2] *Birds and Mammals of Shetland*, 1955, pp. 199-200.

wanders about in the winter months, but this point will be discussed more fully under another heading.

In Ireland the hen-harrier seems to have been finally exterminated as a breeding species about 1913, if not earlier. A pair bred in Co. Kerry in 1908 and probably subsequently, while the Knockmealdown Mountains appear to have been the last locality where they were believed to have bred in Ireland. Colonel Scroope states in *The Birds of Ireland* (1954) that the hen-harrier was formerly resident and not uncommon, and used to nest in mountainous districts in all four provinces, but the numbers decreased rapidly towards the end of last century until, in 1953, it was classed as a rare straggler to the country. There appear to have been about ten records between February 1943 and December 1952. As a winter visitor or perhaps passage migrant there are many records and these will be discussed under the heading of Migration.

The news in the *Irish Bird Report* for 1954 that circumstantial evidence pointed to a pair having bred in that year in a southern county was followed by news of the " extensive breeding " of the hen-harrier in 1955 *in three southern counties* whose names were withheld.[1] Whether it will be allowed to re-establish itself permanently in Eire will depend very largely on public opinion.

DISTRIBUTION ABROAD : The breeding range of the hen-harrier extends from the British Isles east to the Ural Mountains but seldom north of the Arctic Circle. Molineux has stated that it reaches $69\frac{1}{2}°$ N. in Norway, $68\frac{1}{2}°$ N. in Sweden and north Finland and 68° N. in north Russia. Its status and more exact range in Scandinavian countries will be given in a later paragraph. It is rare in the Low Countries. In western Europe it breeds as far south at least as Coimbra in Portugal, whence we can trace its range eastwards through Italy, Albania and Jugoslavia and through much of central and southern Europe to the Caucasus. It is said to be rarely seen in Switzerland. To Spain it seems to be chiefly a winter visitor.

The Asiatic breeding population of the hen-harrier is reported to winter largely in Persia, Baluchistan and India but of that I have no personal knowledge. In *The Handbook of British Birds* the Editors include Burma in its winter range, but it is apparent from the newly issued *Birds of Burma* that there is but a single record from that country !

The European population of this harrier is to be found in winter spread over the Mediterranean area and its islands but by no means do all the hen-harriers migrate. A proportion of them can remain as far north as the Shetlands. There are, however, reports from many islands in the Mediterranean of wintering birds. A few occur at intervals in Corsica and it is also recorded from there on passage in April. It is to be seen in Malta

---

[1] I am greatly indebted to my friend Helen Rait-Kerr for drawing my attention to this interesting occurrence, and to the kind offices of Fr. P. G. Kennedy.

during the same month. In Egypt and Sinai it is the least common of the harriers, but I found it in Cyprus to be fairly common from February onwards. It is rare in Arabia and as far as I know does not reach tropical Africa in its wanderings. In northern Africa it is reported to occur from the northern Sahara to Nubia during the winter. J. I. S. Whitaker had specimens in his collection from the north and centre of Tunisia obtained in spring, and it is reported to be still more often seen in Algeria, but from personal observation in all three territories Tunisia, Algeria and Morocco, I consider the hen-harrier to be an uncommon bird, while the marsh harrier is just the reverse, and Montagu's plentiful during the spring passage, especially in Morocco.

At the western end of the Mediterranean the hen-harrier is reported to be a scarce straggler on migration to Majorca, the dates when it usually appears being in April, but there are September records also and one or two from midsummer: July and August. On the Spanish side of the Straits of Gibraltar the bird is usually seen in winter in suitable localities, but the passage across to the Moroccan coast if it occurs at all must be on a very small scale.

Some remarks on the status and distribution of the hen-harrier in Scandinavian countries may not be out of place, for we still have to account for the origin of those few hen-harriers which are regularly reported during the autumn and winter months from counties in Britain, if they are not all locally bred birds. The hen-harrier is one of several birds which have recently become more numerous and more widely distributed in Norway.[1] A century ago Norwegian naturalists knew this fine hawk only as a rarity. To-day, while still very scarce in some districts, it is in others one of the commoner Raptores.

As far as can be ascertained, the hen-harrier was first recorded as a Norwegian bird in 1832, when an example was obtained on Dovre. Later it was observed, though only sporadically, on passage to and from the uplands.

Conclusive evidence that the species bred in Norway was finally procured in 1884, when Professor Collett and his friend Landmark found two nests on the same marsh. Thereafter very little was forthcoming in the way of records for nearly forty years. Most of these derived from Finmark, where harriers were seen in 1902 (Schaanning), and again in 1923, 1924 and 1926 (Bolam and Blair), in the last-named year under circumstances which suggested that they were breeding. Thereafter breeding took place sporadically in various localities, but in very small numbers.

The strongholds of the harrier in Norway are the great mosses lying between 900 and 1100 metres on the fells around Gudbrandsdal and

[1] The information under this heading is gathered from *Rovfuglene og Viltpleien* (1952) by Doctor Yngvar Hagen and is thoroughly up-to-date.

Dovre. Hardanger Vidda, most of which rises above the 1200-metre contour, seems to be too high for this bird, and it is not common there. Harriers undoubtedly breed in several places between Hallingdal and Gudbrandsdal, although we have as yet only a few records from this vast area. In Finmark this species is very locally distributed and nowhere common.

In Scandinavia the hen-harrier has two very distinct breeding grounds, one in the lowlands of central Sweden with their great reed- and sedge-fringed lakes, the other in the high plateaux. That it has not been found nesting in the lowlands of south Norway is hardly surprising, for there swamps of sufficient extent are lacking. Conditions differ greatly in the two breeding grounds. On the Swedish lowlands prey is always in fairly good supply, and there harriers nest every season. On the high plateaux, on the other hand, it is most unusual to find these birds breeding in any other than a vole or lemming year.

MIGRATION: Although the hen-harrier is stated in textbooks to be a " winter visitor " (*Handbook*) or an " occasional visitant " (Howard Saunders), in addition of course to our small resident population in Shetland, it is not easy to find direct evidence of any Continental passage. Miss Baxter and Miss Rintoul wrote (1953) in their *Birds of Scotland*: " Outside the breeding season the hen-harrier may be seen occasionally in any part of Scotland, but it is difficult to say if these are our own birds wandering about or overseas migrants. We have little evidence from our island stations of any considerable overseas immigration but there are some interesting notes." They then proceed to give some cases which may bear on the possible movements of this harrier from overseas ; notable among these is the " beautiful dark female " which appeared on North Rona on 29th August 1931 and stayed until at least 3rd September. Mr. L. S. V. Venables observes that hen-harriers occasionally " winter in Shetland ", and very occasional visitors to Fair Isle turn up in the autumn.

We cannot, however, be sure of the origin of any of these examples, any more than we can be sure of that of the hen-harriers which visit various localities in England during the autumn and winter months. A perusal of the local fauna reports goes to prove that the hen-harrier turns up at unexpected places certainly much more often than I had supposed, and the authoritative county works such as Mr. Clifford Oakes' *Birds of Lancashire* (1953) support that view. Thus we read that although it has disappeared as a resident it is now a passage visitor to the county in small numbers, more frequent in autumn than in spring, but has occurred in every month of the year and has been known to winter on southern mosses. That looks as if, were a little encouragement offered it, it might become a resident again.

In East Anglia it seems that its status to-day is much as when Claud Ticehurst wrote of it in his *History of the Birds of Suffolk* some twenty-five years ago, small numbers annually visiting the heathlands and marshes of Norfolk and Suffolk. Late October and November is the time when it may be expected, though Ticehurst mentions it from 10th October—his earliest record. It sometimes remains long enough to overlap the breeding harriers, so Major Buxton tells me.

Taking another county, Kent, as an instance that the species may have increased within recent years, Doctor James Harrison writes as follows (1954) : " To this county the hen-harrier is now a regular and by no means an uncommon autumn to winter visitor. It arrives as a rule towards the end of August, remaining until March or even into April ; early examples have been recorded in July. Most of the birds are either females or immature individuals and adult males are relatively seldom seen. The coastal belt of the county is the area most favoured ; while inland records for the species are not numerous. There have been no instances of the species having nested since the middle of the nineteenth century."

In Hampshire during the last four years (1951-54 inclusive) it has been observed fairly frequently in winter, mainly from October to January, but one bird remained until 13th April. The winter of 1952 seems to have been a particularly favourable time, for it was seen on many dates in widely separated places from late October to mid-April. Four were reported between 22nd November and 14th December from the Isle of Wight. I am indebted to Mr. Edwin Cohen for this information in advance of the publication of his forthcoming book on the county.

In south-west England—particularly Cornwall—it is evidently rare, a bird or two in most winters being all that may be expected. The few county reports quoted above will give a fair indication of the relative numbers which may be seen annually throughout the English counties. None now remain to nest south of the Border.

The strongest evidence that some of our wintering hen-harriers are of Continental origin rests on the numbers which are reported, for although a small proportion of the Orkney breeding stock remain the year round, the numbers which actually vacate the islands in winter are not sufficient to account for those which are found scattered here and there in the rest of the British Isles. Where else can these birds come from if not from western Europe ? The late Doctor Eagle Clarke certainly inclined to the view that they came from overseas. The recovery of ringed birds should settle the point.

From information in the hands of the Royal Society for the Protection of Birds it is apparent that the majority of the Orkney Islands' stock move out of Orkney in the winter, so Mr. Philip Brown assures me.

Examination of the reports in *British Birds* of the recovery of hen-harriers ringed when young at the breeding place show that a very small percentage of the 147 hen-harriers ringed in this country up to the year

1952 has been recovered, and those were either recovered on the nesting ground or off the northern counties, especially Caithness. In 1952 the recoveries were more interesting than usual, hen-harriers from Orkney having been recaptured in Sutherland, Aberdeen and Moray at distances from the place at which they had been ringed of sixty-six miles south-west, a hundred miles south-east and a hundred miles south, respectively. There have been no captures of ringed birds in Ireland.

On the other hand we know that Continental hen-harriers migrate for considerable distances. Professor Lönnberg in the English Introduction to his standard work, *The Birds of Sweden*, wrote that more than three score of this species had been ringed prior to 1929 in his country, and the returns amounted to 28 per cent., from which it was learned that some hen-harriers remain at a comparatively northern latitude during the winter, exceptionally even in southern Sweden. As a rule it was found that they proceeded farther south and some were recaptured in western France in November. Professor Lönnberg considered that the winter quarters of the hen-harrier extended over western Germany, from Anhalt to Belgium and south-western France. He drew attention to the possibility of young birds, not yet mature, remaining in the south even during the summer, instancing a specimen which was killed at the beginning of July slightly north of Orleans, when it was little more than a year old; presumably it was a Swedish-born bird.

In Norway it is a typical migrant. Hen-harriers ringed in Norway have been recovered in Denmark, Belgium and Italy. Ringing shows that some adults find their way back to the marshes whereon they were hatched. Many young harriers have by now been ringed on Fokkstumyren: for example, thirteen in 1938, three in 1940, thirty-one in 1941-42, three in 1944 and twenty in 1945-46. The female at the only nest seen in 1943 bore a ring. Two years later ringed birds were seen at three nests, one a male, the other two females.

In autumn the migration commences in Norway in September, to reach its height in October. An example has been seen on the lowlands as early as 8th September, while on the other hand numbers have been still about the high fjeld as late as the 30th. On the coast laggards may be expected up to the end of November. In vole or lemming years conditions sometimes tempt harriers to winter in Norway (one Lister, 24th February 1891, after the lemming year 1890-91; one Bjerkreim, 1st January 1939, after the vole year 1938).

On the return migration in spring the time of its arrival in the south varies from year to year, but the majority of the birds probably pass through the lowlands in April (earliest date 23rd March, Fredrikstad; latest 9th May, Larvik).

Considering that the bird has certainly increased its footing in Norway of recent years it is likely now to be seen more often in Heligoland than was the case when Heinrich Gätke was recording the passage migrants through that island and wrote of the subject of this essay : " During all the time I have been collecting, only three old males of this species have been shot, also an old female and two or three young autumn birds . . . the old males [were shot] in the winter during snowstorms and frost." He then observes : " The very scanty appearance of this bird in Heligoland seems also to point to a very narrowly confined southern line of their autumn migration ; for the least westerly deviation from such a line on the part of the birds nesting in upper Norway, both as regards the old birds and their young, would not fail to carry them frequently across to Heligoland."

As a vagrant the hen-harrier has been obtained in the Faeroe Islands, a very strange place in which to occur.

HABITS : In the far distant days when the hen-harrier was an abundant species in parts of the British Isles, its colloquial name was acquired from its habit of harrying poultry—as every housewife knew to her cost. The name " harrier "—as we read in Newton's *Dictionary of Birds*—has now come to be used in a generic sense for all the species ranked under the genus *Circus* of Lacépède, while that of " hen-harrier " is restricted to the particular species which is *Falco cyaneus* of Linnaeus and the *Circus cyaneus* of modern ornithologists.

It requires a practised eye indeed to be able to distinguish between the flight of the hen-harrier and that of Montagu's, if indeed there is any real distinction at all. I know all four harriers on the British List in their winter quarters and only the marsh harrier seems to have its own distinctive flight. Harriers fly nearer the ground than any other birds of prey and though I have heard them described as slow-flying birds, yet they can cover a plain surprisingly fast, as soon becomes evident when it is desired to keep a bird within focus of field-glasses. When hunting for prey in the nesting season they keep just above the scrub or marsh, rarely rising to more than five feet, though at times a bird will hunt at a height of twenty-five to thirty feet. In its winter quarters I have constantly seen this harrier searching the plains and hills, following the contour of the ground as a shearwater will follow the waves.

The hen-harrier is much less wedded to swamp and reed-beds than is the marsh harrier. Its hunting ground in Norway is of a more varied nature, including nearly every type of terrain except dense woodland. Open the ground must be, although the harrier will sometimes resort to the sparrow-hawk's wiles and approach a prey under cover of trees or bushes, or it may take a line through the forest. Very often it can be seen quartering some grassy marsh broken by pools and drier mounds, or a chain of moraine heaps with pockets of swamp between them. In its search for prey it will make an occasional sally on to the barren heights to snatch a dotterel or snow bunting.

On Hardanger Vidda Doctor Blair observed a male harrier capture a meadow pipit on the wing. The big hawk moved with surprising speed as it followed the pipit's twisting flight, and it finally made the kill rather as a sparrow-hawk would, stretching out one long talon to grip its quarry as it closed.

Compared with Norway there is much less variety of habitat in the British Isles, especially in the Orkneys. " Here there are no snowy peaks and grim deep-cut glens upon which the shadow of the golden eagle falls. . . . Instead squat hills, brown, barren and storm-swept, rise gradually from those countless lochs and lochans which twinkle in the sunlight like blue eyes in the deep brown faces of the valleys. Here corn buntings jingle incessantly by the wayside, and corncrakes rasp in the meadows ; golden plover creak mournfully and whistle plaintively alike on moss and hill-top, and, in the long northern twilight, dunlins purr noisily over the surface of the bog." To Desmond Nethersole-Thompson, fresh from the haunts of the golden eagle and the greenshank, the contrast was tremendous between the terrain chosen by the hill birds of Scotland and that of the hen-harriers on their breeding ground in the Orkneys, of which he has given us the description just quoted.

Prior to the researches of Doctor Yngvar Hagen in Norway comparatively little was known of the feeding habits of the hen-harrier. Norwegian data must always be of considerable interest, as the species there lives under conditions very different from those obtaining in the Swedish lowlands, Britain or central Europe.

In their restricted habitat in the Orkney Islands voles supply the harriers with their favourite food when they are in sufficient numbers, but in these islands young rabbits are their chief food and we may hope for the sake of the harriers that the horrible rabbit disease, myxomatosis, will not be introduced into Orkney. Their unfortunate habit of lifting chickens has not made the harriers popular with the crofters, but thanks to the rigid protection which has been accorded them, they appear to be in no danger of extermination. In places where the hen-harrier and grouse occur in the same area there cannot be any doubt that the harrier will pick up young grouse, but in the estimation of Mr. Nethersole-Thompson and other competent naturalists the game-preservers and their keepers have greatly exaggerated the damage which a pair of harriers can inflict on a moor.

That the hen-harrier when hard put to it will not scruple to attack fairly large birds is apparent from the extraordinary case recently made public in *British Birds* magazine [1] of a hen-harrier attacking a duck on the water in mid-December. The attack was witnessed off the Hampshire coast by three observers who described what they saw as follows :

We were looking at wigeon (*Anas penelope*) and mallard (*A. platyrhyncha*)— no other species of duck were present—when some 500 yards off-shore the hen-harrier

---

[1] P. R. Griffiths, G. Bundy and G. Kinsey, *British Birds*, xlvii, 1954, p. 25.

swooped low over the sea and picked up from the surface what was probably a wigeon. With very laboured flight the harrier, impeded by the duck's struggles, flew about ten yards, rising a good five feet, before dropping its burden. It then made repeated attempts to pick the duck again from the water, though it had now attracted three herring-gulls and a great black-backed gull which were mobbing it. At each approach of the hawk the duck splashed violently yet did not attempt to dive. Finally it was again picked up but dropped within a yard or so.

But to return to its feeding habits beyond our shores. When voles and lemmings are in abundance in Norway mammals may be expected to outnumber birds by more than two to one and in some instances which Doctor Hagen cites the proportion of birds to mammals has dwindled to less than 5 per cent. In these " vole " or " lemming " years the harriers breed under the most favourable conditions possible.

In " depression years ", when there is an almost complete dearth of voles and lemmings, conditions are very different. As will appear later, in such years most harriers fail to raise broods ; indeed, only a very small minority amongst the females get as far as laying. In the few nests in which the eggs hatch, the broods as a rule perish through lack of food, or, at the best, only one nestling survives, perhaps having devoured the others. Now and then the old birds succeed in rearing their young if they are clever enough to turn to bird-hunting. One pair, for example, brought off three young in the " depression year " 1943, a most exceptional occurrence for a bad season. Only a few remnants of food could be procured from this nest, but amongst them birds greatly predominated, there being three pipits, a willow wren, a grouse chick and two unidentified birds, but only one mammal, a vole. In 1946, when voles rapidly became scarce, another pair of harriers proved to be exceptionally skilful at capturing birds. They reared four, possibly five, young, despite conditions so precarious that the broods in other nests nearly all succumbed. At this nest Doctor Hagen found thirteen mammals, six mountain voles, four field voles, a water rat, an unspecified rodent and a fair-sized leveret—quite a respectable total at a time when such prey was fast becoming scarce. But the list of birds identified amongst the captures was certainly more interesting : six teal (mostly ducklings), a large wigeon-duckling, three ducklings unspecified, a full-grown willow grouse, a golden plover, a wood sandpiper, three field-fares, five other thrushes, three pipits and another small bird—in all twenty-three birds. One of the harriers had besides captured a dragonfly. It was at this nest that Doctor Hagen made a most interesting discovery. Amongst the prey was an adult teal duck with a badly united fracture of one of the wing bones which rendered it incapable of flight. More surprising still, it had been ringed in Dorset on 23rd January of the same year.

Doctor Hagen's list of prey-animals taken by hen-harriers collated from his own notes and other sources follows. It covers the period 1938-46 inclusive, though owing to war conditions not much could be done in 1940 and 1944. Of the other years, 1938, 1941, 1942 and 1945 were vole years. 1943 was a " depression year ", while in 1946 small rodents suddenly and rapidly diminished in numbers.

Lemming (*Lemmus lemmus*) .	1	Cuckoo (*Cuculus canorus*) young .	3
Water rat (*Arvicola terrestris*) .	3	Hen-harrier (*Circus cyaneus*), young	3
Field vole (*Microtus agrestis*) .	80	Teal (*Anas crecca*), mostly young	11
Mountain vole (*M. ratticeps*) .	166	Wigeon (*A. penelope*), duckling .	1
Grey-sided vole (*Clethrionomys*		Ducklings unspecified . .	3
rufocanus)	10	Golden plover (*Pluvialis apri-*	
Bank vole (*C. glareolus*) . .	4	*carius*)	7
Rodents unspecified . . .	57	Dotterel (*Eudromias morinellus*)	3
Total small rodents .	321	Greenshank (*Tringa nebularis*) .	1
Water shrew (*Neomys fodiens*) .	2	Wood sandpiper (*T. glareola*) .	4
Shrews unspecified . . .	3	Snipe (*Capella gallinago*) . .	1
Hares (*Lepus timidus*), young .	6	Great snipe (*C. media*) . .	1
Mammals unspecified . .	1	Snipe unspecified . . .	3
Total mammals . . .	333	Waders unspecified . . .	2
Snow bunting (*Plectrophenax*		Willow grouse (*Lagopus*), mostly	
nivalis)	3	chicks	18
Mealy redpoll (*Carduelis flammea*)	1	Grouse chicks unspecified . .	20
Finches unspecified . . .	45	Black grouse (*Lyrurus tetrix*),	
Reed bunting (*Emberiza schoeniclus*)	11	chick	1
Meadow pipit (*Anthus pratensis*)	5	Chick either black grouse or	
Pipits unspecified . . .	45	capercaillie . . .	1
Willow warbler (*Phylloscopus*		*Total birds*	228
trochilus)	17	Lizard (*Lacerta vivipara*) . .	2
Fieldfare (*Turdus pilaris*) .	10	*Total vertebrates* . . .	563
Ring-ouzel (*Turdus torquatus*) .	1	Dragonfly (*Linellula*) . .	1
Thrushes unspecified . .	10	Grasshoppers (*Saltatoria*) . .	1
Wheatear (*Oenanthe oenanthe*) .	7	Beetles (*Coleoptera*) . more than	3
Bluethroat (*Luscinia suecica*) .	8	Insects unspecified . . .	2
Small birds unidentified . .	27		

This list shows the hen-harrier's diet to be rich in species, amongst which all the smaller birds of the fjeld are included. None is at all well represented, however, apart from the meadow pipit, willow warbler, fieldfare, grouse chicks and ducklings. It is quite otherwise with the smaller rodents, for here two species alone make up almost the whole of the imposing total, namely the big mountain vole and the field vole.

Cannibalism was noted on three occasions, the victims being either found half-eaten in the nest or identified by fragments in pellets.

To analyse the material so far forthcoming, we find that mammals constitute 57 per cent. of the total diet, small rodents 57 per cent., and shrews and leverets each 1 per cent. Birds amount to 41 per cent. of the total. Ducks and game constituted 10 per cent. Perhaps the twenty waders should be added to the game-birds, but they are all so common that the toll taken cannot be regarded as serious. The other birds on the list (27 per cent.) are of species of no importance to the game-preserver. So far there is no Norwegian record of the harrier eating eggs. Egg shells are occasionally found in pellets, it is true, but these have been the remains of the birds' own hatched-out eggs.

Finally, to review the harrier's success in rearing broods in " good " and " bad " years on Dovre. Data from two years are not included, as opportunities for investigation were limited (1940 and 1944). The totals for 1938 are too small also, but these are included. However, the material suffices to show how dependent the harriers are upon the small rodents, a four-yearly cycle being apparent for both birds and mammals.

Year		Breeding pairs	Eggs laid	Eggs hatched	Young flew
1938	(mouse year)	6	16	14	14
1939	(depression year)	0	0	0	0
1940	No records .	—	—	—	—
1941	(vole year) .	8	37	23	19
1942	(vole year) .	9	45	24	12
1943	(depression year)	1	4	3	3
1944	No records .	—	—	—	—
1945	(vole year) .	5	24	20	15
1946	(year of decline)	6	22	18	7
		—	—	—	—
		35	148	102	70

It will be seen from the above analysis that in Norway the hen-harrier varies in numbers from year to year, the conditions being best indicated not by the number of pairs breeding but by the number of young reared. It is obvious that there is a close relation between the number of young brought to maturity and the food supply and it is significant that in the year of decline 1946 six pairs of harriers reared less than half the number of young reared by five pairs in the preceding vole year.

The proportion of eggs or young that come to nothing is large, even in the best years, as the proportion of seventy young which flew from 148 eggs goes to prove. That means a mortality of more than 50 per cent.

Hen-harriers when hunting are frequently mobbed by other birds. Nethersole-Thompson recalls one male harrier which used to work a hillside on which was a nesting colony of lesser black-backed gulls and while it was quartering the ground the gulls deafened the ear with their hoarse cries and fell like snowflakes upon the big blue hawk, which neither called nor retaliated but pursued the even tenor of its way. Curlews also harass the hen-harrier, while a merlin rarely misses an opportunity of dashing at the larger bird. A cock merlin is particularly aggressive when harrier and merlin are both nesting in the same valley. Then, as Nethersole-Thompson has witnessed, the cock merlin throws himself with eager dashing flight at the harrier. One moment he is high in the air, and the next swooping straight and true at the gliding form beneath him. The merlin's excited screams sometimes draw his mate from her eggs. Then the two little falcons will stoop, check and throw up, as they buzz round the harrier like a pair of angry hornets. When merlins, short-eared owls and hen-harriers are neighbours many a great battle takes place.

While rather silent at other times, these hawks are often very noisy about the nest. The note most frequently heard during the breeding season is the female's mew—a much higher-pitched sound than that of the buzzard—which may be rendered as *pee-ah*, *pee-ah*. Each note lasts about three-quarters of a second, and is repeated at intervals of about two seconds. Hagen regards this call as closely resembling the whistle of a drake wigeon, with which he admits he has confused it. A male bringing food to the nest calls his mate off the eggs with a subdued *tjukk-ukk*. This seems to be only a variation of the alarm note. When the nest seems in danger, the male's protest is a weak *tjukk-ukk-ukk-ukk*, delivered at a rate of about seven or eight *ukk*s to the second ; while that of the female is sharper, and may best be represented as *kekk-ekk-ekk-ekk*. Individual variation is large, the call with some birds running to ten *ekk*s to the second. Both birds are often very bold and aggressive at the nest, stooping time and again at the trespasser.

On the Norwegian fjelds conditions are not likely to allow of a harrier breeding until the next vole or lemming year after that in which it is hatched. In other words the bird must wait two or three seasons for an opportunity. Occasionally, however, a male will pair in the brown dress of immaturity. Collett noted one such on Dovre in 1884, and Hagen another in 1945.

Of the beautiful spring flight of the hen-harrier—the " dance ", as one writer calls it—much has been written, and it is certainly one of the most remarkable spectacles of the bird world. On a sunny morning in May the gull-blue male leaves the scrub with an odd flight which recalls that of a tern, his wings at times almost touching each other beneath his breast. Then, having gained height, he will soar over the marsh for a while. Suddenly he mounts almost vertically with strong, swift wing-beats, to as suddenly drop headlong, with wings pressed to his body, towards the scrub below. Recovering, the ecstatic bird rises steeply again, and once more plunges down in a breath-taking dive. Before closing his handsome, black-tipped wings, he may turn onto one side, or even somersault, and all the time he calls to his mate circling beneath him. And so the dance continues over the marsh. Sometimes the ringtail herself " dances ". The sky may be overcast, and a cutting wind searching the marsh, but still the brown hawk circles above the willow brake that will later hold her nest. There she tumbles in the air, falling like a plummet, swinging up, somersaulting, and falling again.

A variation of this courtship flight as seen in Norway was witnessed in the Orkneys by Nethersole-Thompson, who stresses the advantage to an observer of studying the courtship habits of elusive birds, for, as he remarks, they are at such times more inclined to cast caution to the winds and disclose their secrets.   He writes :

Before the eggs are laid the hen-harriers often betray the approximate position of the nest by their love of aerobatics.   The two birds will then play in the air above their nesting site.   Both will ring up to such a height that one is left wondering whether they are birds or mere playthings of the fancy.   From time to time the blue male will dive at his more robust partner and playfully buffet her as she turns over on her back to meet his onslaught.   At other times the male glides smoothly over her, dipping as he passes, or he may tumble like a raven, drifting on his side for a few yards.   Again they may pass and repass one another in ever narrowing circles until the two seem knit in one.   And from time to time the sharp courtship cry *kwee-ah* rings out as they answer one another.   Then, with a loud downward glide, either one or both birds come earthward, checking the descent when only a very few feet from the heather.   Their mood may now change and the female may drop stealthily into heather and rushes and commence to build.   The discovery of the nest is then an easy task.

BREEDING HABITS [1] :   In the storm-swept Orkney Islands the hen-harrier breeds on lonely ground which is visited only by the peat-digger or the wandering naturalist ; it is unusual to find a pair breeding away from the solitude of the hills, though an odd pair may select a site within a few hundred yards of a crofter's cottage.   For neighbours some pairs have merlins and short-eared owls ; others share the haunts of curlews and golden plovers.

A favourite nesting place in the Orkneys is a dense bed of rushes in the ankle of the hills, or a long valley of mixed heather and rushes.   Some nests are built in rank heather and are noticeably larger and higher than those built in rushes.   On rare occasions a nest will be found in a tiny hollow on the hilltops but the bird normally prefers a sheltered valley to the summit of the hills.

In Norway, according to the accounts which Doctor Hagen and Doctor Blair have given me, matters are a little different.   Hagen comments that it is remarkable how tolerant the hen-harrier becomes of human neighbourhood.   No fewer than twenty-one nests were found close to some trace of man's handiwork, such as a ditch, a fence, a snow-brake, a railway line or a station.   Five were within thirty metres of high snow brakes, which, however much shelter they afforded, certainly obscured the view.   To crown all, three nests lay within ten metres of the railway track, along which the expresses between Oslo and Trondhjem and various long goods trains

---

[1] In writing this account the nesting habits of the hen-harrier in the Orkneys are taken from Mr. D. Nethersole-Thompson's notes which he published in the *Oologists' Record*. Those which refer to Norway are from Doctor Y. Hagen's observations and from those of Doctor Blair.

rumbled several times a day, quite apart from the passing and repassing of railway personnel.

On the Norwegian fjelds the harrier usually builds amongst willow scrub, rarely less than sixty centimetres or more than a metre in height, and dense enough to conceal the sitting bird and yet not hinder her when she takes wing. Sometimes the nest is amongst mixed scrub or it may even be in birch scrub. Level ground is preferred, only two out of thirty-nine nests found by Doctor Hagen being on slopes. While an isolated birch often stands quite near the nest, the birds always choose a site at least thirty metres from the margin of the wood, and, in most cases, well beyond the forest.

Although many harriers nest on damp ground, the chosen hummock is generally dry and secure against the spring thaw, only one of the nests mentioned being flooded. Of these thirty-nine nests, thirty-five were amongst willow or birch scrub on level ground, two were on drier mounds rising a metre or two above the marsh, and two were on sloping hillsides. In 1941 two pairs of harriers built within a hundred metres of each other, while in 1943 another pair reared their young only forty-three metres from a short-eared owl's nest. A breeding place is often reoccupied in the following season, and sometimes at longer intervals. While the same mound is never chosen, as the growth of vegetation and the snow have altered its appearance, the new nest often lies only three or four metres from the old.

This occasional habit of nesting in close proximity to another pair has also been noted in the Orkneys, but more frequently the nests are separated by a mile or more. In these islands the nests vary considerably in size and structure. The outer fabric consists of heather branches of different lengths and thickness and the lining is of coarse grass and broken leaves of the rush. Now and again a few pieces of down from the breast of the sitting bird cling to the wiry heather and so give a clue to anyone searching for the nest. On occasions a feather or two may be found in the nests.

Conditions are again rather different on the Norwegian fjelds. There the nest is a scrape in the moss lined with fine grass or sedge and surrounded by a ring of willow or birch twigs or the like. On wet ground the grass-lined cup rests on a stout foundation of twigs built up to a thickness of as much as ten centimetres as a protection against damp. Occasionally fresh material is added to the nest after the eggs have been laid—it may be even after the young have appeared. A new nest will be from thirty-five to forty centimetres across, while one of the larger, built on wet ground, measured sixty-six by eighty-one centimetres. The inner cup generally measures eighteen to twenty centimetres across, and a few in depth. About the nest there is commonly a clearing about a metre square so that the bird can at once take wing if surprised.

The task of building the nest is shared by the sexes, the male collecting material while the female alone fashions the nest. At times a male will tire, leaving the work entirely to his mate. Rosenberg, the Swedish observer, notes that unattached males also build nests, which they use as roosts.

In an account of the breeding habits of this harrier which Mr. Nethersole-Thompson wrote a good many years ago he stated that both he and his friend were of the opinion that the hen-harrier is at times bigamous, but although he had strong evidence in that direction he did not consider it conclusive. He stresses the fact, however, that mortality is much greater among the males than among the females.

The date of laying in the Orkney Islands varies very much and is greatly influenced by the weather. Nethersole-Thompson found that a few pairs have laid clutches before the end of April and most hens are sitting by 10th to 15th May. In backward seasons, when the harriers have been delayed by heavy snow, the majority of clutches are laid between 15th and 25th May. In middle Europe eggs may be found from the end of April onwards but as a rule May is the month when clutches are usually laid—that is to say, as Jourdain has pointed out, about two weeks earlier than those of Montagu's harrier.

On the Norwegian highlands the hen-harrier generally lays in the closing days of May, but the date varies considerably with different birds. Some have an egg as early as 14th or 15th May, while others do not begin their clutches until well into June. The latest date recorded by Doctor Hagen for the laying of the first egg is 20th June. As an average date Hagen gives 29th May.

The eggs appear at rather irregular intervals. The first two or three must be laid at the rate of one a day, but with large clutches—and sometimes with the smaller—the last can be laid three or even four days after its predecessor. A clutch of four eggs may therefore be completed in five days, while one of five may require as many as eight. Norwegian harriers lay from three to six eggs, clutches of five or six being the most frequent, because this Raptor, like many others, nests chiefly in vole or lemming years. Of thirty-nine nests, five contained three eggs, eight contained four, fifteen contained five, and eleven contained six, the average being 4·82. In years when prey was scarce, the average clutch for four nests was 3·3, while in rodent years it rose to five. Clutches of seven have been recorded from Sweden.

In the Orkney Islands the normal clutch consists of four to six ; a five is probably the most usual sett but some hens produce six eggs regularly. If robbed a second clutch is generally laid in about a fortnight, but the number of eggs in a second clutch is smaller. When a nest is robbed a new site is chosen for the second laying.

It has been remarked that harriers' clutches include a high proportion of infertile eggs.

The eggs of the hen-harrier are bluish-white in colour and are coarse-grained. Most eggs are unmarked. A minority show spots or streaks of rust or reddish-brown. Very rarely, a clutch will be quite heavily marked. In *A Vertebrate Fauna of the Orkney Islands* Harvie-Brown refers to " two most beautifully marked " eggs, which were as well coloured as buzzards'. A clutch of four in the collection of the late J. J. Baldwin Young was quite exceptional, being blotched with rich reddish-brown. Mr. Staines Boorman has another sett of heavily marked eggs.

Norwegian eggs of the hen-harrier measure 40 to 52·8 × 32 to 40 mm. 100 British-taken eggs measure (after Jourdain) on the average 46·23 × 36·13 mm. Max. 52·1 × 38 and 49·5 × 40 mm. Min. 40 × 32 mm.

The incubation period for individual eggs is either twenty-nine or thirty days, and the bird begins to sit as soon as she has laid one or two. Young harriers therefore always differ from each other in their development. Newly-hatched young weigh twenty grams. The little creatures' large owl-like eyes are surrounded by brown rings, and as they often sit with their eyes closed, they bear a ludicrous resemblance to short-sighted people peering through horn-rimmed glasses. For the first nine or ten days the female covers the brood continuously except when she leaves the nest to take food from her mate. The young birds grow rapidly, putting on as much as twenty-five or thirty grams a day in the second week of their existence. By the third week their plumage is appearing. The ruff develops early, giving the nestling a most distinctive appearance, quite unlike that of any other young bird of prey. At the same time they move three or four metres into the scrub around the nest, where they remain for the greater part of the day. They reassemble in the nest at night time and whenever the parents bring prey, and also during heavy rain, when the female covers them.

At the age of three weeks, the sexes in a brood can be distinguished. The females weigh 500 grams and more, have larger and more powerful feet, and stay longer in the nest; the males are the smaller by 100 grams, and develop more rapidly. A most important distinction between the sexes is to be found in the colour of the eyes. At first each has a brownish-grey iris. Later this darkens in the female to a mahogany-brown, while in the male it lightens to an ash-grey with a slight brown ring round the pupil.

Young harriers attempt their first flights on the thirty-first to thirty-fifth day, the males preceding the females by two or three days. At the end of July or the beginning of August the majority of young birds are on the wing. They follow their parents for a further two or three weeks, and then fend for themselves.

From the day the female harrier begins to sit until the young are well-grown her mate provides for both her and her brood. Even before the eggs are laid the female may spend the greater part of the day waiting for the male to bring prey to her, and once the nest is completed, he rarely goes near it. The female meets him, receives the prey, and flies to a quiet place to eat it, or if she has young, bears it to the nest, while the male takes a rest or sets off hunting again. If the female is brooding, the male generally announces his return with a low *tjukk-ukk*. At once the female takes wing and begins to mew.

Later, when the eggs have hatched, the female has a look-out near the nest, such as a stone or a post. From this she watches for her mate, being able to distinguish him from other males at two or three kilometres distance, and also to tell whether he is carrying a prey. As the two harriers meet the male keeps above and slightly ahead of the female. When she draws nearer she swings towards him and calls once more. This is the signal for him to drop the prey, which she seizes as it falls. Hagen, who has often watched the " pass ", has only once seen the female miss the prey in the air. Both birds then dropped to retrieve it. When the young are on the wing the parents drop food to them in the same fashion.

Sometimes the male disappears when the young are well-grown—perhaps wearied of his duties—and the female must then do all the hunting. More than once Hagen found only the female in charge of a brood—clearly, he says, either a widow or a divorcée—and he noted that these birds never reared more than two or three young.

REFERENCES : Original Description. *Falco cyaneus* Linnaeus, Syst. Nat., 12th ed., 1766, p. 126. Type locality near London.

PLATE 24   **PALLID HARRIER**

Circus macrourus (Gmelin)

An Accidental and Rare Visitor

IDENTIFICATION : Anyone seeing the male pallid harrier for the first time must be struck by the extreme paleness of its plumage, more particularly if the grey males of the hen-harrier and Montagu's harrier are known to the observer. It may without much difficulty be mistaken at a glance for a seagull, so pure white are its underparts, the black terminal part of the primaries assisting the illusion. A closer view reveals a true harrier with long tapering wings and the fairly long yellow legs tucked under the tail. The absence of any grey on the throat or breast at once distinguishes a pallid harrier from the males of the other two species mentioned. The whole of the upperparts is pale silver-grey, including the three inner pairs of tail feathers. A white patch at the base of the tail is caused by the grey and white upper tail-coverts. There is no black bar on the wing as in the male Montagu's harrier. The easy sailing flight as the bird skims along fairly close to the ground is a sure guide to its harrier relationship. In

PLATE 24

BLACK KITE
Milvus migrans migrans (Boddaert)

PALLID HARRIER
Circus macrourus (Gmelin)

Left Figure . . Adult Male
Right Figure . . Immature Female

form it is closer to Montagu's than to the hen-harrier, and in my opinion is the most lovely and graceful of them all. The wing span of an adult male is three feet, four inches, and the total length in the flesh eighteen inches.

The female is so like the females of *Circus pygargus* and *Circus cyaneus* as to be indistinguishable in the field, and the same applies to the immature bird. The female has perhaps a more decided ruff than even the hen-harrier, and the markings of the face are more owl-like, with the white cheek patches and dark facial disc, but these are characters which do not assist identification unless the bird is handled.

The pallid harrier may be distinguished in all plumages from Montagu's harrier by the wing formula : the emarginations of the primaries on both the outer and the inner webs are higher, *i.e.* nearer the bases of the feathers ; that on the outer web of the second primary is almost or entirely hidden by the major coverts. In Montagu's harrier the emargination on the outer web of the second primary begins fifteen to thirty mm. beyond the tips of the primary coverts. The following is a brief technical description from specimens in the British Museum.

Adult male : Forehead and line over eye white ; crown and remainder of upperparts, including all wing-coverts, pale gull-grey, more smoky on the mantle. Primaries black terminally, white basally ; outer web grey towards base, browner towards tip. Secondaries pale grey on outer web and on either side of shaft ; inner web mainly white and tips white. Upper tail-coverts barred grey and white. Middle pairs of tail feathers grey like the back, remainder white irregularly barred with grey. Lores, cheeks, throat, entire underparts, axillaries and inner lining of wing, white.

Adult female : Forehead and line over eye white ; crown and mantle dark brown, feathers white at base and margined with rufous-buff. Rest of upperparts dark brown ; upper tail-coverts white barred or spotted with brown ; quills mainly brown, barred with darker brown, basal half of inner web cream. Innermost rectrices brown, outermost rufous-buff with three or four broad brown bars. Underparts, including thighs, creamy-white or buff streaked with rufous-chestnut.

Eye in fully adult yellow, brown in immature. Bill black, cere greenish-yellow, legs and feet bright orange-yellow.

Young birds have a white patch over and beneath the eye and a blackish patch on the cheeks. Upper surface dark brown margined with rufous, particularly on the lesser wing-coverts. A distinct collar or ruff of rufous or buff. Underparts rich rufous-buff, either uniform or more or less streaked with dark chestnut or rufous-brown. Upper tail-coverts white, unstreaked.

The only way to distinguish the young birds of the pallid and Montagu's harriers from one another is by the position of the emargination in the second primary as described above.

OCCURRENCES IN GREAT BRITAIN : The first example of the pallid harrier to be recorded in this country was the male bird killed on Fair Isle, Shetland, on 8th May 1931 by George Stout and sent to the Royal Scottish Museum. It was reported to have been present on the island for at least a fortnight before it was secured, and was recorded by P. H. Grimshaw in the *Scottish Naturalist*, 1932, p. 1.

The second to be obtained was an adult male shot in east Dorset about twenty miles from Ringwood on 11th April 1938 (cf. F. C. R. Jourdain, *British Birds*, xxxii, p. 150). This was the first record for England.

The third record is that of an adult male seen but not secured on Fair Isle on 6th May 1942 by George Stout, who had already procured the first Scottish specimen. This bird, which remained for a week on the island, is the second recorded from Fair Isle. The information was made public by George Waterston in *British Birds*, xxxviii, p. 230.

The fourth record refers to an immature male shot at Hutton Cranswick, near Driffield, Yorkshire, on 2nd October 1952 (one of two flying together). It was identified at the British Museum and preserved in the Mortimer Museum, Hull (cf. *British Birds*, xlvi, p. 259).[1] It was said to have been accompanied by another bird when shot, but whether of the same species we are left to conjecture.

DISTRIBUTION ABROAD : The pallid harrier has a wide range in eastern Europe and western Asia, ranging from the Baltic States to central Siberia and south to Roumania and southern Russia. The bird has bred sparingly in northern Germany (Mecklenburg) in 1952,[2] and during the same year there was a small invasion into Sweden, where a few pairs nested. Doctor Stresemann tells me that in 1953 and 1954 the pallid harrier has not reappeared in Germany. There were also records from Denmark.

Concerning the Swedish records Count Gyldenstolpe, in reply to my enquiry, writes to me as follows :

The occurrence of *Circus macrourus* as a breeding bird in 1952 was absolutely accidental. As far as I know four or five pairs bred on the islands of Öland and Gotland that year. Their occurrence in Sweden was certainly caused by mere accident. At the beginning of May 1952 there was a heavy belt of fog and warm air over the Baltic and several people actually observed a flock circling around the coasts of those two islands. When the fog-belt disappeared the harriers simply remained in Sweden, where they bred. The birds kept to the same environment as *C. pygargus*, viz., open meadows. Several trustworthy ornithologists here in Sweden

---

[1] A misleading reference to the number of pallid harriers which have occurred in Britain is made in *British Birds*, xlvi, p. 259. In an unsigned article it is suggested that the specimen which T. H. Nelson in his *Birds of Yorkshire* recorded from Flamborough was in reality an example of *C. macrourus* rather than *C. pygargus*. That is clearly disproved by Nelson's reference to the wing formula, which is obviously that of Montagu's harrier.

[2] A special article on this event appeared in the *Journal für Ornithologie*, 1953, pp. 290-299, with three plates.

made observations in 1952 but up to date nothing has been published.[1] The harrier did not, so far as I know, breed in Sweden either in 1953 or 1954.

It seems obvious from the above information from most reliable sources that the much advertised westward extension of the pallid harrier's breeding range has not been maintained.

As an accidental visitor in the past to Sweden the pallid harrier is certainly rarely recorded. I am again indebted to my friend Count Gyldenstolpe for the following Swedish records of *C. macrourus* :

Specimens Preserved in the Royal Natural History Museum, Stockholm

Gotland, 9.5.1834 (mounted)
Norrköping, 16.4.1863 (mounted)
Vaglehem parish, —.8.1895 (skin)
Österby, Dannemora, Upland, September 1914 (mounted)
Vagnhärad, Södermanland, 2.5.1952 (mounted)

Specimens Recorded from Observations (*from* Fauna och Flora)

Gimo, Province of Upland, 1924
Strömsberg, Province of Västergötland, 29.4.1952 (♀ adult)
Dannemora, Province of Upland, 10.5.1953 (♂)
Also seen at the same locality from 21.6.1953 to the middle of July of the same year but no sign of breeding.

RANGE OF THE PALLID HARRIER IN RUSSIA [2] : Within the European countries of the U.S.S.R. the pallid harrier, so Madame Kozlova informs me, ranges north to about Tula, Kazan and Ufa, and in the south to the Black Sea and the steppes on the northern borders of the Caucasus. Westward its range extends to Dobrudja, Podolia and the basin of the Pripiat River in western Ukraine. In Siberia the pallid harrier penetrates in the north to Sverdlovsk (formerly Ekaterinburg), Tiumen, Omsk, Minussinsk and Krasnoiarsk. We find it also inhabiting the western Altai. Its southern range reaches the Aral Sea, the middle course of the Syr-Daria River, the northern fringe of the Tian-shan Mountains and Ferghana. Single individuals are on rare occasions recorded during the winter months from the Crimea, north-western Caucasus, the mouth of the Volga and the Aral-Caspian steppes.

[1] Professor Doctor Portmann, Secretary-General of the Tenth International Ornithological Congress, informs me that a full account of the Swedish nesting of *C. macrourus* will be published in the *Proceedings* of the Congress by C. F. Lundevall and E. Rosenberg, but only a brief summary of this is available at present.

[2] Kindly communicated in December 1954 by Madame E. Kozlova, Academy of Sciences, Leningrad, from the latest Russian surveys.

Circus macrourus is commonly found in dry open steppes, and sometimes in river valleys. In the forest-steppe zone of the U.S.S.R. it is to be met with sporadically. From the plains it penetrates at times to the mountains to about 1000 m. (3300 feet) above sea-level in both the Caucasus and the Altai ranges.

In the Ukraine, the Caucasus and Turkestan spring migration takes place in the second half of March and the beginning of April. The autumn migration in the European area of the U.S.S.R. begins about the middle of August, but single birds may be met with up to the beginning of October.

The winter range of the pallid harrier will be discussed under the next heading, when an attempt will be made to follow it on its journeys to far distant lands, with special reference to the population which has its breeding habitat in eastern Europe.

MIGRATIONS AND HABITS IN WINTER QUARTERS: The migrations of the pallid harrier are very extensive, for the bird ranges all over Africa south to the Cape, the Asiatic population reaching India, Ceylon and Burma. It has even been recorded from the mouth of the Yangtse River in China, while stragglers have been reported from many countries in Europe outside its breeding range, including the British Islands, Norway, Denmark, Holland, Belgium, Luxembourg, France and Switzerland. It is remarkable that a bird whose regular breeding area lies mainly east of longitude 20° E. should find its way in the non-breeding season to the Guinea Coast of West Africa. I recently summed up its distribution in the western half of the African continent in the following words [1]:

To West Africa it is a winter visitor from Europe. It may be expected in October, when it appears in some numbers in the French Sudan, spreading southwards all over the vast area of grassy plains from the borders of the desert to the coast, where it remains until the end of March and sometimes into April. Large numbers have been observed in the vicinity of the Niger near Niamey in mid-October. The birds will travel great distances and have been noted in every political area, reaching the coastal plains at many points. They are equally well known in the province of Zaria in Nigeria from mid-October to April, and on the grass prairies of Owerri province as they are in Gambia or the Accra plains of the Gold Coast. It may, in fact, be encountered in the whole of the West African grasslands and orchard-bush.

The pallid harriers which breed in eastern Europe must have a strong tendency to migrate in a south-westerly direction, as many find their way into the African continent via Tunisia, where J. I. S. Whitaker considered it "undoubtedly the commonest of all the harriers, being particularly abundant during the periods of migration, when considerable numbers of the species may sometimes be observed together". Mr. Whitaker added that it also occurred in Algeria, though sparingly, throughout the winter months. It can then only be found south of the Atlas.

[1] *Birds of West and Equatorial Africa*, 1953, vol. i, p. 304.

Personally I have never seen the pallid harrier in winter in Tunisia, Algeria or Morocco, in all of which countries I have travelled extensively both north *and* south of the Atlas ranges. It is said to be the commonest of the harriers which regularly pass through Malta on passage but is rare in the western Mediterranean generally; the farther east we travel the more abundant does it become.

Colonel Meinertzhagen wrote of its status in Egypt that it is the most abundant harrier in that country, passing through on both migrations and many remaining the winter; it is equally numerous in autumn, winter and spring in the Faiyum, Wadi Natrûn, Kharga and Dakhla oases. It has often been observed in the desert many miles from water. The date of its arrival in Egypt from the northern breeding grounds in Europe and Asia is early September and it leaves again at the end of April. In his much more recent *Birds of Arabia* (1954) Meinertzhagen refers to this species as the usual harrier of the country—and of Sinai also—observing that it has been obtained almost throughout Arabia from late September to early May, but mainly from February till April. Presumably, therefore, some remain in, at any rate, the south all the winter, and do not trouble to cross the Red Sea, though others must assuredly do so to gain the African continent by way of Eritrea, the ornithology of which country is so imperfectly known.

As a rule the spring passage of birds of prey is everywhere more noticeable than the autumn passage, but in Darfur,[1] where Admiral Lynes and Willoughby Lowe spent over eighteen months studying the migration of birds through that Province, the opposite was the case, for where this species was concerned " there was no noticeable spring migration-passage ". On the other hand, the pallid harrier was a common winter visitor from east to west in the plains north to Meidob, in Jebel Marra up to, but rarely so high as, the upper zone. There Lynes found it equally at home quartering the arid prairies and bush as the glades of the woodland country: it was found to live chiefly off insects, reptiles and small birds. At Zalingei the species began to arrive about 7th October, all apparently young of the year until 18th October, when adult males began to be seen. Lynes continues: " The place was then alive with Pale Harriers in all types of plumage, much to the anxiety of the domestic chicks and their owners, although the swarming orthopterous insects were actually their chief diet. Most, if not all, of these birds passed on farther south and normal winter proportions were assumed at the end of the month. The winterers all emigrated in March."

What direction the pallid harriers take on their southward journey after leaving the great prairies of Darfur can only be conjectured; I have been struck by the fact that in their recent work, *Faune de l'Equateur Français*, Doctors Malbrant and Maclatchy make no mention of this

[1] Admiral H. Lynes: " Birds of North and Central Darfur ", *Ibis*, 1925, p. 411.

species whatsoever, not even in the savanna area which their work covers. It appears therefore that the Great Equatorial Forest proves an effective barrier to this harrier's passage, though one might have expected it to occur in the savanna country of the Middle Congo, by which to reach the plains of Angola and of south-west Africa.

On the other hand Doctor James Chapin's notes [1] on this bird are of the greatest interest. " The pallid harrier," he writes, " reaches the north-eastern savanna of the Congo basin every year in October and November, and is common there during the whole dry season, leaving again about March. The earliest date of arrival noted was October 18. . . . This species hunted not only over open marshes, but went flying everywhere low over the drier parts of the savanna, alighting occasionally on the ground or on termite hills, very seldom on trees. . . . The brown females and young, of course, greatly outnumber the adult males, but even these latter are frequently to be seen."

Commenting on how this harrier reaches South Africa Chapin observes that the birds must either go round the forest or else go over high above it, without any stop. It seems that the latter is the most likely, for in the Lower Congo—as already observed—this harrier appears to be wanting and Chapin failed to find a single individual from Kwamouth to Boma in December or January. Examples which were eventually collected elsewhere were found to have been living on weaver birds, lizards and mice.

It is, I think, safe to conclude that the pallid harriers which pass through Darfur either spread out along the northern borders of the Congo forest or else continue to Uganda and Kenya, in both of which territories the bird is well distributed between October and February. There it is subject to local movements and rarely remains longer than a month in any one locality, so Sir Frederick Jackson observed when he governed the former Colony. He considered that these movements of the pallid harrier are influenced by the growth of grass, and possibly to some extent by its prey becoming wary and accustomed to its regular up-to-time methods of hunting. Its habitat in that area consists of grassy plains, marshes, open bush-veld and the outskirts of forests and woods. Sir Frederick remarked how this harrier would for a month at a stretch appear punctually at a certain hour to search a favoured place for its prey, such as a marshy water course, the shady side of a belt of trees or even the rose garden at Government House. Just as Sir Frederick learned to watch for its visits at a particular hour, so, with more reason, would the mice !

Directly it detects anything suitable it stoops with startling suddenness in a downward somersault-like twist just as if it had been shot. One bird was seen to take a wagtail out of many hundreds crowded together on the shore of the lake by Entebbe.

The pranks of the pallid harrier on the shores of Lake Naivasha are

[1] *Birds of the Belgian Congo*, i, p. 599.

recounted with some bitterness, for the bird is a great source of annoyance to a gunner " lying on his stomach in a cloud of midges " waiting until the duck on the lake come within his range.   There this harrier could frequently be observed, skimming along above the water and making stoops at the ducks and coots as they sat congregated on a sandspit quietly preening their feathers, to scatter them in all directions, for the sheer fun of the game. Never was this harrier seen to attack seriously the numerous waterfowl or waders on the lake.   On the other hand, it has earned for itself a bad reputation in Uganda as a chicken thief, at which pastime all the members of the genus seem to be adept.

In his delightfully written book on the birds of Somaliland Sir Geoffrey Archer has expressed the opinion that the pallid harriers' main migration route follows the African coast, and as far as Eritrea that may well be so for great numbers pass through Asia Minor and Egypt at the appropriate seasons, and yet do not appear to follow the Nile.   In British Somaliland they are evidently rather rare but farther west in Ethiopia they are numerous.   Von Erlanger obtained specimens in Abyssinia, as it then was, in many localities between October and January, and it was in that country that Major R. E. Cheesman describes finding about twenty harriers assembled in the evening to roost on the ground in long grass and on a slight rise.   " They came singly and must have come in from long distances as they had not been hunting there during the day, and the last few arrived when it was almost dark. . . . The next evening exactly the same assembling for roosting took place after sunset."   With the exception of one marsh harrier all those seen—and three were secured—were pallid harriers, most of which had been feeding on big grasshoppers.   Major Cheesman adds that the pale harrier is plentiful on the big grass plains on the high plateau during the winter months, getting scarce towards April, and they are not seen after June until the following September.   When present they work all day ceaselessly patrolling the long grass.   Many must continue their long flight south, for Doctor Austin Roberts reports that it is a common migrant to South Africa, where, owing to its predilection for chickens, it is not looked upon favourably by most country people.

I will end my account of this harrier in Africa by quoting a graphic passage from the pen of my old friend Sir Geoffrey Archer, who has known the bird intimately in Somaliland, Uganda and the Egyptian Sudan, of which three territories in turn he has been Governor and Commander-in-Chief, devoting all his leisure hours to the study of birds.   Here is how he pictures it on the Somali coast :

Let us now for one moment watch one of these attractive birds in its temporary surroundings.   Probably it will first be seen quartering some open piece of sandy or stony ground near the sea or one of the many stretches of salt-encrusted hard-pan. Or, again, it may be observed hovering over the gleaming white sand-dunes which are fringed on the seaward side with the tamarisk-like and evergreen *harun* bush.

In this setting of dazzling blue and white, propelled by the leisurely beats of long pinions, it sails silently along with slow, undulating, and even hesitant flight, on the look-out for the lizards, voles, locusts, frogs and larger insects on which it feeds. So easy, so graceful, and withal so buoyant is the flight, that it is a joy to behold. Suddenly it checks, mounts into the air a few feet to gain a better view, and then drops to earth on some hapless quarry which has rapidly darted into hiding. But it does not stop long. Rising with uplifted wings and perhaps a small rat in its claws, it takes a few powerful strokes and then makes off for the nearest sand-mound to perch on a stone or on some hummock amid the grassy flats, there to devour its prey. At other times it will be seen resting on some low stunted thorn-bush but two or three feet from the ground. It has been said that harriers are protected at night by a powerful sense of hearing. This may be true, seeing that otherwise on their ground perch they would fall an easy prey to the many jackals and mongooses which prowl about the Guban day and night.

Winter and spring travels in North Africa have made me familiar with both Montagu's and the marsh harrier, but not till I visited Cyprus in 1954 had an opportunity occurred to observe the pallid harrier and the hen-harrier at the same time. The first of the former species was seen on 16th March ; it had evidently just arrived, sailing over the forest of Salamis close to the ruins of the ancient Roman city. The extreme whiteness of its face and underparts, without a tinge of grey, and the wonderfully buoyant flight so well described by Archer, proclaimed its identity, though we had to look twice to make sure we were not meeting for the first time a lovely unknown gull. Later in the same month more were encountered in other parts of the island ; one fine male in particular gliding to and fro along a hillside on the Karpas peninsula kept to a regular beat, turning at exactly the same spot as if tied to a measured mile. As it turned from side to side with a slightly rolling motion the palest grey of its upperparts came into view, the grey wings gracefully set off with black tips, but there was no black line on the secondaries, this distinction separating it at once from a male Montagu's. Marshlands are uncommon in Cyprus and both hen- and marsh harriers were seen more often quartering the cornfields and the dry slopes of the hills. Moreover, it was not uncommon to see hen-harriers flying along or above the immense precipices which are such a feature of the northern range of mountains ; the birds must then have been two or three thousand feet above the maritime plains. The pallid harrier has been seen in Cyprus until the late summer but no actual case of nesting has been recorded ; it passes through the island in considerable numbers in the month of April on its way to its breeding grounds. It is of interest to record that when the late Charles Horsbrugh was collecting in Cyprus he shot a pallid harrier whose crop contained the remains of a little owl.

BREEDING HABITS : Curiously little is known about the breeding biology of the pallid falcon and even in the Soviet Union few appear to have found its nest or written about it. A bird of the open steppes, as

Madame Kozlova has stated, it has been found nesting in Kasachstan in rank grass. A nest discovered north of Lake Balkash by Dolgushin on 20th June 1947 was situated on a rather steep slope of a small river valley in the steppe country. On that date it contained three highly incubated eggs and two newly hatched young.

Some years earlier Spangenberg found a nest of this harrier hidden in grass on the lower reaches of the Syr-Daria River, on an island near Djulek. This nest contained very small naked young on 31st May 1936. In this area the nests are usually placed in feather-grass (*Stipa*) steppes. They are untidy structures, mostly stems of grasses just thrown on the ground to form a scanty lining.

The full clutch consists of four to five eggs, though a clutch of six has been recorded. F. C. R. Jourdain has described the eggs as sometimes unmarked, but more often spotted or blotched with reddish-brown and not infrequently quite heavily marked. He remarked that only a small proportion of the eggs in collections has been authenticated, most of them having been collected by peasants and identified by appearance. He gives the average size of eighty eggs (thirty-seven by E. Rey) as 44·77 × 34·77 mm. Most of those taken were collected in the latter part of May.

Madame Kozlova informs me from Russian sources that the female alone is said to incubate, and that the period of incubation is unknown. The male has been observed to feed the female on the nest and the newly hatched young, but when the young grow older both parents feed them. The pallid harrier is single-brooded. There is no record of the food actually brought to the young but in Russia the parent birds are known to feed mostly on small rodents (*Stenocranius*, *Microtus*, *Arvicola*, etc.) and also on lizards and birds ; larks, quail, waders of various kinds and young ducks have been identified. Large insects such as beetles, grasshoppers and locusts are likewise preyed upon.

It is seldom that an opportunity arises to study the nesting of *Circus macrourus* in western Europe but such a chance occurred in May 1952, when, as recorded earlier in this essay, a small influx of pallid harriers took place in south-east and central Sweden, Denmark and north Germany. It was followed by breeding of at least six pairs in south-east Sweden and some investigations were made on this happening by Messrs C. F. Lundevall and E. Rosenberg.[1]

In a summary[2] issued in advance of the main publication recording their work it is stated that most of the females were breeding in immature plumage and although the full adult dress is not assumed until the third year, it has been ascertained that the pallid harrier will breed at the age of one. The authors describe a very remarkable case which came to their

[1] *Proceedings of the Tenth International Ornithological Congress*, 1954 (1955).

[2] I am indebted to Professor Portmann, Secretary-General of the International Congress, Basel, for supplying me with this information in advance of the publication of the *Proceedings*.

notice in which the young were fed by two different species of harriers. At one of the nests the female pallid harrier was lost when the young were still in the nest.   The male continued to bring food to the nest but very frequently the young were fed by a female Montagu's harrier (*C. pygargus*), which received larks passed to her in flight by the male pallid harrier. This extreme case of two different species bringing up a family was made even more remarkable by the fact that the female Montagu's harrier was also accompanied by a male Montagu's, which *also* brought food to the same nest.   The young appear to have successfully fledged and flown, for it is recorded that one of them, which left the nest on 15th July, was found dead a month later, *i.e.* on 12th August, at the south-easternmost point of Sweden, at Utlängan in Blekinge.

From the same breeding colony in Sweden there appeared in Yorkshire two young birds, one of which—a male in its first winter plumage—was shot on 3rd October 1952 bearing a ring marked with its country of origin. It seems only too likely that others met with the same fate.

REFERENCES :   Original Description.   *Accipiter macrourus* S. G. Gmelin, Nov. Comm. Acad. Sci. Petropol., xv, 1771, p. 439, Plates viii and ix : Veronezh to River Don.

Genus *ACCIPITER* Brisson

GOSHAWK

Accipiter gentilis (Linnaeus)

PLATE 25 (adult)
PLATE 26 (immature)

1. Goshawk

Accipiter gentilis gentilis (Linnaeus)

A Rare Visitor to England and Scotland which breeds very sparingly

PLATE 27

2. American Goshawk (Eastern race)

Accipiter gentilis atricapillus (Wilson)

A Rare Accidental Vagrant

DISTINGUISHING CHARACTERS OF THE EUROPEAN AND AMERICAN GOSHAWKS [1] :   The North American goshawk, *A. gentilis atricapillus*, differs from the nominate race of Europe in the following particulars. The upperparts in the adults of the former are much greyer, varying from slate-grey to deep grey, whereas in the European bird these parts are always suffused with brownish.   The underparts of adults of the American race are whitish, freckled or vermiculated, not barred, with ashy greyish-brown or brownish-grey, while the European form has the entire under-parts whitish heavily barred with dark brown.

[1] The comparison between these two races has been made for me by Doctor Herbert Friedmann of the Smithsonian Institution, Washington, from material in the United States National Museum.

PLATE 25

GOSHAWK (Adult)
Accipiter gentilis gentilis (Linnaeus)

PLATE 25

IDENTIFICATION :   The goshawk is an imposing, powerful-looking bird, little inferior to a buzzard in breadth of wing.   Overhead its long-tailed, round-winged outline at once brings to mind the sparrow-hawk, but it is considerably larger, the females being as much as two feet in length in comparison with about fifteen inches in a female of the smaller species.

As so commonly occurs amongst birds of prey, the female goshawk is much larger than her mate, often exceeding him in weight by a good half-pound.   Otherwise the sexes, unlike those of the sparrow-hawk, cannot be distinguished.   In maturity both are greyish-brown above, with closely barred whitish breasts and pale eye-stripes fully as prominent as those on female sparrow-hawks.   A feature to observe is the white under tail-coverts. As H. L. Meyer noticed over a century ago, the beauty of a goshawk's plumage is enhanced in life by " a kind of bloom ", which, like the equally delicate tints on eagles and buzzards, fades soon after death.   On adult birds this " bloom " can best be described as " ashen " or " pearly ", and at large, or on the falconer's glove, they appear much greyer than would be expected from a study of museum specimens.   A striking feature of an adult goshawk—and one that contributes much to its air of ferocity—is the deep orange iris.   In birds of the year the eye is no redder than that of a sparrow-hawk, while nestlings lack even the yellow tint, the iris thus early in life being a pale greyish-green.   Immature goshawks are more richly coloured than the older birds, the wings and mantles almost rufous, the buff breasts spotted and streaked—*not* barred—with drop-shaped markings of brown.

LOCAL DISTRIBUTION :   As the late Doctor Eagle Clarke pointed out when editing the 3rd edition of Howard Saunders' *Manual of British Birds*, adult examples of the goshawk are rarely obtained in the British Isles, but immature birds have occurred at long intervals in autumn and winter, and sometimes in spring.

There are, in addition, a very few occasions when the bird has bred or attempted to breed in this country.

Two records are accepted in *The Handbook* for England.   The first record refers to a pair which attempted to nest in Normandy Park, Lincoln-shire, in 1864,[1] the female of which was shot.   The second instance refers to a nest with four eggs found at Westerdale near Grosmont, Yorkshire, in May 1893.[2]   The female was shot at the nest by a keeper and the skin is preserved in the Norwich Museum.[3]   The male was not seen.

Mr. Witherby then dismisses the Scottish breeding records with the sentence :   " Also appears to have bred formerly in Spey Valley and elsewhere."

[1] *List of British Birds*, by J. Cordeaux, p. 18.

[2] *British Birds*, i, p. 319.

[3] The possibility of this bird having escaped from captivity is discussed at length in Nelson's *Birds of Yorkshire*, i, pp. 341-342.

There is no doubt that the goshawk *used* to breed in a wild state in Scotland but whether the English records quoted were genuinely wild birds is much more doubtful, despite the argument used in *British Birds* when recording the first example to be killed. George Lodge was personally convinced that the birds which have nested in England were examples which had once belonged to falconers, but no proof of that is obtainable.

Of fairly recent years the goshawk has bred several times in southern England and successfully reared its offspring, one of which was shot almost as soon as it could fly and sent to the Natural History Museum, where I examined it in the flesh. As this site, or at any rate the area concerned, may be occupied again, it will not be more closely specified. Mr. Philip Brown tells me that a pair which he knew at the nest personally were wild enough in behaviour. There does not appear to have been any reliable evidence of nesting since 1951.

There is no record from Wales, even of a casual visitor.

The Scottish breeding records have been far from easy to disentangle, owing to the confusion which existed between the goshawk and the peregrine. The authors of *The Birds of Scotland* were at pains to discover the genuine records from earliest days, and from their account I have compiled the following list of records which they considered were probably authentic. I have omitted any references prior to that of Pennant.

1769.   Said by Pennant to have bred in the forests of Invercauld.

1795.   Said by Rev. John Lapslie to be a native of Campsie in Stirlingshire, where it " builds its nest upon trees in sequestered places ".

1784.   Colonel Thornton in his *Sporting Tour* mentions seeing some eyries of the goshawk in the forest formed by Glenmore (near Grantown-on-Spey) and Rothiemurchus.

1849.   St. John wrote in his *A Tour of Sutherlandshire* (1st edition) that he knew of it breeding regularly in the forest of Darnaway.

1862.   St. John, in his *Natural History and Sport in Moray* (1st edition), observes that " the goshawk is nearly extinct in this country ", noting that " a few years ago it bred regularly in the forest of Darnaway and it may still do so " and adding (in confirmation of Colonel Thornton's statement in 1784) that " it also breeds in the forest of Glenmore near Grantown-on-Spey ".

1865.   More records it breeding in the woods of Castle Grant and in the woods of Dulnan.

1871.   Two eggs said to have been taken in April at Balmacara, West Ross.

1883.   J. G. Millais had two goshawks in his collection from the woods at Rohallion, Perthshire, shot by a keeper. They had bred for several years previously in the woods. These specimens are now in the Perth Museum. In Millais' opinion these were the last goshawks that bred in the country, and Rohallion was the last stronghold of both goshawks and kites in Scotland.

As vagrants or passage migrants goshawks are reported from time to time in Scotland, usually in winter, November, December and January, but there have been occurrences also in August, March and April. Most of these refer to the eastern or northern counties : Sutherland, Caithness, Inverness, Banff, Aberdeen, Angus, Fife and Perth. There are records also from Shetland and the Outer Hebrides. The birds are rarely seen on the west coast of Scotland or the Isles but there have been records from Mull and Skye, and also from Kirkcudbright on the mainland, all of which are mentioned by Miss Baxter and Miss Rintoul in their account of the birds of Scotland.

To Ireland the goshawk is an even rarer visitor. Ussher and Warren in their *Birds of Ireland* (1900) wrote that " three instances have been mentioned but no Irish specimen is known to exist ". The three instances —Ussher in his *List of Irish Birds* considered their authenticity doubtful— are as follows :

A bird shot in 1844 by Lord Meath's keeper at Kilruddery, Wicklow. Seen in the flesh by Doctor J. R. Kinahan.

An immature male obtained in the autumn of 1846 in Co. Longford. Mentioned in Watters' *Birds of Ireland*, 1853.

An immature male seen in 1870 (March, April or May) in Ballymanus Wood in Wicklow. Recorded in the *Zoologist*, 1870, p. 2283.

The authors of the new *The Birds of Ireland* (1954) do not trouble to specify the above possible occurrences, merely stating : " There have been three or four reports of goshawks in Ireland. Three of these refer to occurrences that took place over seventy years ago." They add that the occurrence of a goshawk reported at Tearaght Lighthouse, Co. Kerry, in October 1922 in the *Irish Naturalist*, xxxii, p. 7, was not fully substantiated. The latter may, as Witherby notes in *The Handbook*, equally have been an example of the American goshawk, and so for that matter may at least one of the three enumerated above ; the American bird has been obtained on four occasions in Ireland and is just as likely to occur as a vagrant as is the European bird, now that breeding goshawks no longer occur in Scotland.

On the east coast of England the goshawk used to be of not infrequent occurrence. In 1912 George Bolam, who classed it as a rare casual visitant to Northumberland and the eastern borders, noted that it had occurred at least sixteen or seventeen times in the district, the majority in Northumberland, but that oddly enough there was no record from Berwickshire across the Border. In Yorkshire the bird has occurred at intervals, generally in the vicinity of the coast. A number of records are tabulated in Nelson's *Birds of Yorkshire* and it has occurred since. In a more recent work, the *Birds of Norfolk* (1930), Rivière mentions seventeen occurrences but nothing more recent than 1901. Since then Jim Vincent and Hugh Wormald have recorded a bird at Hickling in November and Dereham in December 1942. The latest record of which I have a note is of an adult bird seen flying in from the sea on 29th June 1952 by Mr. R. A. Richardson at Cley Bird Observatory. The date is exceptional.

In Suffolk it is seldom recorded and Doctor Ticehurst in his *History of the Birds of Suffolk* (1932) drew attention to the decrease of the goshawk in East Anglia. He could record only three since 1884, one of which was taken at sea.

South of Suffolk—in Essex and Kent—the bird is even more rarely met with.

RECORDS OF THE AMERICAN GOSHAWK IN BRITAIN : The American goshawk, *Accipiter gentilis atricapillus*, has been recorded once in the Scilly Isles on 28th December 1935 ; once in Scotland on the flanks of Schiehallion, Perthshire, about May 1869 ; and four times in Ireland, *i.e.* an adult female in Galtee Mountains, Co. Tipperary, February 1870, a female near Birr (or Parsonstown), King's Co., about 1870, an adult male near Strabane, Tyrone, on 24th February 1919, and an adult female at Carnakelly Bog, near Athenry, Co. Galway, on 23rd December 1935 (within a few days of the Scilly Isles example being recorded on the 28th).

DISTRIBUTION ABROAD : The European goshawk, the most powerful member of a large and widespread genus, is to be found in every wooded country of the Holarctic Region. Over so wide a range local variations in size and colour naturally occur, and upon such differences a number of racial forms have been based. While some of these lack general recognition amongst ornithologists, others are more distinctive, and one or two, such as the handsome American bird, *Accipiter gentilis atricapillus*, for some time ranked as full species ; the latter was so designated in Cleveland Bent's *Life Histories of North American Birds of Prey*. The typical species *Accipiter gentilis gentilis* is that found in Britain and was described by Linnaeus from Scandinavia, with type locality the Scandinavian Alps. There it is resident and far from rare, ranging northwards to the limits of the big timber. It becomes more plentiful south of the Arctic Circle in both Norway and Sweden, although persecution has reduced it to the point of scarcity in many places. Old returns of awards paid for the destruction of " vermin " show that the number of goshawks breeding in these northern forests varies from season to season, a marked increase being apparent whenever game becomes plentiful.

In Denmark and Holland the goshawk at one time seemed perilously close to extinction, but more recently it has been regarded with greater tolerance. Shooting and trapping never made such disastrous inroads on the breeding stock in France, Germany and central Europe, and most of the great woodlands in these countries, like those of the western Russian

PLATE 26

GOSHAWK (Immature)
Accipiter gentilis gentilis (Linnaeus)

Governments, continue to harbour this fine hawk. As immature goshawks from central Europe are mostly lighter in colour than those from further north some ornithologists regard the birds of the former region (*i.e.* Europe north to East Prussia and Denmark) as belonging to a valid race, originally named *gallinarum* by Brehm, with type locality Germany, but this, in the opinion of Hartert, Witherby and others, cannot be upheld.

Goshawks are generally distributed throughout the Iberian Peninsula to within sight of Gibraltar, being most plentiful in Portugal and Spanish Castille. Whether the typical race crosses the Pyrenees, and how far it penetrates into Spain, cannot be determined from the scanty material available. Breeding birds from central Spain and Andalusia are certainly smaller and darker than French examples, and agree rather with the race indigenous to Sardinia and Corsica, described by Kleinschmidt as *Accipiter arrigonii*.[1] The Italian peninsula, on the other hand, and Sicily besides, lie within the range of *Accipiter gentilis gentilis*.

Beyond the Adriatic this is replaced by a second dark race, *A. g. marginatus*, in the Balkans, Asia Minor and the Caucasus. Largest and palest of the European goshawks is *A. g. buteoides* Menzbier, of northeast Russia, which should perhaps be considered rather an Asiatic form, since it ranges farther to the east than to the west of the Urals. The Asiatic distribution of the goshawk is very wide, extending from the limits of the forests to the Himalayas and eastwards to include Japan. Of the races described from this vast area, undoubtedly the most interesting is the almost white *albidus* of Menzbier, found in Kamchatka.

Of the status of the goshawk in Africa little has been published except that it breeds in Morocco, whence Jourdain, among others, received eggs.

WINTER RANGE: Being largely resident throughout its breeding range, the goshawk has been encountered in midwinter as far north as latitude 70°. As will be shown later, many juveniles, with perhaps a few adults, do move south in autumn, and goshawks have then been recorded from Malta, Egypt, Tunisia, Algeria,[2] Palestine, Persia and India.

HABITS: In the breeding season goshawks spend a great part of the daylight hours high over the forest, where they cannot fail to attract notice. They keep more to the trees as the spring draws on, and are, for such large birds, surprisingly inconspicuous. While hunting the forest a goshawk flies low, and is as much at home as a sparrow-hawk, the long tail enabling it to turn sharply as it swerves among the more close-set trees. Like a sparrow-hawk too, it regularly keeps watch from some favourite perch commanding a wide stretch of forest or marsh, ready to dart upon any luckless bird or mammal espied by the keen orange eyes. Often the quarry—whether sighted from the air or a perch—falls to the first onslaught.

[1] Cf. Witherby, *Bull. B.O.C.*, xlvi, p. 5, and *Ibis*, 1928, p. 641.

[2] Hermann Grote, " Paläarktischen Zugvögel in Afrika", *Mitteilungen aus dem Zoolog. Museum Berlin*, xvii, 3, 1931.

Or the hawk may glide along behind it until the formidable talons can be brought into play—a mode of attack known to falconers as " raking ".

For lesser victims death must be mercifully swift, but larger creatures succumb only after a more or less prolonged struggle. Yngvar Hagen traced the fortunes of one luckless victim in the forests along the divide between Norway and Sweden. Here a goshawk had closed with a caper-caillie on the wing above a small marsh. As it lost height, the capercaillie, a big male, ploughed through the willow scrub for more than thirty yards, leaving a trail of down to mark its course. When at last forced to earth, the big game-bird had apparently lain still long enough for the hawk to strip it of nine quills and as many tail feathers, besides much of its body plumage. Other handsome feathers littered the peat beyond, lost in a second tussle as the wounded capercaillie revived. Then it had floundered across the marsh and into the forest, still firmly gripped by the hawk, which even succeeded in wrenching out more flight and tail feathers. The trail ended in a dense thicket of young spruce-firs, a good sixty yards from the spot where the capercaillie had been struck. There it had escaped its assailant, but too badly mauled to fly. A hare seized by a goshawk can travel as far as this capercaillie, and falconers have noticed that the hawk will then clutch at the grass with its disengaged foot in an endeavour to halt the quarry.

Lord Lilford, who knew his birds of prey well, described a hungry goshawk as ready to " go at anything that offers a chance ". British records of prey taken by goshawks, other than those entered in falconers' game-books, are naturally few. Continental observers, more fortunate in their opportunities, have compiled long catalogues of animals killed by these destructive creatures, ranging from full-grown hares and male capercaillies to titmice and a lesser shrew. These show that mammals form a con-siderable proportion of a goshawk's food. Material gathered about Norwegian nests, chiefly by Yngvar Hagen, yielded the remains of 101 mammals as against 306 birds, and a lesser number of autumn and winter records gave an almost similar result. The squirrel always figures promin-ently amongst the furred quarries of the goshawk. In Hagen's list for the breeding season it is represented by thirty-five examples, followed by the hare with twenty-five. Of the smaller mammals the field vole appears to be the commonest victim in Norway (twelve in Hagen's list), while lemmings are as rarely taken as shrews. The weasel and stoat appear one and four times respectively in Hagen's account, which suggests that they are excep-tional captures. From other sources we learn of fox cubs surprised outside the earth, and Jourdain cites a Continental record of a wild cat, doubtless a kitten.

As might be expected, birds killed by goshawks in the breeding season are chiefly forest-haunting species. Besides thirty-five pheasants, Hagen specifies one hundred game-birds in his analysis of prey-remains collected at that time of year : ten capercaillie (four of them adult males), nineteen black grouse, thirty-five willow grouse, twenty-seven " grouse " (probably all willow grouse) and nineteen birds, mostly chicks, which were either capercaillie or blackgame. Norwegian goshawks also account for large numbers of thrushes in spring and summer, the majority of them nestlings or fledglings. At one time or another Hagen himself has discovered amongst the litter around goshawks' nests the remains of all the six thrushes indigenous to Norway, as well as those of all the *Corvidae* of the northern forests. Waders, duck, owls and kestrels all fall victim in their turn and it is stated that a goshawk will often wipe out a brood of one of the smaller Raptores, sometimes before they make their first flights.

In autumn and winter goshawks' " kills " are more scattered, and so less easily discovered, than in the breeding season. According to Hagen's personal notes, the proportion of game now rises to as much as two-fifths of the total, or—if birds only are considered—to more than half. It is his experience that goshawks will travel as much as two miles from the nest in search of prey, while in winter they tend to cover even more ground in their hunting.

In captivity goshawks can be trained to attack animals many times their size. Readers of Richard Burton's little-known work on falconry[1] will remember Joseph Wolf's grim portrait of one of these birds harrying a fleeing gazelle. To Burton's Baluchi hosts, the goshawk was the " hawk-king " (shabbaz),[2] most esteemed of the falconer's birds and procurable only—and that at great expense—in the hills along the North-West Frontier.

Falconers of all periods have been interested in this hawk. Charles St. John in one of his books[3] observes that it is rather a favourite with some falconers and is flown with great success at rabbits and even hares. He mentions that when flown at birds, the goshawk, if unsuccessful in its first dash, is apt to perch on the nearest tree or hedge and there remain patiently as if expecting the reappearance of its prey. This habit and its less interesting manner of flight rendered it less a favourite with that naturalist than the peregrine. In support of his opinion St. John adds :

The temper of the trained goshawk, too, is said to be more capricious and change-able and to require much humouring. Our ancestors, who understood hawking far better than we do, had the same opinion of the goshawk and I find in an old book on the subject the remark that " she is very choice and dainty, and requires to have a nice hand kept over her ". The same work remarks the habit of a goshawk of taking to a tree when disappointed in her first flight. This kind of hawk, however, seems to have been much used for all sorts of game, and particularly for the larger kinds, such as the wild goose, etc.

Those who may be interested in training a goshawk should consult

[1] *Falconry in the Valley of the Indus*, 1852.
[2] Burton points out that the peregrine was all but unknown in the valley of the Indus.
[3] *Natural History and Sport in Moray*, p. 242.

the long account contributed by Mr. J. G. Mavrogordato to the *Bulletin of the British Ornithologists' Club*[1] entitled " Flights with a Trained Goshawk ", in which the author gives much valuable information on the goshawk as a hawking bird. I once had the pleasure of seeing Mr. Mavrogordato's goshawk in action and shall not easily forget the impression of grace and power which this fine hawk made upon me.

But to return again to the ways of the wild bird. By all reports, the old goshawks are comparatively sedentary. It seems equally certain that the yearlings in most years undertake quite extensive migration, those hatched in Scandinavia wandering as far as the Mediterranean. Schaanning, who spent more than a decade in Arctic Norway, noted a regular passage of goshawks through the Pasvik forests between mid-August and late September.[2] The native stock is then reinforced by a varying number of pale birds, presumably of Siberian origin, some of which remain to winter. According to Kolthoff and Jägerskiöld,[3] some of the goshawks which leave Scandinavia in autumn return as early as February, and the vernal immigration is commonly over by March. The same two authors note that in " grouse years " some young goshawks do not move south on the onset of cold weather.

In Scandinavia, while goshawks are at all times most plentiful about woodlands, many appear in open country after the breeding season is over. In autumn it is not unusual to see some of these big hawks about the Norwegian coasts at Jaederen and Lister, unlikely spots for goshawks under ordinary circumstances but rich hunting grounds for birds of prey when the southward migration reaches its height. It is at this time of the year also that goshawks make their way into the birch woods high up the fellsides and well above their breeding haunts.

Compared with the other large woodland hawks, buzzards and kites, a goshawk seems anything but a noisy bird. The alarm note is a hoarse *kek*, repeated five or six times within the second, and louder and deeper-toned than that of the sparrow-hawk. The male's voice is the higher-pitched. At many nests the birds make little protest, and one female kept complete silence. When the hawks feel secure, their usual note is a long-drawn *kee-ah*, *kee-ah*, compared by Tucker to a buzzard's wailing, though not so prolonged. A low *whee-u* from the female Hagen believed to be the " begging " note of hunger. Nestlings, he found, resent intrusion on the nest with a sharp, whistling *kikk*, *kikk*, *kikk*, while the fledged young call for food with a penetrating *kee-kee*.

While many of the observations in this account of the goshawk have been made by naturalists of repute in northern Europe, it must not be overlooked that this fine bird of prey is also resident in the Mediterranean

---

[1] *Bull. B.O.C.*, liii, 1933, pp. 218-238.
[2] *Östfinmarkens Fuglefauna*, p. 54.
[3] *Nordens Faglar*, p. 172.

area, where the late Lord Lilford, an ornithologist of international reputation, was one of the first to study it. He frequently came upon it on the pine-clad sierras near Madrid and had in his collection eggs of the species from the stone-pine country along the lower Guadalquivir.

In Andalusia, where Irby considered it rare, it shows a decided partiality for haunts about swamps or near running water. Colonel Irby knew of a nest in a marshy wood near Gibraltar and one seen by Doctor H. M. S. Blair in the sierras further inland actually overhung a swiftly-flowing stream. How seldom the goshawk is actually seen, though it is known to inhabit the locality, is recounted by Colonel Willoughby Verner in his book.[1] He too found it nesting in Andalusia in the midst of the almost impenetrable jungle which covers the deep " sotos " or marshes in the wood-land districts. He first found the nest in 1871 and in 1903 goshawks were still haunting the same place, if not the same tree, even though the " soto " had been cleared and drained.

The breeding race of the goshawk in Spain has never been satisfactorily settled. Harry Witherby allied those from the south with *A. g. arrigonii*, the Sardinian race, but those from the north and from the western borders have never been collected and the race is undetermined. The Duque de Medinaceli[2] considers that the goshawk emigrates from central Spain and even from Granada (which lies high up) in winter, but that it is sedentary in the extreme south.

The goshawk has likewise been recorded as a breeding bird in northern Morocco. The eggs in the Jourdain collection from this area are excep-tionally small. This is likely to be the same race as the one which occurs in the south of Spain and is equally likely to be resident and non-migratory. I have never seen it during my travels in Morocco and it must be restricted in its range to the forested areas of the Atlas.

BREEDING HABITS[3] : Winter has barely passed—even in Norway it is still March—when goshawks show above the trees on the first of the flights which so grace their courtship. Soon they become very active, particularly in warm, sunny weather with light winds, and their aerial displays may be looked for, day after day, until the nest is ready for eggs. Sometimes the pair do little more than circle together over the forest, but even so they cannot but impress. In a more elaborate display flight the bird repeatedly mounts and loses height, often holding the wings stiffly above the body rather as a wood pigeon does. In another, the two hawks swing backwards and forwards with noticeably deliberate wing-beats, which, as Tucker pointed out, resemble " the long, slow strokes " of a harrier. At the same time they spread their under tail-coverts until the

[1] *My Life among the Wild Birds in Spain*, p. 173.

[2] *Aves de Rapiña y su Caza*, Madrid, ? 1925, p. 88.

[3] This full account has been specially written for this book by Doctor H. M. S. Blair, who has made use of many of Doctor Hagen's observations.

white feathers stand out on either side. The male sometimes brings his display to a close in a headlong stoop to the tree-tops below.

Goshawks sometimes breed in the striped plumage of immaturity, but only very exceptionally, and Hagen believes that most Scandinavian birds do not find mates before they are two or three years old.

An experienced forester or gamekeeper rarely has much difficulty in locating any goshawks' nests within the woods under his care. Long acquaintance with the big hawks has taught him that, unless shot or trapped, a pair will return every year to a favourite stretch of forest and there rear a brood in one of the two or three nests they have built. He knows too that he must not be content with the destruction of only one of the birds, for the survivor is sure to find a new mate. Even if he succeeds in killing the entire family, another pair will sooner or later put in an appearance and, as often as not, repair one of the old nests. Indeed, should a nest be thrown down, the newcomers may build on the same fork. One pair of goshawks, finding the pine that held their old home cut down, built afresh on the ground beside the stump, although there were many suitable trees close by.

While the goshawks of northern Europe generally favour pines as sites for their nests, tall birch trees are almost as frequently selected amongst the higher-lying Scandinavian forests. Poplar and oak are also recorded, both from south Norway. In central and southern Europe goshawks' nests have been found in a greater variety of trees, both evergreen and deciduous. Major Congreve[1] heard of two on tall, solitary pines in central France, and conifers are preferred on the sierras near Madrid. The only nest recorded by Irby[2] from the vicinity of Gibraltar was in an alder, while one examined by Doctor H. M. S. Blair further inland was in a black poplar, a tree to which birds of prey appear to be very partial. In the great Roumanian forests Kirke-Swann and McNeile[3] found goshawks breeding in limes and a kind of sycamore.

Whatever its species, the tree selected is very likely to be one with a trunk forking into tough, arm-thick limbs amongst which the nest can be firmly secured. Almost as frequently the goshawk, like the sparrow-hawk, builds close against the bole, where two or three stout branches grow close enough together to form a support. A typical nest will be half-way up the tree, or at the most two-thirds, in contrast to that of an osprey, which is often affixed to the topmost branches. While these hawks often build as much as sixty to seventy feet up in tall, well-grown trees, they sometimes decide upon a site no more than fifteen or twenty feet from the ground.

In Witherby's *Handbook* Jourdain described the nest of the goshawk as " built partly if not altogether by the female ". Vagn Holstein,[4] on the

---

[1] *The Oologists' Record*, xxv, p. 5.
[2] *Ornithology of the Straits of Gibraltar*, 2nd ed., p. 185.
[3] *Two Ornithologists on the Danube*, pp. 27 and 36.
[4] Duehögen, *Biologiske Studier over Danske Rovfugle*, i, 1942.

other hand, makes the remarkable statement that a new nest is entirely the work of the male, and that the female only assists in the repair of an old structure. The nests are built of branches and twigs of varying size, the majority of them about half an inch in thickness. The eggs lie in a shallow bowl of finer twigs, lined with green leaves, or, in the north, with fresh pine or spruce foliage. One nest seen by Hagen was padded with grey witch-hair lichen (*Usnea*), and occasionally the birds resort to flakes of bark for the lining. A Spanish nest was lined with leaves of the black poplar in which it was built.

Newly built nests are not particularly large—no more than twenty-five centimetres high, and about seventy-five to ninety in width, with egg-bowls six to eight centimetres deep and thirty centimetres across. One measured by Hagen was rather more bulky, being seventy-five centimetres broad, 120 centimetres long and fifty-five high. Long after incubation has commenced, and even when the young are well grown, the hawks continue to enlarge the nest, chiefly with newly plucked foliage, and Hagen notes that they can sometimes bury the eggs with disastrous results. As earlier mentioned, these solidly built nests are often utilized again and again. One visited by Hagen had been built up, through four or five seasons, into a compact mass a metre high and of equal breadth, and Doctor H. M. S. Blair climbed to one as large on the Pasvik. Yet more massive was the first nest John Wolley inspected. " I found it to be of prodigious thickness," runs the account in *Ootheca Wolleyana*. " As I stood in the branches on which its lower part rested, the level of the top was some inches above my head." [1]

Occasionally the old nest of some other bird of prey serves as a foundation for that of a goshawk. On the other hand, in the absence of the hawks, their nest may find another tenant. In Arctic Norway this may be a Lapp owl or a rough-legged buzzard ; farther south, the Ural owl, rarely, and the common and honey-buzzards, both frequently, have all been recorded as temporary occupants.

Goshawks and buzzards will occasionally breed in fairly close proximity, as Mr. James Taylor discovered in two large forests in western Germany.[2] One goshawk's nest was found within 200 yards of that of an occupied buzzard's nest, while in another forest two buzzards' nests were discovered, one 300, the other 500 yards from the nest of a goshawk. The two buzzards' nests in this forest were almost half a mile apart.

Within the Arctic Circle the first goshawk's eggs are generally laid in the second week of May. Farther south in Scandinavia, the birds are three or four weeks earlier, one nest in southern Norway containing an egg on 9th April. While some of the goshawks of southern Europe lay in March, others are very little in advance of Scandinavian birds. Eggs

[1] *Ootheca Wolleyana*, i, p. 75.
[2] *British Birds*, xl, 1946, p. 89.

brought to Congreve by a French gamekeeper had been laid in the closing days of April, and the clutch recorded by Irby from near Gibraltar had yet to hatch on 15th May. Farther to the east, on the Danube, Kirke-Swann and McNeile[1] found fresh eggs on 27th April, only three days before the first young were seen.

Colonel R. F. Meiklejohn found nests in Esthonia on 7th May with four eggs incubated about a week, and describes in his diary another massive nest—built in a pine on a hillside near Corte—of the Corsican race, *A. g. arrigonii*. Unfortunately, he omits to mention the date, which would have been of interest.

Goshawks lay from two to six eggs, four being the normal clutch. It is interesting to note that with this species the size of the clutch does not appear to vary markedly according to latitude, sets of five and six eggs being as unusual in Norway and Sweden as they are in Roumania.

The eggs of the goshawk lack gloss, and vary in shape, some being pointed, others ovoid. When freshly laid they show a faint tinge of blue in their white ground colour, but this disappears with incubation. The great majority are immaculate. Occasionally one, or even a whole clutch, will be found with small blotches of rust-coloured pigment, but such specimens are as rare as they are with the marsh harrier. John Wolley first called attention to a very interesting variety with curious " vermiform " markings of pale olive, which had " the character of those occasionally seen on the eggs of ducks ".[2] As Jourdain and others have pointed out, goshawks' eggs tend, on an average, to be smaller in the southern part of the species' range than in the north. The average of twenty-five Finnish eggs measured by V. Pousan was $59 \cdot 64 \times 45 \cdot 68$ mm. Central European eggs were smaller, sixty from Germany averaging $57 \cdot 3 \times 44 \cdot 7$ mm. (Moebert and F. Groebbels), and Spanish examples least of all, with an average of $56 \cdot 3 \times 43$ mm. The largest eggs known to Jourdain came from Lapland, and measured $65 \times 47 \cdot 9$ and 62×51 mm.[3] Hagen gives the weight of a fresh egg as 60 grams.

Goshawks' eggs soon become soiled in the nest, especially in wet weather. In south Spain they have been found so deeply stained as to resemble incubated eggs of one of the grebes. It is interesting to note that the eggs of the booted eagle, which also lines its nest with fresh leaves, are often as heavily discoloured.

According to Holstein, goshawks lay at intervals of three days. In northern Europe at least, incubation commences with the first egg. As the bird at first broods intermittently, the embryos in the earlier-laid eggs develop slowly, and the whole clutch hatches within at the most two or three days. The incubation period for individual eggs appears to be rather

---

[1] *Two Ornithologists on the Danube*, p. 39.
[2] *Ootheca Wolleyana*, i, p. 77.
[3] Jourdain in Witherby's *Handbook*.

variable, the normal being from thirty-five to thirty-eight days. While the male goshawk has occasionally been found incubating, the major share of the long task falls upon his mate. From the first, the male hunts for both. When successful, he calls the female off her eggs to receive the prey at some place at a little distance from the nest. As they meet he drops his booty, which she either seizes aloft or, more usually, retrieves from the ground. Each female has several regular feeding places, generally stumps or mounds, to which she resorts in turn. While she is feeding and exercising herself, the male warms the eggs.

Individual goshawks vary in their behaviour at the nest, some remaining on the eggs until the tree is struck, others taking wing at the first alarm, even when incubation is far advanced. Once flushed, they mostly keep well out of shot, and it is almost unknown in Europe for a goshawk to show as bold a front in defence of its clutch as American birds so often do. The sole exception, to Doctor Blair's knowledge, was a particularly reckless female which inflicted an ugly scalp wound on a Norwegian as he climbed to the nest.

When just out of the shell young goshawks weigh from thirty-five to forty grams. In high latitudes the female covers them almost continuously until they are about eight or ten days old. A little over a fortnight later, it is possible to distinguish the females of the brood from the males, for they are much the heavier, weighing on an average 1200 grams as against 850, and the more strongly built. The males, however, mature more rapidly, and can use their wings at seven weeks, five days before the females attempt to fly. During the first weeks of the brood's existence, the old male does the hunting, while the female breaks up the prey and shares it amongst the young. Later, when they can safely be left, she too goes foraging. Should she be away when her mate returns, he lays his " kill ", more or less thoroughly plucked, on the nest, and then flies off. If the female is killed while the young are small, the male rarely attempts to feed them, although he continues to bring prey to the nest. The brood will then gradually starve to death in the midst of an abundance of food. In one nest from which the female had been shot, Schaanning found two of the small young savagely pecking the third.

In Norway young goshawks occasionally leave the nest towards the close of June, but July is usually well in before the majority are on the wing. For about a week they haunt the neighbourhood of their old home, but by September they may have wandered as much as a hundred miles away.

REFERENCES : Original Description. *Falco gentilis* Linnaeus, Syst. Nat., 10th ed., 1758, p. 89 : " Habitat in Alpibus " ; restricted type locality Scandinavian Alps.

Note on the American Goshawk

PLATE 27   *Accipiter gentilis atricapillus* (Wilson)

The following brief account of this bird in America is from the pen of Doctor A. Wetmore[1] :

The goshawk, one of the fiercest and most destructive of our birds of prey, exceeding some of the falcons in this respect, inhabits the forests of the north and of the western mountains. It comes south sporadically from the far north during winters when there is a failure of its food supply, but at other times seldom is seen except along our northern border. Its flight is swift and powerful and I have seen it easily overtake grouse and other fast-flying birds on the wing.

In the north the goshawk eats Arctic hares, lemmings and ptarmigan. In its southern invasions it is the foremost enemy of the ruffed grouse, so that in the year following a goshawk flight there always is noted a decrease in these game birds.

It kills with the greatest ferocity, so that any creature marked as its prey may escape only with difficulty. While it ranges the country on the wing when hunting, it also has the habit of watching quietly from a perch until prey appears, when it dashes out to pounce upon it. It is relentless in its pursuit and when its quarry takes to heavy cover, the goshawk often enters the thickets and hunts on foot.

With these propensities, naturally this hawk is highly destructive to poultry, seizing chickens and bodily carrying them away. When its hunting instincts are aroused, it seems to lose all sense of fear, so that it will return for chickens even after having been stung with shot. It does not hesitate to attack other predatory birds and will fight with large owls until both combatants are killed.

This is one of the hawks trained by falconers that have been used extensively in hunting.

In its periodic invasions from the north it spreads in hundreds through the Northern and Central States. At such times many are killed by hunters.

The goshawk builds bulky nests of sticks in either conifers or deciduous trees, but usually in heavy forest. The bird is fierce in defence of its home and will not hesitate to attack a human intruder.

The eggs vary from two to five, with three or four as the usual number. They are pale bluish white, often unmarked, but sometimes with a few spots of brown. The call is a shrill note sharply repeated, being heard principally in the breeding season. The young in the first fall have the undersurface streaked like the immature Cooper's hawk.

Two forms are recognized. The eastern goshawk . . . paler in color, breeds from Alaska, Quebec and Nova Scotia south into British Columbia and the northern United States, extending south as far as western Maryland. In its sporadic southern flights it comes into the Central States and irregularly into the Southwest. The western goshawk nests in the Pacific coast region from Alaska south to California and northern Mexico.

It is of course the eastern race of the American goshawk which has occurred in Britain (cf. p. 234).

REFERENCES : Original Description. *Falco atricapillus* Wilson, Amer. Orn., vi, 1812, p. 80, Plate 52, fig. 3 : Philadelphia.

[1] An extract from *The Book of Birds*, by A. Wetmore and others.

PLATE 27

AMERICAN GOSHAWK (Eastern Race)
Accipiter gentilis atricapillus (Wilson)

SPARROW-HAWK

PLATE 28

Accipiter nisus nisus (Linnaeus)

A Resident breeding bird in all four countries of Britain which has its numbers reinforced in winter by Continental visitors. Also a Passage Migrant.

IDENTIFICATION : The male sparrow-hawk is easily described but so swift is its flight that when on the wing there is small opportunity of noting its colouring. An adult bird has the crown of the head and the entire upperparts slate-colour with some white mottling on the nape. The wings are like the back, but the tail, which is noticeably long, is greyish-brown tinged slate, with four or five dark bars across it. The throat is pale buff streaked with brown, while the rest of the underparts is buff closely *barred* with reddish-brown and dark brown. The face and cheeks are rufous ; sometimes the chin is nearly white but more often buff. The iris is orange. The legs and feet are yellow and the middle toe is very long and slender. The cere is greenish-yellow.

By far the best character is the barred, not streaked, under surface, which can usually be seen as the bird flashes by.

The female is a much larger bird than the male, the difference in the size of the sexes being striking. In plumage she is altogether browner on the upperparts with only a tinge of slate in many examples except on the crown, which is slate-colour. There is less rufous and more brown on the cheeks. The whole of the underparts below the throat, which is like that of the male, is whitish or pale buff banded with dark brown. There is usually a rufous patch on the flanks and often a considerable amount of rufous on the breast. The under tail-coverts are barred. The tail is browner than in the male and less grey. The axillaries and under wing-coverts are strongly barred with dark brown. The soft parts are as in the male.

Young sparrow-hawks are brown above with rufous margins to the feathers, the underparts white barred with rufous-brown. The iris is yellow. Both sexes are known to breed in their first summer plumage.

It cannot be too often stressed that the European sparrow-hawk is liable to considerable variation in the tone of its plumage and also to a lesser extent in the intensity of its barring. When the late Mr. Kirke-Swann bestowed a new name on the sparrow-hawk of Ireland[1] a heated controversy took place at the meeting of the British Ornithologists' Club, when Mr. Swann, Mr. Harry Witherby and myself were the principal speakers.[2] Mr. Swann contended that the Irish sparrow-hawk, which he named *Accipiter nisus hibernicus*, was duller and darker than *Accipiter nisus nisus*, that the barring below was heavier and closer, and that in size it was noticeably smaller. His action came in for considerable criticism at the time, mainly on account of the poor material at Mr. Swann's com-

[1] *Bull. B.O.C.*, xliv, 1924, p. 79.
[2] *Bull. B.O.C.*, xliv, 1924, p. 93.

mand. Twenty-six years later, with a much larger series for comparison, this race was judged on its merits by the British List Committee and their findings published.[1] The race was not accepted as valid, the Committee observing : " It is well known that the sparrow-hawk, in both sexes, shows much individual variation in the colour of the mantle, the barring underneath and the amount of red on the underparts of the male. The darkest bird examined came from Sweden (terra typica of *Accipiter nisus*) and whilst admitting that many dark birds come from Ireland, so also do pale ones."

Finally Mr. Witherby added a note on this matter in *The Handbook of British Birds*.[2] He observed : " Birds (of both sexes) from Ireland and also Great Britain tend to be slightly darker than Continental examples, but there is too much individual variation to justify the separation of the British bird as a distinct race."

In fairness to Mr. Swann, who was a known authority on the birds of prey, it may be mentioned that the controversy has not entirely died with the findings of the List Committee, and it may be that *Accipiter nisus hibernicus* will yet become the name for the resident sparrow-hawks of the British Isles, not of Ireland alone.

LOCAL DISTRIBUTION : Throughout England and Wales the sparrow-hawk is evenly distributed and despite considerable persecution is still tolerably common. Being for choice a woodland bird it is naturally scarce in open moorland country, where its place is adequately filled by the merlin. With the exception of the kestrel it is probably still our commonest bird of prey, and with the disappearance of gamekeepers on so many sporting estates, its numbers are likely to increase. Not that the sparrow-hawk ever did much damage to game, though chicks would fall victim when opportunity occurred, and every gamekeeper's gun and trap are against it. In well-wooded counties such as Devon it is frequently to be seen but in the more open county of Cornwall it occurs only in small numbers and has evolved a somewhat different method of nest building in the treeless country in the west. Probably there are more sparrow-hawks in the wooded parts of Wales than in any other area in Britain. In Norfolk and Suffolk they will never be permitted to become numerous so far as the breeding population is concerned, for in these game-rearing counties the sparrow-hawk is looked at askance. The country, however, is well suited to its requirements.

North of the Scottish Border its numbers decrease to some extent but it nests in every mainland county, with the possible exception of Angus. The authors of *The Birds of Scotland* state that it is nowhere an abundant species and is naturally less common and more sparsely distributed where trees are few, as in the north-west Highlands and Caithness. It occurs

[1] *Ibis*, 1950, p. 138.
[2] 1938 edition, p. 79, footnote 1.

in a number of the islands, to which Miss Baxter and Miss Rintoul give a reference in their standard work, but is nowhere common. Two or three pairs are reported to breed regularly on Mainland in Orkney. To the Shetlands and Outer Hebrides it is now only a bird of passage, though it used to nest sparingly in Unst and in Lewis.

From the up-to-date information supplied by Colonel C. F. Scroope in *The Birds of Ireland* it would seem that the sparrow-hawk is more abundant in that country than it is anywhere in the rest of Britain, with the possible exception of Wales. He reports that it is " very common and widespread in woodland areas, where it usually outnumbers the kestrel " ; the latter, however, predominates in the wild and mountainous areas. The sparrow-hawk nests on the Mullet but not on the marine islands of the west, with the exception of Achill.

DISTRIBUTION ABROAD : The breeding range extends in Europe as far north as the forest growth, *i.e.* to about 69½° N. in Norway, whence it ranges eastwards through Lapland, the Baltic Provinces and north-west Russia to western Siberia, merging with an eastern race east of the Yenisei River.

In the south its breeding range reaches the Mediterranean but it is said to be an uncommon bird in Spain except in winter and during migration. It breeds, however, in the vicinity of Gibraltar and is resident in Andalusia and probably sparingly throughout the Peninsula.[1] In the north of Portugal it is common and resident and the late Mr. William Tait had eggs from various parts of Portugal sent to him when he was resident in Oporto. Eastwards the southern range of the typical race follows the northern shores of the Mediterranean basin to Asia Minor, whence it extends eastwards north of the Caspian and Aral Seas in the direction of Dzungaria. That is a very rough distribution of *Accipiter nisus nisus*.

In the winter the population from the extreme north moves southwards. Swedish birds take a south-westerly course and some have already reached Belgium and northern France by September and others central France in December. The population of southern Europe is then considerably increased by arrivals from farther north. It is doubtful whether British-bred birds leave these islands except under extreme conditions and even then they can reap a rich harvest of starving Passerine birds.

It has been said that the European sparrow-hawk winters in North Africa. I am doubtful if it does so to any great extent. Actual specimens are very rare in collections. I know of one from Tunisia, and Whitaker believed that a few must come from Europe to account for the additional

[1] It does not appear to have been definitely settled which is the breeding race of sparrow-hawk in Spain. H. F. Witherby wrote in *Ibis*, 1928, p. 641, that specimens which he examined from south and central Spain did not appear to differ from a series of the typical form but added that few were definitely breeding birds. There is little doubt that a number of *A. nisus nisus* migrate to southern Spain in winter and only a series of summer-killed birds will enable the resident race to be determined. I do *not* think they will turn out to be the North African *punicus* as has been suggested.

numbers seen during the migration season in that country.   Farther west
Irby noticed some " passing " the Straits of Gibraltar in March but he
does not mention in what direction.   In the Balearic Islands the sparrow-
hawk occurs occasionally on migration, and during the winter, but according
to the late Captain Philip Munn, is not common and does not remain to
breed, though erroneously stated by earlier foreign writers[1] to be resident.
There is apparently some migration through Corsica, as birds are said to
be more common there during the winter months.   There is, however,
an indigenous race on the island.   This hawk also passes through Malta
in spring and autumn but is evidently scarce, though formerly said to be
fairly common.

In the recently published *Birds of Arabia*, Colonel Meinertzhagen
states that the typical subspecies visits Arabia from early October to late
March from Aden to Muscat and Riyadh and throughout the Hejaz, but
is not very common.   On the eastern side of Africa it is reported to be a
scarce visitor in winter to the Sudan and Abyssinia, one having been taken
in the Arussi country south of Harar.   There is no known occurrence in
Somaliland.   Sir Frederick Jackson only once saw a bird in Kenya—on the
lower Molo River in February.   South of that there is but a single record—
a European sparrow-hawk, verified as such by Herr Grote, obtained between
Kilimanjaro and Meru in Tanganyika Territory.

From the above it seems certain that *Accipiter nisus nisus* does not
normally occur south of the Sudan and even there it is extremely rare.
Admiral Lynes had several notes of sparrow-hawks " of sorts " seen in
Darfur in late autumn and winter, which he concluded must be wintering
individuals of the European bird, but he failed to obtain any, and, as he
himself wrote, their species and status must remain doubtful.   In Egypt,
on the other hand, they were often seen from the end of October to the
end of November near Port Said, evidently birds on passage.

The latest review of the European and Asiatic sparrow-hawks appeared
in Colonel Meinertzhagen's *Birds of Arabia*, where a distributional map
indicates the range of the six subspecies recognized.   Leaving aside the
Ethiopian representatives, which the present writer would keep distinct
under the specific name *rufiventris*, there are two principal Palæarctic
subspecies : *Accipiter nisus nisus* throughout the greater part of Europe
and western Asia, and *Accipiter nisus nisosimilis* ranging over the rest of
Asia to the Pacific, with a wide zone of intermediates in between.   Then
there are two insular races : *granti* in Madeira and the Canaries, and
walterstorfii in Corsica and Sardinia.   To these Meinertzhagen would
add *melanoschistus* from the Himalaya and Tibet.

Even excluding the Ethiopian forms it will be seen from the above
what an immense area is covered by the range of the sparrow-hawk *Accipiter
nisus* in Europe and Asia.

[1] Barceló and Ponseti.

HABITS : In the preceding section much is included which would normally have appeared under the heading of Migration, but in this species winter quarters and migrations are so closely bound up that it has been found easier to deal with both subjects together.

As Mr. Witherby pointed out a long time ago, the recovery of over fifty British-ringed nestlings in the country of their birth indicates that our island birds are sedentary. Continental birds certainly are *not*, and already there is a short list of migrants ringed in Heligoland and Holland which have been recovered in Flintshire, Kent (two), Somerset, Essex, Yorkshire, Stafford and (a Dutch bird) Co. Monaghan, Ireland.

In recent years four particularly instructive recoveries have been reported by Miss Elsie Leach of sparrow-hawks captured on migration :

Ringed as Adult on Passage to Britain		*Recovered Abroad*	
Gibraltar Point, Lincs	6.11.50	Valdres, Norway, 60° 52′ N.	30.6.52
Fair Isle, Shetland	17.9.51	Vendée, France	21.10.51
Gibraltar Point, Lincs	16.9.51	Jutland, Denmark	1.4.52
Gibraltar Point, Lincs	16.9.51	Valdres, Norway	14.7.51

Passage migrants from overseas have been recorded from time to time from the Inner and Outer Hebrides, Orkney, Shetland, Fair Isle and the Isle of May, but on the whole, as Miss Baxter and Miss Rintoul have emphasized in their *Birds of Scotland*, there is little evidence of movement of this species at our island stations. In Ireland Major Ruttledge proved by ringing that a small-scale leisurely movement probably takes place through the Mullet in September and October, but Irish sparrow-hawks have even less reason to migrate than those from the Scottish Highlands and we can be fairly certain that the majority are sedentary.

On the east coast of Scotland there is a decided immigration of Continental sparrow-hawks in the autumn and they have been taken at Norfolk light-stations during September and October. In the adjoining county of Suffolk Ticehurst found that in some years " considerable numbers " arrived in autumn from overseas ; he instances among others the year 1911, when remarkable numbers came into east Suffolk and a keeper on part of an estate killed over a hundred.

Among Doctor Ticehurst's patients in his practice at Lowestoft were many members of the fleet of herring boats based on that port and he was therefore in an excellent position to receive any birds which might be captured when the trawlers were at sea. On many occasions he had sparrow-hawks brought ashore which had been caught on the boats, generally between 18th September and 9th November. He was struck by the fact that females greatly predominated over males, and that has been so in the isolated " invasions " which have occurred on our coasts.

The return spring passage does not come much under notice in East Anglia.

The autumn migration of small Passerine birds over the little island of Heligoland is invariably accompanied by sparrow-hawks and the extent to which the unfortunate migrants are harried by these hawks has been described by the old naturalist of Heligoland, Heinrich Gätke :

As early as the middle of August, simultaneously with the arrival of the young chats, the first young sparrow-hawks make their appearance. These young birds continue to arrive during the whole of September and October, the first old examples not reaching here before the beginning of the latter month ; these old birds, as well as scattered young birds, may still be met with during the whole of November.

Gätke's account continues :

Like all diurnal birds of prey this species performs its migration journeys during daylight, the birds arriving suddenly as though they had dropped from the clouds, and mostly in large flights, but not until late in the afternoon ; they seem to have travelled a very long distance for their crops are perfectly empty. . . . The sparrow-hawk flies during its migration at a very great height. . . . On one occasion during an October afternoon I saw this hawk arriving in exceptionally large numbers. The sky was covered uniformly with high and somewhat striped white clouds, or rather cirri, which form the most favourable background for perceiving an object at a very great height, when viewed vertically overhead. My attention was attracted upwards by some descending hawks. Both I and " Old Oelk ", who was in my company, saw at various heights above us many of these birds descending together in small circles of twos and threes. As their numbers kept continually increasing we directed our attention to portions of the sky where no birds were to be seen, and observed, after a short and strained look upwards, some scarcely discernible small dark points which after a short time we recognized to be hawks.

Gätke estimated that these tiny specks in the sky were at not less than 5700 feet from the ground when they came first within human vision, and at what altitude they had performed their migration can only be conjectured. It will be remembered that Swedish birds, according to Professor Lönnberg, take a south-westerly course on their migration, and the birds which pass in such numbers over Heligoland may even have been of Finnish origin. A course over Denmark and Heligoland would eventually lead to the British coast-line somewhere in the neighbourhood of East Anglia and it has already been shown that there is a small but regular migration every autumn to these islands by way of Norfolk and Suffolk. The majority of the sparrow-hawks which cross Heligoland are likely to continue their passage by way of the west Continental coast-line rather than cross the North Sea and so through Holland, Belgium and France. Only exceptionally, as in 1881 and 1911, does the drift westwards bring the sparrow-hawks in any considerable numbers to our shores ; in ordinary years the east coast of Britain is only on the fringe of the sparrow-hawks' trek southwards from the countries in the far north where many have reared their young.

In the days before the First World War game preservation in England —and indeed throughout Britain—was at its zenith and in consequence the sparrow-hawk was greatly persecuted. Being a hawk it was shot at sight by every keeper but its method of hunting is such that the damage it does to game preserves has been on the whole grossly exaggerated. Some well-known naturalists whose names carried weight in 1914—among them Heatley Noble, W. H. St. Quintin, Doctor F. G. Penrose, E. G. B. Meade-Waldo and Menteith Ogilvie—wrote in defence of the bird and carried out experiments in sporting areas to try and ascertain the true facts ; the result to a large extent vindicated the sparrow-hawk. Menteith Ogilvie on one occasion examined the stomach contents of thirty-five sparrow-hawks killed on highly preserved Suffolk estates and out of these only three had the remains of game chicks in them. St. Quintin too located three nests where there was a rearing field within less than a mile of each and watch was kept on the parents. In three weeks during which the young were being watched not a single game-bird's remains were found about any of the three nests. Partridges too were plentiful in the neighbourhood.

A correspondent to *British Birds*, Mr. W. Farren,[1] had much the same experience as regards a chicken farm. " It seems evident," he wrote, " that it by no means follows that sparrow-hawks are certain to prey on young pheasants in coops adjacent to their nest. In the orchard about fifty yards from the nesting tree were many fowls, and coops of chickens of all ages, and so far as I could ascertain *not one was taken*."

A rogue kestrel is much more of a danger in a rearing ground than the sparrow-hawk, who is not quite the villain he is painted, though he cannot be considered blameless. Mr. Eric Hosking tells a tale in one of his books of a sparrow-hawk's nest that he and Cyril Newberry were watching in Suffolk. To their dismay they found that the youngsters were being fed largely on the chicks of red-legged partridges. Old partridges are seldom killed but before it is fully grown a young partridge is no match for a sparrow-hawk in full flight determined to capture its quarry. When a sparrow-hawk is itself fully mature, and has become practised in the art of hunting small birds, it is much less of a menace to game than in the early days of its life. Mr. J. H. Owen, who studied its habits so meticulously, held the view that it was after the parents had ceased to feed the young birds that the latter were the greatest danger, for, as he wrote : " The young hen birds seem to hang about the rides of the woods and it is at this stage that they do most harm to game and chicken rearers. They cannot hunt properly yet and find pheasants in the rides an easy prey and will kill birds larger and much heavier than themselves." His observations tended to show that the old birds continued to bring food to their offspring for about three weeks after the nest had been vacated but that they cease entirely to do so before the young have properly learned to hunt for themselves.

[1] *British Birds*, viii, 1914, pp. 154-160 : " Feeding-habits of the Sparrow-hawk".

The dexterity exhibited by the sparrow-hawk in the capture of its prey has been the subject of several excellent articles. Doctor Tinbergen's researches in this field are of course well known and will be referred to later in this account when we come to consider the economic aspect of the bird under discussion. For English readers the work of Mr. J. H. Owen is more accessible and his exhaustive observations[1] on the sparrow-hawk form the basis of the following account.

Mr. Owen was greatly struck by the many variations in the method of the bird's attack. While agreeing that most observers, including himself, were inclined to consider the speed at which various birds fly greater than it really is, he put the chasing flight of the sparrow-hawk at approximately fifty miles an hour or more. Should a sparrow-hawk wish to hunt at some distance from its headquarters it reaches its destination by means of a rapid glide, very close to the ground and as straight as an arrow across the fields. When a hedge is reached the bird just glides up, over and down again, and flies on as before. Once the hunting ground is reached the usual method is to follow a fence, flying fast and low and every now and then slipping over to the other side and back again. If some unfortunate small bird is perched on an outstanding twig the hawk's pace seems to increase greatly. It swoops over the bird and as it passes it drops a foot and picks the victim up with absolutely unerring skill. The hawk may then stop in a few yards and eat its prey, or it may carry it off to some regular feeding place.

The flight is mostly done by gliding and very few wing-beats can be seen in the course of a hunt.

Several writers have been amazed that this hawk can crash into a bush or hawthorn fence after its victim without doing itself mortal damage, and though it will not disdain to hurt itself on thorns, it will avoid a briar in which it would become entangled. Its boldness in following its victim has led it even into the rooms of houses, as Colonel Meinertzhagen has remarked elsewhere, and many have fallen victim from striking window panes. Mr. Owen in the article I have cited gives many instances of unusual prey; he has seen a sparrow-hawk take a house martin off a nest under the eaves of a barn with but a momentary pause, and scoop up a young moorhen that was swimming across a pond without even making a splash, and he has watched them try to catch lapwings but never with success. The element of surprise in many cases forms the essence of the bird's attack. The victim is a victim before it is aware that it has been picked out, and, as Mr. Owen points out, even when it has to catch a flying bird it usually obtains an advantage by having already accelerated and so reaches its victim before the latter has a chance to get up speed, as for instance when it dashes into a crowd of sparrows, finches or buntings in rickyards or on stubble and takes one of them as they rise.

[1] Published over a series of years in *British Birds* magazine, vols viii, x, xii, xv, xx, xxv, xxvi and xxx.

PLATE 28

PLATE 28

SPARROW-HAWK (Female with Nest and Young)
Accipiter nisus nisus (Linnaeus)

Colonel Meinertzhagen recounts how as he was walking up quail in Arabia a sparrow-hawk was sitting on a cactus hedge when one of the quail flew in the direction of the hawk. As the quail topped the hedge the hawk jumped up and seized it in full flight, both of them tumbling to the ground.

One does not suspect the sparrow-hawk of paying much attention to woodpeckers but Mr. Owen gives two instances of one chasing a green woodpecker. In the first case the hawk was out to scare the woodpecker rather than kill it, and scare it it did, the frantic screams of the fleeing bird showing how little it appreciated that form of sport. In the second instance the woodpecker made a wonderful but vain effort to escape from its pursuer by going through a small wood but the hawk was practically its equal in twisting and turning through the branches. Again the noises the woodpecker made in that last frenzied minute were dreadful to listen to.

Accounts of sparrow-hawks flying at stoats and squirrels came to Mr. Owen's notice but such cases, he believed, were more in the nature of ragging than an attempt to secure a meal.

One remarkable feat on the part of a sparrow-hawk must be recounted. Mr. J. H. Owen was again the observer and sent an account of the incident to *British Birds*.[1] He was visiting a marsh in Essex at the end of March to see if any snipe were nesting when he put up four birds. They flew away and then circled back. Suddenly a hen sparrow-hawk appeared and travelling at great speed seized one of them within twenty yards of where he was standing. It carried the snipe about half the distance towards him but on seeing him released it, apparently unhurt. Both birds went off in different directions.

In a long list of victims which Mr. Owen has compiled[2] a surprising number are fairly large birds; partridges, wood pigeons, stock doves, jays, green woodpeckers, cuckoos, lapwing and a little owl may be mentioned, together with a large list of smaller species very few of which at one time or another do not figure on the menu.

Reference has been made earlier in this essay to the exhaustive study by Doctor Tinbergen " On the Sparrow-hawk as a Predator of Passerine Birds ".[3] His investigations aimed at discovering the rôle of *Accipiter nisus* as a cause of mortality among the species upon which it preys, thus— to use his own words—" contributing to the problem of the regulation of numbers in wild animals ". Investigations were directed at discovering what percentage of the mortality of the house sparrow, chaffinch, great tit and coal tit could be attributed to the depredations of the sparrow-hawk. The work was undertaken in the Netherlands. It was found that collective predators play a very great rôle, exceeding that of all other mortality factors. In the chaffinch predators cause about 50 per cent. of mortality and in the

[1] Vol. xix, p. 312.
[2] *British Birds*, xxvi, p. 40.
[3] *Ardea*, xxxiv, 1946, pp. 1-213.

particular district of Holland where the investigations took place the same holds good of the great tit.   In the coal tit the influence of predators is practically negligible, this rapidly reproducing species being checked by other factors.

Then Doctor Tinbergen turned his attention to the amount of damage done by the sparrow-hawk to game preserving.   It was discovered by investigation that in a terrain rich in pheasants *and* sparrow-hawks less than 7 per cent. of the annual mortality among the pheasant population was caused by the hawk.   As to its danger to partridges, nothing could be ascertained with certainty, but it was believed to be negligible, as partridges inhabit open country much less favourable to the sparrow-hawk than coverts.   Finally Doctor Tinbergen made a strong point in the sparrow-hawk's favour by stressing the bird's influence in keeping the jay in check. Taking all factors into consideration, Doctor Tinbergen concluded that its economic rôle is indifferent.

BREEDING HABITS[1] :   That sparrow-hawks can, and do, breed within a year of being hatched is evident from the numbers killed at the nest in first plumage.   Amongst these, females are naturally in the majority, a bereaved male being particularly likely to replace his lost mate with a bird of the previous season.   More rarely it is the male of a pair that is the yearling, and very exceptionally both partners prove to be immature.

Now and then a male sparrow-hawk has been known to mate with two females.   In the *Scottish Naturalist* for 1925 (vol. cliii, p. 95) Lieutenant-Commander G. Hughes-Onslow gave an account of a nest from which he flushed two hawks " looking like hens ".   The birds were later killed and found to have brood patches, the sex in each case being verified by dissection.   A boy brought down from the nest the unusual number of eight eggs, all slightly incubated.

While the sparrow-hawk in Britain is chiefly a bird of the evergreens, it is by no means scarce in deciduous woods.   Though a planting of some acreage is always the most likely site for a nest, the birds will sometimes take to an insignificant spinney or wind-break.   Less frequently a pair will build in a rather isolated tree, perhaps one of a number thinly scattered along a moorland stream or forming a straggling hedge on a lonely farm. On the Downs Walpole-Bond and others have come upon nests in dense thickets of hawthorn and the like.   Certain woods, or parts of woods, seem more attractive to these hawks than others, and in such a favourite haunt the old nests of different seasons may be seen within a hundred yards or less of each other.   If the wood is preserved the keeper can kill a pair of hawks there every year, in the certainty that the dangerous territory will be retenanted in the following spring.

Normally very wary, sparrow-hawks will at times so far forget their

---

[1] The notes on the nesting of the sparrow-hawk have been supplied by Doctor H. M. S. Blair.

habitual distrust of human neighbours as to nest close to a building. G. E. Lodge speaks of a nest in the grounds of a busy hotel, and of another only thirty yards from a house, in a cypress used both as a shelter by children and as a support for a hammock. Rather more secluded was the Cambridgeshire orchard where our artist found another pair of hawks established.

Most reports of sparrow-hawks breeding in treeless country depend upon evidence which cannot be regarded as entirely satisfactory, but credence must surely be given to Saxby's account of nests he had seen in the Shetlands, as well as to the Orkney record quoted by Harvie-Brown.

Sparrow-hawks abroad resemble British birds in their preference for coniferous forests. On the Scandinavian fell-sides more nests occur where pine and spruce predominate than amongst the birch woods, although the latter appear the better stocked with suitable prey. Near the southern limit of its distribution, in Tunisia, forests of Aleppo pines are the strongholds of this widely ranging bird.

In Britain the sparrow-hawk generally builds in a well-grown conifer, larch, spruce or Scots pine. Nests in oaks are common enough, however, particularly in purely deciduous woods, where they may also be found, though less frequently, in birches and hawthorns. It is only rarely that any other species of tree is favoured. The nest seen by Lodge in an orchard was in a cultivated apple tree, a most unusual site, and was the more noteworthy in being built out on a branch and not against the trunk.

When prospecting likely sites sparrow-hawks look for one which allows of their leaving and returning unimpeded by thick covert. The tree finally selected, therefore, nearly always stands hard by a drive, along a water course or on the fringe of the wood.

As already mentioned, sparrow-hawks' nests have occasionally been found on cliff ledges. From Sweden comes a unique record of these hawks building on the ground, and that amongst tall trees.

In Britain a pair of sparrow-hawks will decide upon a site and begin to build early in March. From the middle of the month onwards the birds, otherwise so retiring and inconspicuous, fairly betray the whereabouts of the nest by the spring flights described with such a wealth of detail by J. H. Owen. Until the female is ready to lay the two will be on the wing together early each morning and again, though for a shorter period, towards sundown. With slow measured wing-beats they fly along the wood, keeping at the one height, and with now the male ahead, and now his larger partner. When the hawks turn they rise abruptly and sharply. The same line, the length of the wood, is always followed, regardless of the prevailing wind. Sometimes the displaying birds mount until they are far above the wood, when they will either turn suddenly away from each other or dive headlong towards the trees before continuing their evolutions. As the nest progresses towards completion the female hawk takes less and less part in these flights, and just before laying time her mate alone will be seen on the wing. Still flying in the same deliberate fashion, he will now and then break off to hurtle downwards to where the female is perched. A similar headlong dive precedes the actual mating, which takes place either on a bough or, though less frequently, on the nest.

Sparrow-hawks normally lay in nests of their own building. Unlike goshawks, they build anew each spring, and the home of an earlier season is rarely put to use even as a foundation. Should a pair of hawks lose their nest as it nears completion, the female's need for a platform of some sort for her clutch may become too urgent to allow of one being built. The birds must then be content with the hurried repair of some old nest, one of their own if it happens to be available, otherwise that of a crow, magpie or pigeon, or even an old squirrel's drey.

A typical sparrow-hawk's nest can easily be distinguished from that of any other woodland bird, the broad, rather flat platform being attached to its supporting branches close to the bole and several feet below the summit of the tree. Most hawks build between twenty and thirty feet above the ground, but these limits are often exceeded, and the eggs or young can occasionally be inspected without the trouble of climbing. Viewed from below, the nest may appear no more than a loose, carelessly assembled faggot of sticks and twigs. Yet, artless though it seems, it will survive the gales of several winters, and if dislodged it will fall to the ground intact. Indeed considerable force is required to pull apart the closely interwoven material. George Bolam was once fortunate enough to surprise a sparrow-hawk building in a hedgerow birch which could be approached under cover. The bird was busy on the framework of the nest, already a foot in depth and as big as a small clothes basket, and most carefully constructed of birch branches, all fresh enough to be pliable. By the time it was ready for eggs this nest had lost its original neatness of outline, the cavity being filled up with branches, many of them larger than those used for the foundation.

Entirely new nests of the sparrow-hawk measured by Owen varied in their dimensions from fourteen by thirteen inches to twenty by fourteen, with depths of from six to thirteen inches. One Norwegian nest was exceptionally large, measuring more than a yard across.

The finishing touch to a sparrow-hawk's home is the lining of small twigs, commonly of larch or birch, which are interwoven with each other and the larger sticks beneath to form an almost flat platform. In some nests the eggs rest upon dead leaves, rotten wood or fragments of bark, while in the far north the sparrow-hawk, like so many other birds in those regions, felts the whole structure with black witch-hair lichen. The completed nest often stands empty for seven to ten days, and as much as three weeks may pass before an egg appears. In Britain the first eggs are laid in April, and a nest will sometimes contain its full number by the end of the month, but the first or second week of May is usually quite soon enough to look for clutches. A few fresh sittings—usually second attempts—may be found towards the close of May and even in June. Data from the Mediterranean countries show that the sparrow-hawks there are very little earlier, if at all, in going to nest than ours. Fresh eggs have been taken near Gibraltar between 8th and 17th May, and in Greece between 20th and 24th May. In Scandinavia laying becomes general about the end of May, but here, as in Britain, some nests hold an egg or two in the preceding month. Like many other Raptores, the sparrow-hawk generally lays on alternate days, the pause between the appearance of two eggs being sometimes prolonged by twenty-four hours.

Five eggs appear to be the normal clutch with the sparrow-hawk, but many of the birds lay one more or less. Genuine clutches of seven do occur, though not very frequently, but where a nest holds eight, nine or ten eggs two females are probably concerned. A full clutch of three eggs is either the produce of an old bird or of one nesting for the second time in the season. Large clutches are no commoner in Scandinavia than in Britain, despite the difference of latitude. Five is not an unusual number for eggs in Spain, but with the North African race, according to Whitaker, the full complement rarely exceeds three.

The largest sparrow-hawk's eggs known to Jourdain measured $46 \cdot 7 \times 35$ and $54 \cdot 5 \times 36$ mm., the smallest $35 \times 25 \cdot 4$, the average for his series being $39 \cdot 82 \times 31 \cdot 83$ mm. Typical eggs are rounded ovoid in shape, but the variation is considerable, and Hewitson had specimens as pyriform as waders'. When fresh the white, glossless shell shows a bluish or greenish tint, which fades with incubation. In an extreme, very rare variety the ground is deep green. Most eggs of this hawk are most handsome, with their bold, chocolate blotches and streaks. Some are beautifully zoned, while on others the markings are concentrated towards the smaller end, and it is not very unusual to find one on which the ground colour is almost hidden. Types with chestnut rather than chocolate blotches are common but those marked with pale brown seem rather rare. Some clutches are comparatively poorly marked, and many include an egg apparently lacking in pigment. Whole sets of unmarked eggs have been recorded but some of these have been known to be second layings.

While one sparrow-hawk sits closely on her first egg, another will not settle down to brood before she has two or three, if she does not wait until the clutch is complete. Walpole-Bond and others have reported the male sparrow-hawk as occasionally relieving the female. Such an occurrence must be very exceptional, for Owen never saw the male take his turn on the eggs at any of the scores of nests he and his assistants kept under observation. The male can indeed have little time for anything other than hunting throughout the incubation period, as his mate depends upon him for food. This he brings, not to the nest, but to some older structure nearby, or to some favourite feeding place, such as a mossy mound or stump.

Individual sparrow-hawks vary greatly in their behaviour when disturbed at the nest. Many will slip quietly away on the first alarm, others can only be persuaded to take wing by much whistling and shouting, and a few crouch on the eggs until the climber is all but on them. Once flushed, some females become very noisy and demonstrative. As Owen was examining one nest the owner repeatedly passed within a few inches, sometimes even brushing him with her wing, and an even bolder bird earned a place in Stevenson's *Birds of Norfolk* by leaving her mark " in deep scratches " on an intruder's hand.

Typical of the sparrow-hawk is the persistence with which a female will return to her eggs despite narrow escapes from the gun. Such devotion only too often proves the bird's undoing but one owed her survival, and that of her brood, to George Bolam's knowledge of this trait. Her nest, built in a low birch tree, was most conspicuous and clearly doomed if left there. When incubation had fairly begun, Bolam transferred the nest to the top of a high rock not far from the tree, a change to which the hawk took kindly. Concealed amongst the heather which crowned the new site, she escaped the eye of the keeper and Bolam later had the satisfaction of watching her brood on the wing.

During the incubation period the sparrow-hawk frequently " top-dresses " the nest, and she adds further material, mostly fine twigs, while the young are growing. Owen believes that the purpose of these later additions is to cover any pellets, dung or fragments of prey which have sunk into the nest beyond the bird's reach, where they might become offensive. While brooding the bird sheds her down freely about the nest until it becomes attractively plumed. These down-tufts disappear soon after hatching time, being swallowed by the female together with any chance feathers from the prey she feeds to the young.

Even after the long weeks of incubation the shell of a sparrow-hawk's egg remains surprisingly tough, and as much as four days can elapse between an egg chipping and the nestling's final emergence. Sometimes the parent will help the little bird to free itself by breaking the shell with her bill. The incubation period therefore varies somewhat, but most young are clear of the egg by the thirty-fifth day. For the next fortnight the female covers the family almost continuously, and as long as they keep to the nest she will endeavour to protect them from the weather. Given the opportunity, she may now and then attempt a kill close to the nest tree, but otherwise she leaves hunting to her partner. Until the young can safely be left the male brings all food to the nest, first announcing his return in a succession of plaintive wailing notes. His captures at this stage are usually completely plucked, besides being drawn and beheaded. After a few days, unless the weather is very bad, the female leaves the nest when she hears the male calling and flies to meet him at one of the feeding places. There she takes the prey from him, either on a branch or stump or, more rarely, while still on the wing. Now the carcass is less likely to be thoroughly prepared, and sometimes it is still untouched when the male relinquishes it.

A young sparrow-hawk receives no food until it has been hatched for some hours. At first the female must put each morsel of flesh to the youngster's bill as it sprawls about the nest, and it is not until its fourth day that the little bird can reach up and take food from its parent. Each nestling receives a fair share in those early days but the old bird becomes less careful of this later, although she always gives particular attention to the last-hatched. After feeding the young the hen goes thoroughly over the nest, removing droppings and pellets, before carrying away the remains of the prey.

Should the female sparrow-hawk be killed, the male makes no attempt to feed the young, although he continues to bring prey to the nest. If the young are small, they must die of starvation, often surrounded by an abundance of food. One of MacGillivray's correspondents, being curious to know whether a male sparrow-hawk could feed the brood, returned to the nest nine hours after shooting the female. A boy who climbed to the nest found the four young almost suffocated by dead birds, of which he threw down no less than sixteen—larks, buntings, chaffinches, greenfinches and hedge sparrows—all untouched.

Young sparrow-hawks begin to pull at carcasses on about the seventeenth day of their existence, but they cannot feed themselves until they are more than three weeks old. Towards the end of their stay in the nest the female gives up dismembering prey for them, each one making a meal in turn. At the age of one month the young wander away from the nest into the surrounding trees. They continue to use the nest as a dining-table for some time, flapping hurriedly back whenever they hear the male on his way with a kill. The male still provides the bulk of the food, and Owen believes that he now kills bigger game—young pigeons, jays, blackbirds and starlings, in place of the finches and warblers of the earlier weeks. Owen further remarks that the larger the victim the more thoroughly it is dressed before being brought to the nest. Such hunting as the female does is largely on her own account, nor does she now concern herself with the cleansing of the nest, which soon becomes littered with bones. Some seven weeks after the young have hatched the family move off through the wood and the nest is finally abandoned.

REFERENCES : Original Description. *Falco nisus* Linnaeus, Syst. Nat., 10th ed., 1758, p. 92 : Habitat in Europa. Restricted type locality Sweden.

Genus *MILVUS* Lacépède

PLATE 29

KITE

Milvus milvus milvus (Linnaeus)

Resident, a very few breeding in central Wales ; otherwise a very rare
Accidental Visitor to Britain

IDENTIFICATION : The kite is a bird which should be easily recognized in this country, where there is very little danger of its being confused with the black kite, as is the case in southern Europe. The present species is often termed the red kite, on account of its rufous colouring. The head in the adult bird is white, streaked narrowly with black, the streaks very sparse on the forehead but heavier on the nape and hind crown. All the rest of the upperparts is reddish-brown, the feathers with paler margins and dark middles. The wings are like the upperparts, the wing-coverts with broad rufous edges, the secondaries mostly brown and the primaries with long black tips. The tail feathers are bright reddish-chestnut ; the whole of the underparts below the whitish throat is chestnut with black streaks on the breast. The feathers of the thighs are long and droop over the tarsus well below the joint ; in colour they are rufous-chestnut with black streaks. The bill is yellow at the base, as is also the cere, with a black tip to the bill. The legs and feet are yellow and the iris is amber.

When in flight the kite, which is a large bird measuring two feet in total length, may be recognized at once by the markedly forked and rather long tail, by the conspicuous white area on the underside of the wing forming a light patch immediately next to the black wing-tips, and finally by the whitish head and throat.

When flying overhead or circling over a hillside or plain, the gliding buoyant flight is sure to attract attention, and then the long wings with splayed open fingers and the abrupt angle of the bend at the carpal joint are notable features to observe. The wing span of an adult bird is as much as five feet, three inches. George Lodge, whose picture of the kite adorns this book, had studied the bird in Sweden in his younger days and wrote that on the wing, when merely travelling, it looks very like a heron both in size and in the slow flapping of the wings, but to appreciate its grace the bird must be seen soaring : " The kite rises into the sky in spirals on motionless wings, just tilting its body as it circles to get full advantage of air pressure, when it ultimately disappears into the blue."

The distinctions between the red kite and the black kite will be given under the latter species.

FORMER STATUS IN GREAT BRITAIN : It is difficult to believe that the kite was at one time perhaps the most familiar bird of prey in Great Britain and that, as Newton pointed out in the *Dictionary of Birds*, foreigners were struck with its abundance in the streets of London, where it acted as a useful scavenger. A Bohemian gentleman who visited England about 1461

PLATE 29

KITE
Milvus milvus milvus (Linnaeus)

declared that he had nowhere seen so many kites as around London Bridge, and his statement is confirmed by Belon, who in 1555 observed that they were scarcely more numerous in Cairo than in London, feeding on the garbage of the streets and even of the Thames. In those days both kites, and ravens also, were protected by law in the City. There are reasons for thinking that the kite was not so common in the rest of England as has been generally inferred, especially in the northern counties, for, like its cousin the pariah kite of India, it tends to congregate where garbage is most plentiful. Its place has now been taken around the London bridges by the black-headed gull, which is itself a comparative newcomer.

How it came about that protection was later denied to such a useful scavenger has never been clearly told but its fondness for chickens helped to seal its doom and it was hated in consequence by every housewife. In country districts when game preservation came to the fore its fate was finally settled but even at the beginning of the eighteenth century it is reputed to have formed a feature of many a rural landscape in England.

In the year 1734 it is recorded that some kites still nested in the trees round St. Giles-in-the-Fields in company with rooks and magpies, while Pennant, in a letter written in August 1777, mentions some young kites taken from a nest in Gray's Inn with frogs in their stomachs! The final disappearance of the kite from London is not chronicled and it is considered probable that they ceased to breed in London before the end of the eighteenth century. According to Mr. James Fisher's researches[1] the story of the kite in London concludes with one seen flying over Piccadilly on 24th June 1859.

In the account which he prepared on the extermination of the kite from most of England Mr. Fisher observes : " Most of this early persecution, directed against the kite as a chicken-stealer, was in the breeding season. Most of the ' heads ' paid for by the churchwardens in parishes all over England were those of young taken from the nest. . . . The game-keeper, armed with new and more effective weapons, exterminated the kite most effectively. . . . The kite just disappeared without trace from the records of half the counties of England at the beginning of the 19th century."

The last breeding kites disappeared from Yorkshire early in the century, from Cumberland about 1840, from Kent about 1815 ; in 1830 or there-abouts they nested for the last time in Berkshire, Oxfordshire, Cambridge-shire, Northumberland, Norfolk and Suffolk. They held out in Hunting-donshire until 1837, Rutland to 1840, Northampton until about 1845, Worcestershire about 1850, Essex possibly to 1855, and the last *English* breeding kites (with the exception of two which attempted to breed early in the twentieth century) were exterminated in Lincolnshire in the spring of 1870.

The same tale of destruction comes from Scotland, where the last pair are believed to have nested in 1880 in Perthshire. The history of the

[1] Annual Report for 1947 of the R.S.P.B. : " Natural History of the Kite ".

kite's former distribution in and final extermination from Scotland is told by Miss Baxter and Miss Rintoul in their recently issued *Birds of Scotland*, and as that standard work is accessible to all, the story need not be repeated here. According to these authorities " the principal feature of the disappearance of the kites in Scotland was the rapidity with which this was affected ". The second half of the last century saw the virtual extirpation of this fine bird north of the Border, where from all accounts it was once fairly numerous. There is no satisfactory evidence, as pointed out by Doctor Eagle Clarke in Howard Saunders' *Manual of British Birds*, that the kite ever occurred in Ireland other than as a vagrant.

Whether or not the disappearance of the kite was affected by its pursuit by trained falcons, it is recorded that in the earliest days of falconry the kite was looked upon as a supreme prize, for it showed excellent sport, though the taking of it was quite beyond the powers of any but the most highly trained falcons. In consequence this came to be considered the sport of kings, for only royal personages were in a position to acquire, at vast expenditure, the very exceptional hawks capable of tackling a kite successfully. The tale has been told [1] that the Master-Falconer to King James I, being determined to outdo the performance of the French king's falconer, who when sent to England to show sport " could not kill one kite, ours being more magnanimous than the French kite ", at last succeeded after an outlay of £1000 in getting a cast of hawks that took nine kites running— " never missed one ". On the strength of this James was induced to witness a flight at Royston, " but the Kite went to such a mountee as all the field lost sight of Kite and Hawke and all, and neither Kite nor Hawke were either seen or heard of to this present ".

One other factor—the weather—may have played a greater part in the extermination of the kite in England and Scotland than has been credited. It was observed by Miss Baxter and Miss Rintoul that the end of the kite came in Scotland with extreme rapidity and we find the same thing happening in England. This induced Lord Lilford,[2] when pondering the reason for the bird's disappearance, to write : " I have also heard it stated that the Kites were exterminated by a very severe winter, and this I think is more likely, for although most of the records sent to me are somewhat vague as to date, from what I can gather, our Kites seem to have disappeared suddenly, and not gradually diminished in numbers as though shot and trapped off by gamekeepers."

In Wales alone a few pairs survived in a remote part of the country but owing to their rarity their eggs were soon in demand. By 1900 the kite population was down to three pairs, and had it not been for the unprecedented action of the British Ornithologists' Club, the species would

[1] *A Dictionary of Birds*, p. 489, footnote 3. The same anecdote appears in different form in Yarrell's *History of British Birds*.

[2] *Birds of Northamptonshire*, i, p. 32.

undoubtedly have been exterminated. It was due in the first place to W. R. Ogilvie-Grant and his friend E. G. B. Meade-Waldo that the Fund for the Preservation of the Kite in Wales came into being, but many members of the Club at the time assisted actively with their support.

LOCAL DISTRIBUTION : The kite in the year in which I am writing, 1955, is confined to an area in central Wales where it is very strictly protected, and with the close collaboration of farmers and landowners, every effort is made to permit the few pairs to nest in peace. The story of the fight to save the kite in these islands has been told in a report, now made public, which Mr. James Fisher made in 1949 to the Royal Society for the Protection of Birds. Mr. Fisher traces the fluctuations of the small kite population from the days when the birds almost ceased to exist until 1948.

In the early days of the present century the increase was very gradual but by 1912 a great improvement had taken place and in that year nine or ten pairs had nests. Then the numbers dropped again and in 1921 only three pairs bred. By 1927 this number had more than doubled. Then followed an experiment by a private person to introduce fresh blood from overseas.

In the years 1927 and 1928 an attempt was made by Mr. C. H. Gowland to restock Britain with kites. At considerable expense he imported a number of fresh eggs from Spain. In 1927 twenty-one eggs of Spanish kites—the same race as our bird—were sent by air from Seville and placed in buzzards' nests in central Wales. Of this number only two hatched out but the young birds were seen for some weeks afterwards. The next year, 1928, fifty-three eggs were sent by sea and these were eventually dispersed in the nests of *Buteo buteo* in north and central Wales. Greater success attended this effort and thirty-one hatched, the young being observed on the nest and the buzzards proving good foster-mothers. The subsequent history of these birds was hard to trace. The next year some young birds were seen about in central Wales which may have been from this hatching ; none appears to have returned in the subsequent years to North Wales, and, as stressed by the recorder, there is no positive evidence that the hatching of these Spanish eggs contributed to the permanent kite population. The number of young which flew, dispersed, never to return, and, as we are pertinently reminded, the Spanish red kite, unlike its British counterpart, is a migratory bird. The experiment seems therefore to have been doomed from its conception and has never been tried again.

For the next twenty years [1]—until 1949—the kite population was

[1] In the year 1937 Miss Dorothy Raikes took charge of the Kite Preservation Fund and worked indefatigably to preserve the few known breeding places from molestation.

The fund is administered to-day by the Kite Committee, representing (1) the Royal Society for the Protection of Birds, (2) the Society for the Promotion of Nature Reserves, (3) the West Wales Field Society, (4) Cardiff Naturalists' Society, (5) Montgomeryshire Field Society and (6) the Council for the Preservation of Rural Wales. On the councils of the first two of these the writer has had the honour to serve for a number of years.

subject to the same fluctuations as were apparent from the start of the intensive preservation campaign, but I learn from a reliable source that a marked improvement took place in the number of pairs known to the Protecting Societies in 1950, and that this improvement has been maintained. The reason perhaps is that the young kites are spreading farther afield, and although that would be all to the good and ultimately prove the kite's salvation, it is likely to make still heavier demands on those who so generously give their time in the breeding season to keeping undesirable visitors from the bird's haunts.

RECORDS BEYOND THE NORMAL BREEDING AREA: Kites which were presumed to have strayed from central Wales to other parts of Britain have been recorded from time to time. For instance, in 1913 kites were seen in Somersetshire in December by A. F. R. Wollaston, in Derbyshire in April by D. Palmer Pearson, and in Buckinghamshire by Guy Robson of the British Museum. The two Devonshire records certainly do not point to these having been visitors from the Continent, as at that date the northern-breeding kites would long since have completed their usual southward migration. In the same year, 1913, James Hale and Clifford Borrer were able to record the attempted nesting of a pair of kites in Devonshire, the nest being destroyed by boys.

One more attempt at nesting has been recorded, this time in Cornwall, during the breeding season of 1920, but again it came to nothing, and the sad fact remains that whenever the Welsh kites have tried to breed far beyond their own protected area the attempt has come to grief through human interference.

Seldom does a year pass without reports of a red kite being noted in some distant part of England or Scotland and on one occasion a bird appears to have made history by crossing the Irish Sea. English counties from which such reports have come include Cornwall, Devon, Somerset, Shropshire, Northamptonshire, Leicestershire, Norfolk, Bucks and Sussex.

In Scotland it has been reported from the Mull of Kintyre (June 1911), from two districts in Perthshire (spring and August 1917), from Loch Fyne, Argyll (June 1919), from Strachan, Kincardine (April 1929), and again from Perthshire (1936).

There are few winter records of wandering kites in comparison with those which have been noted between June and September inclusive.

The history of the kite in Ireland is most unsatisfactory. R. J. Ussher in his *List of Irish Birds* records (on p. 28) that the supposed occurrences cannot be substantiated, but in his *Birds of Ireland* (1900) he wrote that the only record of a kite shot in Ireland is that of Sir Ralph Payne Gallwey, who describes finding a young male, which he killed, in Co. Kerry during the severe winter of 1880-81, at the mouth of the Cashen River, which flows into the sea outside the mouth of the Shannon (*Fowler in Ireland*, p. 307). In the new *Birds of Ireland* the authors, after noting that there are

several alleged occurrences which cannot be substantiated, observe (on
p. 106) that there are two *authentic* Irish records : a mounted specimen in
the National Collection labelled as having been obtained " in November "
near Kilcoole on the Wicklow coast, and a bird satisfactorily identified
at Slane, Co. Meath, on 15th November 1951 (cf. *Field*, January 1952,
p. 135).

Whether the kite ever bred in Ireland there is no evidence to prove.
As Irish writers have pointed out, harriers go by the name of kites in that
country and old references to kites in Irish literature cannot necessarily
be taken as referring to *Milvus milvus*.

DISTRIBUTION ABROAD :   The breeding range of the kite has been
greatly reduced by persecution but in northern Europe it still nests in
Sweden and through the Baltic Provinces, Germany and Poland to
Roumania.   Its southern breeding range in Europe reaches the
Mediterranean in southern Spain and extends east to Palestine and
northern Persia.   It is reported to be absent as a breeding bird from the
Mediterranean zone of France, from Greece and from much of the Balkan
States.   We find it breeding in the western Mediterranean in Spain, in the
Balearic Islands, Corsica, Sardinia and Sicily but not apparently in the
eastern Mediterranean.   In northern Africa it nests in Tunisia, Algeria
and Morocco, in the last-named both in the Riff and in the Middle Atlas
ranges.   The southernmost area inhabited by the red kite is the Canary
Islands, where the same race occurs in four out of five of the western islands ;
its absence from Palma is notable.

Another subspecies occurs in the tropical Cape Verde Islands, *Milvus
milvus fasciicauda*, which is the only representative beyond the Palæarctic
Region.   In western European countries its range is local and may be
summarized as follows :

Norway :   The red kite is now one of the rarest of Norwegian birds,
only two examples, both immature, having been reported in the last fifty
years, one from Mandal on 2nd August 1906, and the other from Rendal
on the same date twenty years later.   At one time this species bred, though
only sparingly, in the neighbourhood of Halden (then known as Fredriks-
hald), where the last recorded nest was found in 1896.   Collett notes that in
the first half of the nineteenth century kites used sometimes to occur in
the Oslo district in spring.   As a straggler the kite has wandered as far
north as Gudbrandsdal and as far west as Stavanger.

Sweden :   When Kolthoff and Jägerskiöld wrote on the birds of their
country no birds of prey had lost so much ground in Sweden as the kite.
At one time it was a fairly common breeding bird in the south of the country
up to Mälaren and central Upland, possibly to Gävle and Storsjön
in Jämtland.   Gradually its numbers diminished and at one time its
extermination in Sweden was imminent.   Everywhere it was scarce or had
totally disappeared.   Since being protected in 1919 it has slowly increased

and in 1945 (when the report [1] I have before me was written), its distribution became concentrated in Skåne, Småland and Södermanland, in which area there were some forty breeding pairs. With the rigid protection afforded them and the huge area of forested country available for their expansion they are likely to have spread to other districts. These northern-breeding kites depart from Sweden in winter and are then recorded on migration through southern Norway.

Finland : A very rare straggler.

Denmark : The kite has been exterminated for a number of years as a breeding bird until one pair successfully bred on Lolland in 1949, after having unsuccessfully attempted to do so the previous year. The kites appropriated an old buzzard's nest in a beech tree which they duly decorated with rubbish. Incubation began about 24th April and three young left the nest on 13th July and were fed by both parents until 8th August (L. Hansen, *Dansk. Orn. Foren. Tidssk.*, xliv, 1950, pp. 5-15).

France : On its distribution in France I have received the following information from M. Georges Olivier, who writes : " Both *Milvus milvus* and *Milvus migrans* are decreasing in our country. As regards the red kite, formerly the species was breeding in western France and *occasionally* is still breeding there (Vendée, 1935, 1952 and ?1953). It breeds regularly in the east and south-west, either in mountainous or in hilly or even in rather flat country." In Lorraine, M. Olivier tells me, he has often seen it nesting in woods and forests, and sometimes even in the trees along the roads. In 1953 it was observed at Rambervillers (Vosges) and also in wooded country in the south-west near Rabastens and near Pau. In Normandy the kite, if seen at all, is very rarely observed as a migrant, and the same applies in the north, north-west and west of France.

A note received in 1955 from M. François Hüe informs me that *Milvus milvus* does *not* nest in the Mediterranean zone [2] of France, and consequently the distribution map in Peterson's *Field Guide to the Birds of Europe* should be corrected. Since 1950 a colony is spreading towards the Montagne Noire (Aude-Tarn).

Spain : For an account of its breeding distribution in the Iberian Peninsula the reader must turn to the end of this essay, to the section headed " Status and Habitat in Spain " (p. 269).

WINTER DISTRIBUTION : Those birds which breed in the northern part of the kite's range migrate in winter to countries on both sides of the Mediterranean, especially to the south of the Iberian Peninsula and northern Africa. They are not known to reach the tropics and probably all those which reach Africa remain north of the Atlas range of mountains. In numbers there is no comparison between the present

[1] Bo Österlöf in *Vår Fågelvärld*, 1945, pp. 101-136.

[2] M. Hüe draws attention to the fact that his statement refers only to the Mediterranean zone of France and not to the Midi, where the position is entirely different.

species and the black kite, the latter being very much more numerous, but that bird winters almost entirely in tropical Africa, and none remain north of the Atlas. The red kite is seen much more commonly in winter in Algeria and in the forested area of Tunisia than in Morocco according to my own experiences in these three countries.

When writing of the birds of central Spain H. F. Witherby instances a kite ringed in Denmark which was recovered at Cordoba as proof that birds from the north enter Spain in winter, but nevertheless it appeared to him that the kite was much scarcer in central Spain in autumn than it was in summer, which prompted him to suggest that a proportion of the kites which breed in central Spain move southwards when cold weather sets in. That seems to me extremely likely from my acquaintance with that country, for central Spain lies very high and in winter the sierras and most of the high ground lie deep in snow ; birds of prey are hard put to it to find a living and the red kite is no exception.

HABITS : As the study of our native kites is rightly deprecated by all who are interested in their preservation, those who would become familiar with them must travel far afield, for only by allowing our own small stock to remain *completely undisturbed* is there any chance of their survival. My own experience of the red kite was gained in the first instance many years ago in the Canary Islands, still, I believe, a stronghold of the species. I have met with it since in several lands—in Spain, Morocco, Algeria and Tunisia—but nowhere is it so easily observed as in Tenerife and Grand Canary, and nowhere is it such a common feature of the landscape, not even in Andalusia. Oddly enough, in the Canaries, its southernmost habitat, the red kite is resident—as in Britain—all the year round. In eight successive years I never saw the slightest sign of migration.

Its distribution in the Archipelago is rather peculiar in as much as it inhabits four of the five western islands but is absent from Palma, the most suitable of the lot one might think, for there the Canarian pines reach their highest and finest growth. The Egyptian vulture too shuns Palma, though it is exceptionally common in the two largest islands, and one can hardly suppose that the competition of the chough, which formerly, if not to-day, swarmed in Palma, would be the cause of the vulture's absence, though it may have some bearing on the kite's preference for islands where the chough does not dominate the horizon, and in fact does not occur at all.

As in most country districts the kite is disliked by the country people on account of its thieving nature. Young chickens prove an irresistible bait to the Canarian kites, which exhibit extraordinary boldness in their capture, dashing down into the farmyard and stealing the young hens from under the very nose of the farmer's wife. Carrion forms a considerable portion of the kite's fare but it loses no opportunity of seizing live prey as well—rats and mice, rabbits, large grasshoppers and wounded or ailing birds, whenever they can be found. Moreover, of all the birds of prey in the Canaries the kite is the most persistent feeder on the entrails of fish. I well remember one glorious day at Maspalomas in the south of Grand Canary watching a fleet of native fishing boats heading for the shore. The sky was cloudless and brilliantly blue and not a bird was in sight save a solitary raven flying along the coast-line while uttering its deep throaty croak. As the leading boat ran aground there appeared, literally out of the blue, a dozen or more red kites which, perhaps beyond human sight, had been watching the fleet heading for land, knowing what was in store. The great birds just dropped from the heavens and within a few minutes were flying screaming round the boats as the fish were gutted. They reminded me of gulls crowding round the stern of a liner, jostling and fighting amongst themselves for every morsel thrown into the sea. It was a remarkable sight to anyone familiar with the kite's usual wariness, even when feeding on carrion washed up on the shore.

The powers of flight of the kite are difficult to beat even by the vulture, and in the clear atmosphere of the Canary Islands can be seen to perfection ; in the Cumbres of Grand Canary, where extensive views are obtained, one or more kites is seldom out of sight. I have watched individual birds soaring upwards in great spiral curves until they appear but specks in the sky and during these manœuvres the tail is clearly used as a rudder. Each pair of kites was observed to have their own territory, over which they would beat backwards and forwards, but that is probably only in the breeding season, for one cannot imagine a bird of its wing-power allowing itself to be unduly confined. More often in the winter time they are encountered sailing along the barren hillsides in huge curves, covering a great area with very little effort. When the wings are used they move with a slow beat.

The kites in the Canaries are used to good weather, and rain and mist have a depressing effect on them. At such times the birds will seek out some old dead tree and sit for hours on end in thoroughly dejected mood, feathers ruffled and head sunk low between the shoulders. I found that they continually returned to the same roosting places, choosing habitually very high pines. At such times they are difficult to approach and, being gifted with astonishing eyesight, are not easily taken by surprise. The usual cry, to be heard in the silence of the pine wood, is a sort of mewing whistle. The pine country in the Canaries lies at a fair altitude and what the kites can find in these deserted woods is difficult to guess ; partridges and rabbits are few and far between and unless crippled are seldom captured. Nevertheless kites were often seen at considerable altitudes in the mountains gliding along close over the tops of the trees, scanning the ground below. Suddenly, without warning, they would appear to change their minds and the direction of their flight to float down in great sweeps, with effortless motion of wings, to the valley far below.

The arrival of a kite overhead, or even its passing shadow, had a miraculous effect on the other feathered inhabitants, even domestic pigeons, which would show little alarm at the approach of a buzzard, scattering in panic at the sight of this brazen chicken-thief, but for all its wicked ways the kite is a glory to behold. Would that we at home had the same opportunities of observing it as have the natives of " the Fortunate Isles ".

STATUS AND HABITAT IN SPAIN : In the seventies of the last century the red kite was a well-known resident throughout Spain. If this no longer holds good of some districts, kites remain plentiful enough in others, and especially in some of the provinces of Andalusia.

The chief strongholds of the red kite in Spain to-day lie amongst the woodlands from Seville southwards. Here it ranges to within sound of the Atlantic, and one pair had their nest at the very foot of the great sand-hills which every year encroach yet further onto the Coto Doñana. That one-time royal preserve remains much as it was when the authors of *Wild Spain* first set foot there. For some miles from the margin of the Guadal-quivir, the traveller rides amongst stone pines overhanging dense tangles of brambles, broom, myrtle and lentiscus, with here and there an open glade where the soil—hardly distinguishable from sand—gives roothold to little more than grasses. These attractive " pinares " hold a wealth of wild life, including that most characteristic of Spanish birds, the azure-winged magpie, an active sprightly creature almost as brightly hued as the roller or bee-eater. Raptores abound. As the little cavalcade plods along, a snake-eagle takes wing from a commanding perch. A little further on a pair of imperial eagles are circling uneasily above the flat-topped pine that supports their eyrie. Then two hobbies delight the eye with their mastery of wing, and over every clearing hangs a kite of one or the other species.

Beyond the pines lies more open, park-like country where the mule tracks twist amongst breast-high scrub between scattered groves of cork oaks. In the scrub the Spanish form of our magpie replaces the azure-winged bird and a pair or two are always in sight, often in hot pursuit of a greater spotted cuckoo. This is the country also of the vinaceous-breasted southern grey shrike. If not more plentiful than in the pine forests, eagles and hawks are certainly more conspicuous. The red kite is generally distributed throughout the whole preserve, breeding both in the " pinares " and amongst the little cork woods, and often in close proximity to its darker ally. At times the two species will be found incubating in adjacent trees, while in some particularly favoured places every cork oak holds a nest old or new. Besides the kites, the imperial eagle, the raven and the white stork all build in these great oaks, and kestrels will be found in possession of many of their old nests.

Elsewhere in Andalusia the red kite is less numerous and more local. Scattered pairs frequent the foothills of the great sierras, others the smaller cork woods, but, as Irby discovered, this bird has never been other than a rarity in the vicinity of Gibraltar.

The call of the red kite falls less pleasantly on the ear than a buzzard's mew, being weaker, shriller and more hurried. Early in the spring, and occasionally at other seasons, this is varied with long-drawn, tremulous notes not unlike the whinnying of the black kite. Red kites are, however, far less noisy than either their congeners or buzzards, and Doctor Blair remarks that all those which he saw in Andalusia in April and May have been completely silent.

While the red kite will readily gorge on carrion or offal, it is by no means entirely a scavenger. Chapman and Buck dissected the stomachs of twenty-one kites, some of them black, and found the remains of snakes, lizards, blindworms, small birds, locusts, beetles, a young red-legged partridge, and a rabbit. The characteristic feathers of a red-legged partridge littered the ground beneath one nest seen by Doctor Blair in Spain, and from his experience of the birds there he has little doubt that they maintain themselves largely by hunting. Small mammals, weakly birds, reptiles and insects are recorded amongst this species' kills. The prey brought to one nest in Germany included field voles, young rabbits, weasels, partridges, lizards, fish, a cuckoo and a jay. By one of MacGillivray's correspondents a red kite was " seen to fish in the Loire, which it seemed to do with much success, seldom appearing to miss its prey ". Other records suggest that most of the fish eaten by kites are either driven ashore or have died before they are picked out of the water. In central Europe a pair of these hawks often build in the centre of a heronry, to avail themselves of the remains of fish dropped from their neighbours' nests.

According to foreign observers, a kite will follow another bird of prey —goshawk, peregrine or osprey—which has just made a kill, and pester it until it relinquishes its booty.

BREEDING HABITS[1] : Some Spanish kites have eggs before March has drawn to a close, and laying becomes general amongst them in the next fortnight. Even in the south, however, it is not unknown for nests of this species to remain empty until May ; two seen in 1953 by Doctor Blair contained incomplete clutches on the 9th of that month.

In Spain red kites' nests may be found in stone pines—the most favoured sites—cork oaks, the evergreens of the genus *Ilex,* and black poplars. While the inspection of a nest often involves a stiff climb of as much as seventy or eighty feet, some are no more than thirty feet up in quite small trees. Compared with the nests of other large raptorial birds— goshawks, buzzards or booted eagles—that of a kite appears very untidy, almost dilapidated. It is a rough, often slight basket of sticks and earth, lined with a little moss, dried dung and wool and decorated with all manner of rubbish. Amongst the curiosities found about such nests the authors of *Wild Spain* list " the dead and dried remains of a white owl . . . the long quill-feathers of the spoonbill and other birds, a linen shirt sleeve,

[1] For the nesting habits as observed in Spain I am indebted to Doctor Hugh Blair.

and old matchboxes ". Abel Chapman went so far as to deem it useless to climb to a nest " unless a rag or two fluttered in the breeze ", and Doctor Blair never failed to find at least one worn fragment of cloth beside the eggs, with perhaps a strand of rope, a piece of paper or a scrap of discarded harness. Even in the most remote districts, such rubbish can be picked up within easy flight of the nest, either along the mule tracks or beside some charcoal-burner's camp. But one bird must have travelled far to acquire the " delicate cambric handkerchief, embroidered with the name Antonia M.", which Chapman found covering two handsome eggs. Equally surprising was the good fortune of the Spaniard who, as he afterwards told Lord Lilford, descended from a kite's nest the richer by a purse of nine dollars. What was perhaps the strangest discovery of all fell to the lot of Lord Lilford himself, for it was from a scrap of newspaper brought down from a kite's nest by his climber that he first learned of the murder of President Lincoln.

It is, of course, not only in Spain that the kite bears comparison to Autolycus. Dresser heard of a Danish forester's wife who had to complain not only of raids upon her chicken run but also of a lace window curtain filched through the open casement while the house was airing. From Britain too we have many tales of oddly " decorated " nests taken in the days when the kites were common. One sent from Northamptonshire to John Hancock contained " a bit of saddlegirth, a bit of red worsted binding, a harvester's glove, and many pieces of paper and linen ". Of the last nest built by a kite in the west of Scotland Robert Gray commented that " the materials of which it was built would have almost suggested the idea of the birds having robbed some wandering gaberlunzie of the contents of his wardrobe—a pair of ragged trousers, worn stockings, and part of an old shirt (the latter flapping in the breeze like an old worn banner) being among the articles ".

The peculiar habit above described at such length is well known to be characteristic of all members of the genus *Milvus*, the nest of one—the Egyptian kite—being referred to by Canon Tristram as " the marine-store shop of the desert ". Among the European Raptores, the Egyptian vulture evinces a somewhat similar predilection, but the rubbish accumulated by that foul-feeding scavenger is usually repulsive and hardly " decorative ".

Particularly interesting to naturalists is the close association prevailing in some countries between the larger birds of prey, the red kite amongst them, and—in Spain—the forest-haunting Spanish sparrow (*Passer hispaniolensis*). In central Spain Lord Lilford generally met with large colonies of these chestnut-headed sparrows breeding hard by kites of both species, and more than once found them building amongst the foundations of their larger neighbours' nests. Dresser also saw many sparrows' nests " built in the foundations of the nests of the buzzard, kite, black kite and booted eagle ".

Clutches of two and three eggs seem equally common with the red kite. Exceptionally a nest will hold four, or the bird may be sitting hard on one. A series from Continental sources measured by Rey averaged 56·7 × 44·8 mm., which is slightly less than the mean of fifty-eight British specimens, which Jourdain found to be 56·97 × 45·09 mm. Like those of many other birds of prey, red kites' eggs show a faint tinge of bluish-green when freshly laid, but this soon fades to leave the glossless shell a dull white. The majority can only be described as sparingly coloured, the reddish-brown or chestnut markings taking the form of spots, streaks and small blotches, with a few lilac shell-markings. Some have hardly a trace of pigment, or may even lack it entirely. Very boldly blotched specimens do occasionally occur, and on some of the more striking the markings are a dark sepia. Another handsome type is clouded with colour, but this again is unusual. Characteristic of this species are the peculiar scratch-like markings and small dots or specks of colour found on many eggs. Others can hardly be distinguished, out of the nest, from those of the buzzard, and require the most careful identification.

Most red kites are far from demonstrative at the nest. Those encountered by Doctor Blair in Spain all slipped away without any note of protest, and when they did reappear, it was only to do no more than circle, still silent, high above the nest.

One final word regarding the nesting of the red kite in the Canary Islands—exactly the same race which occurs in Britain and in Spain.

In Tenerife and Grand Canary there is no record of the kite nesting in any other tree than a pine, and even when a nest is built in the laurel zone a solitary giant pine amongst the laurels will be selected. The nest is a gigantic structure built of twigs loosely put together. Koenig found one with pine and chestnut twigs interwoven in the interior, the whole overlaid with the fur of rats and mice.

In comparison with the Spanish population the kite in the Canaries is sometimes an early breeder but the season is protracted. Meade-Waldo found a kite's nest above Santa Ursula on 2nd March and records that the nest contained young more than a week old! In his manuscript notes he further records that Don Ramon Gomez—a well-known collector of his day—had taken two eggs on 22nd February in Tenerife. In his private collection, however, he had two clutches only, both taken in the pinar of Santa Ursula on 19th April in two successive years. These two clutches, now in the British Museum, do not differ from the Continental clutches which I have examined, though one has the markings in the form of lines rather than spots forming a zone round the *pointed* end. These four eggs measure 59 × 45·5, 56 × 43, 55·5 × 42 and 56 × 43 mm.

Two eggs seem to be the complement in the Canaries, whereas in Corsica Colonel R. F. Meiklejohn found three to be laid. In that island the kite nests both in conifers and in deciduous trees. On one occasion the nest was in a thick cork tree and on another some twenty-five feet up in the main fork of an ilex.   Perhaps most curious of all is the fact that in the Balearic Islands Captain Munn invariably found it nesting among the crags in the hills and on the cliffs of the coast, never in trees,[1] though when Howard Saunders visited Majorca he found the nest in pines.

In the preceding account little has been said about the breeding biology of the red kite in northern Europe, where the bird has been studied meticulously by Gerhard Thiede and Adolf Zänkert[2] in the eastern part of Mark Brandenburg (1935) and later by L. Schuster[3] in Vogelsberg, Hesse (1950).   These authors give somewhat different dates for the arrival of the kites at their breeding places.   In Brandenburg the birds arrived in the last week of March or the first week of April, whereas in Hesse they turned up with great regularity, and independently of the weather, between 7th and 12th March, the 10th being an average date.   The sexes arrive at the same time and are apparently already paired.   Large undisturbed pine forests are their preference among places in which to rear their young, and trees of 150 years' growth may be selected.   Nests are placed as much as 97½ feet from the ground.

Thiede and Zänkert quote our countryman Kirkman's assertion that when the young are first hatched the female continues to brood over them, only leaving the nest for short intervals for food, often at about six a.m. Their own experiences substantiated Kirkman's observation.   In a summary of the results of their work these authors affirm that during the fourteen days that followed the hatching of the young the male kite provided all the food.   Schuster on the contrary believed that the young were fed and guarded by both parents in turn, but this appears to be the only point of disagreement between him and the other two observers in Brandenburg.

In the first few days of the young birds' life instinctive fights were observed to take place but they normally subsided harmlessly.   Thiede and Zänkert found that the chief feeding time was early in the morning, the male bird often taking his share in it.   By far the greater part of the prey brought to the nest was freshly killed and it was noted that in almost all cases the head was missing.   The nest was always kept tidy and even the smallest food remains were fed to the young.   Of food identified the authors mention jay, cuckoo, partridge, rabbit, water rat, weasel, lizard, bream, roach and perch, and observe that as far as they could see the prey was principally caught by the kites themselves.

The observations which L. Schuster was able to make in Hesse add considerably to what had previously been published by others.   He found that flight display of the two sexes was frequent over the nest in cloudy as well as in fine weather.   As long as eggs had not been laid the two birds

[1] *Novitates Zoologicae*, xxxvii, 1931, p. 99.
[2] *Beitr. Fortpfl.-Biol. Vög.*, xi, 1935, pp. 121-128 and 169-173.
[3] *Syllegomena Biologica*, 1950, pp. 406-412.

went off hunting together. This they did independently but they always kept near one another. No continual guarding of the territory appeared to take place, as is the case with the peregrine falcon.

It was found that about four weeks after arrival at the nest site the red kite begins to incubate and Schuster proved that the male does share that duty, incubating mainly in the forenoon. When the female is relieved she by no means goes off hunting at once, and the male also takes his time before setting off to forage.

Schuster raises the question of the age of sexual maturity and enquires whether the kite breeds at one year old or two. That question does not appear to have been satisfactorily answered.

In a nest kept under observation by Thiede and Zänkert the period between the time when the young (presumably the first egg) hatched, on 13th May, and the time when the youngster flew, on 1st July, was fifty days. It appears from their account that for fear of disturbing the kites they made few observations before the young had hatched and did not therefore ascertain the incubation period. *The Handbook* gives twenty-eight to thirty days on the authority of F. C. R. Jourdain but he acknowledges that confirmation is desirable. Incubation begins with the laying of the first egg. The parents moult during the breeding season.

REFERENCES : Original Description. *Falco milvus* Linnaeus, Syst. Nat., 10th ed., 1758, p. 89 : Europe, Asia, Africa. Restricted type locality southern Sweden.

PLATE 24   **BLACK KITE**

Milvus migrans migrans (Boddaert)

A very rare Accidental Visitor which up to date (January 1955) has been recognized in Britain five times, excluding a doubtful record in Dorsetshire in May 1954

IDENTIFICATION : Wherever the black kite breeds it passes under a name derived from its sombre colouring. Thus the Spaniard distinguishes it as " milano negro ", to his French neighbour it is " milan noir ", while in Germany it becomes " schwarzer Milan ". The first impression in the field is of a large, uniformly coloured hawk, and on dull days the bird may appear as dark as a raven. It is only under favourable conditions of light that the contrast between the deep brown, almost sepia, mantle and tail and the chestnut breast and greyish head becomes appreciable. Young black kites show pale markings on their underwings, noticeable at some distance though by no means as striking as those on the wing of a red kite, but with age the quills darken and in adults the light patch, smoke-grey rather than white, is absent or only faintly indicated.

Red and black kites differ in structure as well as in plumage. The tail of the red kite is by far the more deeply cleft, the longest feathers exceeding the shortest by more than three inches, whereas with the smaller black kite the difference is no more than two inches. A black kite's wing, besides, is not so long as that of its ally, and therefore appears proportionately broader and less sharply angled.

The black kite's forked tail and angled wings should prevent any confusion with dark examples of the common and honey-buzzards, or—in southern Europe—with the rather scarce dark-breasted phase of the booted eagle. A female marsh harrier in very dusky plumage more nearly approaches the black kite in appearance, but this species, like the buzzards and eagles, has a square-cut or slightly rounded tail.

In some lights, when flying very high, the crown of the head will appear much paler than is really the case and there is then the danger of assuming incorrectly that the bird is a red kite. I have myself been deceived in this way as the birds peered down during their flight.

OCCURRENCES IN GREAT BRITAIN: The first example to find its way to these islands was a mature male trapped in the Deer Park at Alnwick, Northumberland, a few days *prior* to 11th May 1866, on which date it came into the possession of Hancock, who recorded it in the *Ibis*, 1867, p. 253. The specimen was mounted and is in the Hancock Museum at Newcastle.[1]

The second to be obtained was shot near Aberdeen on 16th April 1901 within the city boundary and was recorded in the *Annals of Scottish Natural History*, 1901, p. 133.

The third, a juvenile example, was shot in the Scilly Isles on 16th September 1938 but had been observed in the vicinity of Tresco during the early part of the month. It was recorded in *British Birds*, xxxii, p. 237, by Mr. Arthur Dorrien-Smith.

The fourth example was also recorded from the Scilly Isles, on 28th May 1942, but was *not* obtained. It was, however, identified by Mr. A. Dorrien-Smith and the keeper who had actually shot the other Scilly Islands specimen recorded above. A note concerning this sight record appeared in *British Birds*, xxxvi, p. 74. Had this bird been a red kite the exceptionally forked tail could hardly have been overlooked, quite apart from the colour of the body plumage.

The fifth was shot on 14th May 1947 by Mr. H. Hogg at Beal, Northumberland, and is said to be a male in first summer plumage. The specimen is now in the Hancock Museum, Newcastle, and was recorded in *British Birds*, xl, p. 251, by Mr. S. E. Cook.

DISTRIBUTION ABROAD: The black kite has an extensive breeding range in Europe, ranging from Spain to Asia Minor and across middle and southern Europe. It is absent, however, from the greater part of France, the Low Countries (except as a rare vagrant), and Norway and Sweden, as well as from the British Isles. It has, however, bred in Finland and thence

[1] Cf. also Bolam's *Birds of Northumberland and the Eastern Borders*, p. 290, in which on Plate VIII appears a photograph of the mounted specimen.

eastwards to the River Ob in western Siberia. In Switzerland it is fairly common around the Lake of Geneva.[1] To Sweden it is but a rare visitor as to Britain.

Among the Mediterranean islands it breeds only in Sicily, though reported on migration in the Balearic Islands, Corsica and Malta. In north-west Africa it nests plentifully throughout Morocco, Algeria and Tunisia, ranging from the Mediterranean to the middle of the Sahara ; some details of this will be mentioned hereafter.

In Egypt its place is taken by a closely allied race, *Milvus migrans aegyptius*. Other races have been described from tropical Africa and others again from southern Arabia and Asia, the species having a huge range.

Throughout the whole of its breeding area, lying north of the Atlas Mountains, the black kite departs after the nesting season to spend the winter months in tropical Africa. Whether those which nest in the oases of the northern Sahara migrate or not is not definitely established, but I shall be very surprised if they do not join the vast throng which must annually pass through their breeding places from Europe. Doctor Austin Roberts has stated that the typical race from the north definitely reaches South Africa occasionally on its migrations, but normally there is no doubt that its journey does not extend beyond the Transvaal and south-west Africa.

Passing mention must be made of the black kite's status to-day in France and Spain, for in those countries it may still be seen in considerable numbers. Although reported to be decreasing in France of recent years, the black kite is much more common than the red kite, and is more generally distributed, so I am informed by M. Georges Olivier, who has made a special study of the species in his country. It nests to-day, he informs me, in suitable places in most parts of France except in the north and north-west. In some districts, as for instance the south-west and the south-east, the species is very common. It breeds also in the Camargue. In the French Mediterranean zone it breeds sparsely throughout, M. François Hüe tells me ; many pairs breed alone, and the colonies which exist are small.

While in Spain black kites can be found in most woodlands where birds of prey are not over-harried, it is in Andalusia that this species is most plentiful. It is, however, true to say that from March to September this migratory species is the most numerous and widely distributed of the larger Spanish raptorial birds. As the Madrid express runs clear of the Pyrenees the first bird of note to catch the eye is most likely " el milano negro ", and truly imposing the big hawk looks as it quarters a pasture within easy distance of the carriage windows. The same dark silhouette will be in evidence amongst the gulls circling about a steamer which has entered the mouth of the Guadalquivir, the whole length of the country away.

[1] According to Colonel R. F. Meiklejohn's notebooks.

MIGRATION : While it has once been stated by Castellarnau that the black kite is sedentary in the vicinity of San Ildefonso in the Province of Segovia, Spain, I agree with Harry Witherby that his statement is scarcely credible and do not believe that any but ailing birds remain north of the Mediterranean during the winter months, especially north of Madrid. The great majority cross the Straits of Gibraltar in September. Irby gives 9th October as the latest date on which he saw any of these birds on passage south. Witherby, who visited Spain several times, wrote that he had never seen a black kite in his autumn trips to that country, though in summer he had found the birds in much the same places and about the same numbers as the red kite ; Jourdain, however, found it the commoner of the two. At all points in the Mediterranean the autumn migration is not nearly so marked as the one in spring, and that is the case not only in the extreme west of the Mediterranean but as far east as Tunisia. In that country the vernal passage attracted Whitaker's attention many years ago, but he makes no mention of the birds passing south later in the year.

The migration is generally at its height in the closing days of March, Irby's dates for large flights ranging from the 25th to the 31st. In one year a few black kites passed over Gibraltar on 5th March, while in another Irby saw a small party as late as 5th May. Colonel W. A. Payn records them passing over Tangier on 27th March and occasional flocks have been seen passing Malta at the end of March and early in April.

I have once seen this passage myself across the Straits of Gibraltar, the birds sweeping up the western seaboard of Morocco and passing over the town of Tangier, where my wife and I happened to be, in incredible numbers. The full account[1] of the migration we witnessed between 22nd and 26th March 1951 has been given by us in the *Ibis*, for it was by no means restricted to the black kite, but a resumé of that experience may be repeated here[2] :

Tangier, 22nd March.—We were awakened in the night by the noise of the wind which had increased to gale force—a strong levanter had been blowing for two days, but at Tetuan there was little obvious migration taking place. This state of affairs seemed to have changed during the night of the 22nd, for no sooner had we opened our shutters in the morning than we became aware that the sky was full of birds. Immense numbers of black kites, *Milvus migrans*, were passing over Tangier and heading across the Straits in the direction of Spain. The kites were sailing against the strong east wind with barely a wing-beat ; they were well spaced out—singly, not in bunches. So pale did some of their crowns appear when viewed through field-glasses that we were almost led to believe there were red kites among them, but in this I am sure we were wrong. We were to have a much closer view of the passage later in the day, when all were *Milvus migrans*.

Flying high with the black kites were flocks of bee-eaters, *Merops apiaster*,

---

[1] *Ibis*, 1952, pp. 678-681.
[2] With acknowledgments to the Editor of the *Ibis*.

calling as they flew—in fact it was the voice of the bee-eaters which first attracted us. Unlike the kites, the bee-eaters were flying in flocks and all at a considerable height but clearly identifiable through field-glasses.

We drove quickly round the bay to the lighthouse at Cap Malabata, hoping to see the migrants more clearly, but instead found ourselves too far to the east of the main flight. Swallows, *H. rustica*, were passing in numbers, flying low over the land, dropping over the cliffs and continuing out to sea only just above the waves. A few house martins, *Delichon urbica*, were noted but none were seen to cross the sea.

Of other migrants we saw nothing until we had gained the heights above Tangier on the road to Cape Spartel, where we were to witness the migration in full swing. The hills above Tangier are well wooded, and from a vantage point at the head of a valley we could see the larger birds moving in a steady stream from the direction of the Pont International and over the low ground through which runs the coastal road to Arcila. From the saddle-back where we stood we watched the black kites sweeping up the valley, then low over the trees, some even sailing between the branches, so low were they flying over the steeply rising ground. There were never less than twenty in sight at a time and as long as we remained, the stream of kites continued.

The kites were not alone, indeed the curious thing about this migration was the number of small birds accompanying them, or at any rate moving in the same direction against the very strong wind. Bee-eaters, *M. apiaster*, were constantly passing, though some would rest for a while on the telegraph wires, perhaps birds which intended to remain in North Africa to breed. Swallows, house martins, sand martins and swifts were all on the move in the direction of Spain and several birds of prey were seen flying with the kites.

When we drove down to the sea-shore on the Atlantic side of Cape Spartel to obtain a view of the kites coming over the low ground, we became aware for the first time of the large migration of Montagu's harriers, *Circus pygargus*, which was following the shore-line and the maritime plain. Some of the harriers we watched beating in from the sea, over which they must surely have been blown farther down the coast. All these harriers were flying due north and coming along singly or in pairs. A terrific easterly gale was blowing, making it difficult to stand against it, and many of the harriers, but no black kites, settled on the shore, particularly in a sandy inlet where they could get a little shelter and rest before ascending the high ground between Cape Spartel and Tangier. In this little bay we found a thick-knee, two little ringed plover and two common sandpipers.

Considering that we had seen nothing of this great movement at Tetuan less than fifty km. to the east, though the levanter was already blowing before we left for Tangier, does this not point to the Atlantic coast-line being the main highway of many European migrants, and certainly of the black kites? From all accounts the kites, and doubtless also the other large birds of prey, await a strong cross wind before making the crossing of the Straits—in the case described a fierce *easterly* gale.

We woke on 24th March to a wonderful day—not a cloud in the sky, not a breath of wind, the sea like a lake. The levanter had stopped as suddenly as it began, having raged for three days until, in the evening of the 23rd, it blew itself out. With this abrupt change in the weather all visible signs of bird migration stopped also. Where the day before black kites, swallows and Montagu's harriers were steadily drifting out to sea from the African shores, there was not on this day a feather to be seen after 7.30 a.m., when a few belated black kites were observed passing. Before the sun was well up the astonishing migration we had witnessed on the previous day had completely ceased.

GENERAL HABITS : Compared with that of the red kite, which it closely resembles, the flight of the black kite seems fully as graceful and perhaps even more buoyant. Like the larger bird, the black species will swing for an hour or more in easy circles over the wood that holds its nest, and it hunts in the same fashion, beating backwards and forwards within fifty feet of the ground. It spends more time over water than the red kite, and is as nimble as a black-headed gull at retrieving edible flotsam. Dresser, who knew the kites well, considered the black kite the more wary, and yet the bolder in its hunting, but Doctor Blair could find no difference between the species in this respect.

An opportunity of gorging carrion or offal never comes amiss to the black kite, and some writers describe it as a scavenger by choice, but there can be little doubt that this hawk kills much of its food. The remains of frogs, snakes, lizards, blindworms and small mammals, including rabbits, have all been found in the stomachs of dissected examples, as well as small birds and insects. When large birds are captured it is generally because they are either weakly or disabled. In the breeding season these kites kill nestlings and fledglings of many species, such as the red-legged partridge, of which Major Congreve found two small chicks in one nest. As a result Spanish gamekeepers look rather askance at this bird. Where poultry is reared, the black kite can be as great a pest as the red, and in both Spain and Roumania it bears an unenviable reputation as a chicken-stealer. In the latter country Major Congreve found well-grown chicken-poults in some of the nests he climbed to—in one case as many as four.

That black kites live largely on insects is almost suggested by their migratory habits. They have been seen catching and devouring locusts on the wing, and one shot by Abel Chapman was " crammed " with such food. Colonel Verner supplied Seebohm with an account of a curious habit of the black kite which merits quotation. He had been studying the species in the pine woods by the Guadalquivir and wrote as follows :

These pine-forests are frequently broken by broad strips of sun-baked mud, which during the winter are, no doubt, a series of " lagunas ". The black kites congregated in numbers on these open places, where they crouch very much after the manner of pratincoles. I crept under cover of some scrub to within 150 yards of a party of twenty-two, and watched their proceedings through my binocular. Some were crouching on the ground, while others were walking about, apparently feeding.

When they detected my presence they rose with a shrill tremulous cry. I came upon many such parties of them, and on each occasion tried to make out what they were feeding upon. The ground was as hard as iron, and the scanty vegetation on it brown and dead ; so I conclude that they must have been catching some insects, judging from the frequency with which they picked at the ground.

As earlier mentioned, black kites can often be seen over the waters of a lake or river, either in search of floating refuse or actually fishing. Alphonse de la Fontaine, in his *Fauna de Luxembourg*, gives a picturesque account of the black kite capturing live fish day after day, unless the river happens to be in flood, at which time he maintains that the bird actually plunges into the water. One of Seebohm's correspondents also described the black kite as being very fond of fish, and noted that the nests were often covered with fish bones. According to the Editors of *The Handbook*, however, most of the fish these birds pick up they find dead on the surface.

The call of the black kite can easily be distinguished, after a little experience, from the notes of other hawks. Several observers have found it gull-like but undoubtedly the most faithful rendering is that given by Kirke-Swann (*Oologists' Record*, vol. i, no. 3) : " It starts with a piercing mewing whistle not unlike that of a buzzard, but is followed by three or four tremulous or whinnying notes."

In its winter quarters in Africa there has always been considerable difficulty in distinguishing the European migrant from the other races which are found in that great continent, though when viewed through field-glasses the black bill of the typical race will enable it to be distinguished from all except the Arabian subspecies, a rather doubtful race which usually has a dark bill also. The resident African black kites *aegyptius* and *tenebrosus* and *parasitus* all have yellow bills. For the above reason this bird has not been recognized as yet in western Africa north of the Equator, but many must either winter in the French Sudan or else pass through that territory, judging by the numbers which travel north by way of the Moroccan coast on their way to Europe.

Naturalists in East Africa have experienced the same difficulty in separating the European birds from the residents as Sir Frederick Jackson found in Kenya and Uganda. He identified a few with the aid of glasses and suggests that the European bird is more patient and is more apt to remain stationary than the yellow-billed race, which is more given to flapping and floating round villages than its European visiting relative. Sir Frederick held the view that *Milvus migrans migrans* is much more of a chicken-thief than the resident birds, and believed that the African kites were often wrongly credited with the misdeeds of the migratory race.

On the other hand, Colonel Meinertzhagen has stated [1] that in his opinion the European birds are *not* invariably poultry-robbers, except

[1] *Birds of Arabia*, p. 372.

particular birds which have developed a taste for chickens. He stresses the importance of the black kite as a scavenger and on the whole considers it beneficial to a human community. There is little doubt, as he points out in his *Birds of Arabia*, that the black kite feeds mainly on carrion and offal which it picks off the ground or off water with amazing accuracy. Its daring when in search of food is proverbial and it is recalled that it has been known to snatch a beefsteak from a soldier's plate while he was eating on a barrack-room verandah.

When stationed at Addis Ababa in Abyssinia in March 1932 Colonel R. E. Cheesman witnessed a huge migration of black kites, several thousand in number, some at a great height, wheeling continually and gradually drifting west to east. It is possible, he suggests, that this had some connection with a swarm of locusts which appeared the following day, taking the same direction, but the kites had gone ahead. They always make for the rising air of whirlwinds and soar up to a great height in them, apparently for the fun of it, as Colonel Cheesman noted that they descended to earth immediately after. In this case it was not possible to identify the kites subspecifically but it is probable that they were of the Egyptian race. Black kites appear regularly on the high plateau of Ethiopia after the rains ; almost certainly these birds are one of the resident African forms and not the European migrant.

BREEDING : The black kite, being a migrant, is considerably later in nesting than the other large Raptores, the honey-buzzard always excepted. Major Congreve has a set of eggs presumed to be of this species which were taken by a Spanish gamekeeper on 6th April, but this is exceptional. Generally the last week of April is quite soon enough to look for the eggs of this kite. In Spain many of the birds do not lay until the following month, two of several nests visited on 12th May in 1953 being still empty, while others held fresh eggs. In this connection it was interesting to read Professor Heim de Balsac's observations on the breeding of the black kite *south* of the Mediterranean in his study, " Contributions a l'Ornithologie du Sahara central et du Sud-Algérie ",[1] where he observes : " Bien que la reproduction du milan noir ait été constatée de très bonne heure en Algérie, nous n'avons personellement trouvé que des nidifications assez tardives. Au Dj. Bou-Khaïl des œufs frais nous furent apportés au début de mai et le 13 du même mois à Aïn-Sba nous n'avons trouvé que des nids en construction ou des œufs très frais." At Aïn-Sba the kites not only nest in the rocks on the hills but also come in from all around and on one occasion de Balsac counted a hundred circling around. He recalls that Hartert found this bird nesting at El-Goléa and that he himself found it in unbelievable numbers near Boghari, it being much more numerous in the north than in the south of Algeria.

In Spain, like those of the red kite, most black kites' nests are either

[1] *Mémoires de la Société d'Histoire Naturelle de l'Afrique du Nord*, 1926.

in stone pines or in cork oaks, and they may be anything from twenty to eighty feet from the ground. At times this hawk will appropriate the old nest of some bird of prey, just as its own is often taken over by a kestrel in after-years. Major Congreve found one pair of kites of this species in posssession of a nest which had been built by a snake-eagle two years previously. When the kites build for themselves, the result is an untidy, rough-looking structure in no way different from that of a red kite. Chapman and Buck maintained that the nest of a black kite could always be distinguished by the absence of anything approaching the " decoration " so favoured by the red kite, but all other observers have found the habit common to both species. R. B. Lodge, in his *Bird-Hunting in Wild Europe*, gives an excellent photograph of a black kite's nest, in which the eggs are surrounded by a choice assortment of rags, besides a match-box. All the many nests seen by Kirke-Swann had rag linings, some being quite festooned, together with such curious rubbish as a flattened goldfinch nest and a puff-ball fungus. In the Atlas Salvin found that black kites not only decorated their nests with rags but draped old pieces of Arab clothing of various colours on the branches around.

The Spanish headquarters of the black kite are those of its congener, the woodlands of stone pine and cork oak to the west of the Guadalquivir. Here kites may almost be said to nest in colonies. Abel Chapman counted " a score " of nests in a small wood of hardly two acres, while Kirke-Swann in 1921 found that " the pine-belt literally teemed with nests, new and old, most of them black kites', which birds we saw slipping off their nests in every direction ". From one tree he actually put two black kites off " twin nests almost touching each other ". In the more open cork groves, Doctor Blair came upon a dozen occupied nests of the two kites, besides those of the imperial eagle, raven and white stork, in the course of a short ride. Away from the Guadalquivir black kites are more sparingly distributed, but a pair or two will be found about most woodlands of any size, including those on the lower slopes of the sierras. Like the red kite, this species has never been particularly common near Gibraltar.

Some account has already been given under the heading of the red kite of the pine forests and cork groves so attractive to this species also. Within sight of these, yet many miles away, lies another resort of the two kites—a valley in one of the lesser sierras. The hillsides overhanging the river, which runs as strong and clear as a Scottish trout stream, are thickly wooded with oak and evergreens to within a hundred yards of their crests. Among the trees is a scrub of lentiscus, myrtle, gorse and barberry which extends beyond the woods to a line of rocky outcrops and cliffs, many half-hidden under ivy and bushes. This valley harbours almost as great a variety of raptorial birds as any of the cotos beyond the Guadalquivir. Fully 300 feet above the river a pair of black kites had their nest in a tall oak on the lip of a bramble-filled gully, in winter the bed of a rushing torrent; from this tree could be pointed out the nesting sites of at least six other raptorial species, all within an hour's journey.

In Spain the number of eggs laid by black kites seems to vary according to locality. About Algeciras, where the species is fairly plentiful, most of the nests seen by Major Congreve held two eggs, while in the woods along the Guadalquivir clutches of three are in the majority. As with the red kite, singletons are occasionally found. Major Congreve considers that large clutches are more frequent in Roumania than elsewhere. A nest to which he climbed in that country held no less than five eggs, and two sets of four were seen later in the season. Congreve adds that all these nests were in close proximity to a large poultry farm, which suggests a possible explanation for the unusually large clutches. Jourdain, it should be added, knew of only one other clutch of five.

The association between the Spanish sparrow and the red and black kites has already been discussed under the former species.

The smallest black kites' eggs examined by Jourdain measured 47 × 39·8 and 53·5 × 39·5 mm., the largest 61 × 42·3 and 55·7 × 46·1 mm., the average for his series being 52·92 × 43·33 mm. These eggs have rather coarse-grained shells with no trace of gloss, and a white ground, often faintly tinged with blue. In the character of the markings and the intensity of their pigments they vary considerably. Many have only a few spots, streaks and hair-lines of rust or yellowish-brown. Others are boldly blotched with reddish-brown, a clutch of such eggs being very handsome. One attractive type is clouded or washed with brown, while on another the pigment is distributed in networks of interlacing streakings. Some eggs of the black kite show underlying blotches of lilac, and on an unusual variety these are the only markings. Unpigmented eggs occur but only rarely. It is exceptional for an egg of this species to lack the streak-like markings, as if applied with a pen, which are characteristic of the genus *Milvus*.

While on an average black kites' eggs are smaller than those of the red kite, the larger amongst them exceed some of the latter in measurements. As the eggs of the two species hardly differ in shape and appearance, the identity of many clutches of kites' eggs can therefore be determined only if the bird is seen. Where a sufficient series of the eggs of these birds can be studied, it will be found that well-marked clutches occur more frequently with the black kite. Some eggs of this bird cannot be distinguished from similar varieties of the common and rough-legged buzzards.

While the incubation period for the black kite has yet to be exactly recorded, it is not likely to be less than four weeks. Both sexes take their turn on the eggs, according to German observers, and in an editorial note to an observation published by Mr. Derek Goodwin[1] that he had in Egypt watched the female of the local black kite being fed by the male when she was on the nest Mr. Jourdain gives further instances in support of this.

[1] *British Birds*, xxxix, pp. 121-122.

In Andalusia birds seen by Congreve sat closely, and when disturbed circled around the nest, " mewing " occasionally. Blair, however, found that they differed in their behaviour. One, in the sierras, remained on the eggs until the tree was knocked, and flew silently off, while another took wing as reluctantly but with much mewing protest. In Coto Doñana, where black kites are very common, they proved remarkably wary, the sitting birds all leaving their nests well out of gunshot and flying mutely away, even though their eggs were incubated.

REFERENCES :   Original Description. *Falco migrans* Boddaert, Tables Planches Enl., 1783, No. 472, p. 28 : Typical locality France.

PLATE 30
PLATE 31

WHITE-TAILED OR SEA-EAGLE

Haliaëtus albicilla (Linnaeus)

An Irregular Visitor which has long ceased to breed owing to persecution

IDENTIFICATION :   At all ages the sea-eagle or erne, as it used to be named, can be distinguished from the golden eagle—and also from the imperial eagle of Europe—by the unfeathered tarsi, but in life these are often concealed amongst the loose femoral plumage. When on the wing the sea-eagle can be recognized, again at all ages, from the two eagles cited by the shorter wedge-shaped tail. A fully mature individual should easily be identified, in a fair light, by its white tail and strikingly pale head, but again it is advisable to note the shape of the tail, for young golden eagles unfortunately have white tails with a black band at the tip. A young sea-eagle has a brown tail, but without any dark bands across it as are seen on the tail of an adult golden eagle. For the first few years of its life the sea-eagle has a horn-coloured beak similar to that of the golden eagle at all ages, but later the sea-eagle's beak turns yellow, while that of the golden eagle never does.

Ernest Lewis, the young naturalist who studied this eagle in Iceland, declared that the only clear and certain difference at all ages is that the golden eagle's tarsi are feathered and the sea-eagle's bare. In Doctor Blair's opinion from much experience in Norway, the wedge-shaped tail of the sea-eagle is an even better guide, as usually it can be seen more easily. The only other eagle at all resembling it which conceivably *might* occur in Europe is Pallas's sea-eagle, *Haliaëtus leucoryphus* (Pallas), but in this species the white tail feathers are broadly tipped with black. So far as body plumage is concerned the dark ash-brown colour of the upperparts and rather paler brown of the underparts in the sea-eagle do not distinguish the sea-eagle from the golden eagle.

Haliaëtus albicilla is the largest of the European birds of prey other than the vultures—black, griffon and bearded. The Scottish naturalist

PLATE 30

WHITE-TAILED or SEA-EAGLE
Haliaëtus albicilla (Linnaeus)

McGillivray handled birds with wing spans of seven feet in the flesh, and examined one skin which measured nine feet across. Ernest Lewis gave eight feet as a normal expanse of Iceland birds and the Greenland race, separated on its usually larger size, must be that and more.

A striking characteristic of the sea-eagle, which is shared by the American bald eagle, is the development of the bill, especially noticeable when the bird alights. McGillivray, who had many sea-eagles through his hands, noticed that in every one the bill was nearly as long as the head. In a typical male measured by the great Scottish naturalist the bill was $3\frac{5}{12}$ inches along the ridge, 3 inches along the lower mandible, and $1\frac{5}{12}$ inches high, the same dimensions in a female being $3\frac{11}{12}$ inches, $3\frac{4}{12}$ inches, and $1\frac{8}{12}$ inches. The bill of a large female golden eagle with a span of 87 inches measured only $2\frac{9}{12}$ inches along the ridge and $2\frac{1}{2}$ inches along the lower mandible, with a cere of $\frac{10}{12}$ inches. The only eagles more powerfully billed are the handsome birds of the Pacific genus *Thalassoaëtus*, Steller's and the Korean sea-eagles.

In its movements the sea-eagle appears a more sluggish bird than the golden eagle. It will sit for hours on a tree, stump or ledge of rock, or even in shallow water. Its cry has been described by Jourdain as " a querulous chatter insignificant for so large a bird " and by others as a " loud, shrill *krikrikrikri*". In moments of intense anger or alarm this changes into a deep-toned *gaa-gaa-gaa*, likened by some Norwegian observers to the hoarse note of the lesser black-backed gull.

FORMER LOCAL DISTRIBUTION : The total disappearance of this grand bird from the breeding species of Great Britain is a severe loss to all lovers of bird-life. There was a time when it was even more numerous in some districts of Scotland than the golden eagle, but whereas the latter has managed to survive, the sea-eagle has been completely exterminated. Now and again it pays a visit from overseas but it is too much to hope that it will ever be allowed to breed again in any of its old haunts. Its fondness for new-born lambs has sealed its fate.

In Miss Baxter's and Miss Rintoul's standard work on the birds of Scotland a very full account will be found of its former distribution and status in Scotland and the islands. These ladies begin their detailed analysis, which traces the bird county by county and covers eight and a half pages, with the following sentences : " The White-tailed Eagle used to be widely distributed and abundant, especially along our coasts and islands, and, even up to the middle of last century, was still in fair numbers in Northern Scotland and the Islands. It was remorselessly persecuted and its numbers gradually reduced until it finally ceased to breed, the last records being of an eyrie somewhere in Scotland in 1911 and one in Skye in 1916."

By the end of the eighteenth century the birds had ceased to nest on the mainland, with the exception of a pair or two in the extreme north. Doctor Eagle Clarke considered that it probably ceased to breed on the mainland of Scotland in 1889, but F. C. R. Jourdain is reported to have had a clutch in his collection taken in Sutherland in April 1901. On the islands the white-tailed eagle bred plentifully and pairs managed to exist in remote localities longer than elsewhere. In the days when Robert Gray wrote of the birds of the west of Scotland it was probably more numerous in Skye than anywhere else, nearly all the bold headlands being frequented by at least one pair. At one time, prior to 1871, it is said that as many as forty could be seen together attracted by carrion, but by 1886 they were becoming scarce and a few years later their doom was sealed. Surprisingly, a pair or two hung on until the beginning of the First World War or later. At that date, 1914, Mr. Seton Gordon wrote that " there are, at most, only two pairs of these birds nesting in Britain ". A pair bred in 1916, which is the latest record in *The Handbook*, but when Miss Baxter and Miss Rintoul were in Skye in 1930 they were informed on good authority that a pair of white-tailed eagles had bred on the island long after they were presumed to be extinct.

On the mainland, in the days when they were common, they were to be found in many parts of the country other than the Highlands and Islands, more especially perhaps in the wilder country of Dumfriesshire, Kirkcudbright and the Mull of Galloway. There is even an old record of the species on Criffel, a mountain which rises to 1800 feet, close to which our own farm, Boreland of Southwick, is situated. There were eyries too on Ailsa Craig and on the Bass Rock, among many other well-known landmarks where the white-tailed eagle formerly reigned supreme.

The story of the last resident in Britain, which lived on North Roe, one of the Shetland islands, for about thirty years, has been told by George Lodge in his *Memoirs of an Artist Naturalist*. This bird was an albino and originally had a normal-coloured mate, the pair breeding for the last time in 1908. When its mate was killed the white eagle brooded on its nest each year until 1918, when it too succumbed to the same fate.

About former breeding places in England there is less to record. In the north of England it once bred in Cumberland in the vicinity of Keswick and Ullswater, and it is said to have bred until 1815 in the Isle of Man. Devonshire is another county in which it nested in former days, both near Plymouth and on Dartmoor. In the Isle of Wight a pair bred in the Culver Cliff up to 1780. But on the whole eyries were scarce around the English coasts even in the early eighteenth century. There does not appear to be any breeding record for Yorkshire, in which county with its precipitous sea cliffs the eagle might have been expected to have a footing. Nor are there apparently any records from Wales, unless these are buried in ancient faunal accounts.

The white-tailed eagles in Ireland have suffered the same fate as those of Scotland. When Ussher and Warren published their *Birds of Ireland* in 1900, they recorded that until the middle of that century the eagle bred in the marine cliffs of Munster, Connaught and Ulster and at a somewhat earlier date in those of the Wicklow Mountains. " It is now," they wrote, " on the point of extinction, its last resorts being in the most remote parts of Kerry and Mayo." The new *Birds of Ireland* (1954) quotes Ussher, but adds nothing new with reference to its breeding for there has been nothing fresh to add. Wandering examples turn up now and again between November and March and five are recorded by Colonel Scroope as having occurred between 1935 and 1950.

DISTRIBUTION ABROAD : The typical race of the white-tailed eagle has a vast breeding area in the north Palæarctic Region, ranging in the west from Iceland and Scandinavia[1] eastwards to Mongolia and Kamchatka. Its breeding range in western Europe extends to north Germany and Hungary, and reaches the Mediterranean in Jugoslavia, Albania, Greece and Asia Minor. It is reported to have once bred in Corsica and Sardinia and may still breed in the latter island. Formerly it is reported to have nested on Dragonera in the Balearic Islands but has ceased to do so for many years. I can find no mention of its having nested in Spain and it probably only occurs in the Peninsula as a rare vagrant in winter. It has been reported on fairly reliable evidence about five times from the Canary Islands as a vagrant, but has never been obtained. Canon Tristram's record from Lanzarote is probably the best authenticated, for such an experienced ornithologist would hardly have confused it with the osprey. I have, however, failed to trace a record from Morocco. It has been taken on migration off the north coast of Tunisia on the small island of Galita in the month of December (the skin is in the Whitaker Collection), and is reported also from Tabarka on the Tunisian mainland. Formerly this eagle nested in small numbers in Egypt in the reedy marshes of Lake Menzaleh, two of the adults having been shot and examined by Howard Saunders. To-day it is only a scarce winter visitor to Egypt and is occasionally reported from the Suez Canal and from the northern end of the Red Sea.

The distribution of the white-tailed eagle in the Soviet Union of Russia has not been known in any detail for a number of years. Thanks to Madame Elizabeth Kozlova this gap in our knowledge can now be made good and I quote from a letter received from her in December 1954 in which, in reply to my enquiry, she writes as follows :

Haliaëtus albicilla breeds throughout all the European parts of U.S.S.R. and Siberia as far north as the tundra border, penetrating also within the tundra zone, mostly along large river valleys with tree vegetation. In the north it ranges to the lake district of Kola peninsula, to the southern part of Jamal peninsula to the mouth of the River Ob, along the Yenisei River to 72° N. and to the mouths of the Lena, Indigirka and Kolyma Rivers. In the north-east and east it ranges to Anadyr, Kamchatka and Ussuri Land.

---

[1] I learn on good authority that a pair have bred this year, 1955, in Denmark.

In the south its range extends to the lower Dnieper, the Crimea and to the mouth of the Volga. It is common in the Caucasus and Transcaucasia and is sporadically distributed in Turkestan, there being breeding records from the lower reaches of Amu-Daria and Ili Rivers. Further east the southern limit of the range of *H. albicilla* passes through the Zaissan Depression, Russian Altai, north-west Mongolia and Transbaikalia.

The white-tailed eagle winters partly in Transcaucasia and southern Ussuri Land, where it is very common during the winter months.

Madame Kozlova's personal experiences of this eagle in her native land and her account of finding it breeding both on an island of the Caspian and again on the Kola peninsula are recounted in the section headed " Habits in the U.S.S.R." (see p. 293).

In its wanderings outside the breeding season the white-tailed eagle reaches India and China.

A subspecies *Haliaëtus albicilla groenlandicus* Brehm is recognized from Greenland. It is restricted to the west, where it breeds north to Disko Bay. The difference lies in the greater measurements but there is much overlapping. (See Salomonsen, *Grønlands Fugle*, part 3, p. 420.)

HABITS IN GREAT BRITAIN : Mr. Seton Gordon, than whom there is no greater authority on the eagles of Scotland, stated many years ago, when a pair or two still nested in Skye, that the cause of the white-tailed eagle's rapid decrease may be set down to its partiality for lambs. Unlike those of the golden eagle, its eyries were situated almost entirely along the coast-line, on the west of Scotland, where sheep farming is largely practised. Shepherds and sheep farmers trapped the bird whenever they could and shot the hen at the nest. It was treated everywhere as an outlaw and in Skye at one time a reward of ten shillings was paid for each erne accounted for. On the mainland the bird was equally persecuted and in Wester Ross a single keeper accounted for fifty-two sea-eagles during the course of twelve years. Mr. Seton Gordon believed that if its nesting sites had been more remote and inaccessible, like those of the golden eagle, it would have held its own.

In Britain the prey of this eagle consisted of much more than fish. It was much more a carrion-eater than *Aquila chrysaëtos* and, as already noted, was much more dangerous to lambs. It has been seen, as Seton Gordon recounts, raising and dropping lambs merely for sport, rising to a height and endeavouring to recapture them before they reached the ground. Such habits are unlikely to endear the bird to Highland sheep owners. It had also been seen to chase grouse, and among birds which it used freely to capture were guillemots and kittiwakes. Fish were at times captured when daylight had departed and its plunge into the sea after some unlucky fish has not infrequently been heard, the great form of the eagle passing swiftly by in the gloom. That it can rise from the water with a heavy weight was borne out by a trout of twelve pounds having

PLATE 24

PLATE 31

SEA-EAGLE, MOBBED BY HOODED CROWS
Norway, N. of Trondhjem, 4th October 1899

once been found in an eyrie in the Lake District. A sea-eagle has, Mr. Gordon recounts, been known to attack a sleeping seal and one bird was seen to carry off a pig. It is hardly surprising with such a record that it was not left to enjoy its peace in the Highlands and Islands of our native land.

In these islands the nesting site has usually been a lofty precipice along the sea coast but occasionally an inland one was chosen. Like its relative, the golden eagle, the white-tailed species had often two eyries, placed a short distance from each other, and these it used as occasion demanded. Even where lofty cliffs abound, as in Shetland, the sea-eagle did not always make use of them, for on one occasion cited by Mr. Gordon the eyrie was found on the ground. Normally the eyrie was a bulky structure six to eight feet in diameter and often reached a great age before it was brought to the ground by a heavy snowfall or gale of exceptional severity.

Mr. Gordon found that the nesting materials used by the sea-eagle in Scotland did not differ much from those utilized by the golden eagle, only that fresh-pulled fir branches were not found in the nests of the white-tailed species. As a receptacle for the eggs, the plant *Luzula sylvatica* was chosen, and the eagle sometimes added a bunch or two of seaweed for the adornment of the home. It was usually the first week of April before the two or three eggs were laid in Scottish nests and the first days of August had arrived before the young sea-eagles were ready and able to leave the eyrie.

HABITS ABROAD : If ornithologists in Britain are ever to enjoy the sight of a pair of nesting sea-eagles again it is almost certainly from Norway that the birds will come. The unfortunate bird very nearly met the same fate there as it did with us, but thanks now to a more rigid protection it has managed to survive and some account of it in that country as it is to-day may be of interest in this book. As usual I have to thank Doctor Hugh Blair and Doctor Yngvar Hagen for the details, and especially for the notes on its breeding habits in that country.

Amongst the countries of western Europe Norway can undoubtedly boast the largest sea-eagle population. Nevertheless this fine species was until very recently losing ground to an alarming extent. Less than a century ago it bred here and there along the whole coast-line from Hvaler to Sör-Varanger. There was at one time an eyrie no further from Oslo than Dröbak, and another close to Fredrikstad, in Onsöy. At the latter site the last birds were killed in 1882, and in the course of time resort after resort was deserted, through the agency of gun, trap or poison, until it was believed that the sea-eagle had been banished from the whole coast-line south of Sunmöre, about Aalesund. It was with great satisfaction therefore that local ornithologists learned, in 1949, of the discovery by Doctor J. F. Willgohs (noted curator of vertebrates in Bergen Museum) of an occupied eyrie in Sogne and Fjordes between Bergen and Aalesund. In a letter of recent date Doctor Willgohs tells us that he has since noted sea-eagles elsewhere along the coast between the Sogne fjord and the Stat, where he thinks there must be at least five pairs. Some, if not all, of these may have been overlooked in the past, as this part of Norway has been little explored by ornithologists. Still, Doctor Willgohs' accounts of eyries unmolested and broods reared encourage the belief that in Norway the blackest days for the sea-eagle have passed.

Northwards from the Sogne fjord sea-eagles' eyries are to be found up to the Russian frontier, the majority of them in Helgeland and around Tromsö. Save in the extreme north-east, this is indeed the sea-eagle, confined to the neighbourhood of salt water, and breeding both on the mainland and on all the larger islands, including the most isolated of the Lofotens, Röst. There were a few inland eyries in East Finmark at the beginning of the present century, one being a good seventy miles from the Varanger fjord, with others in Finland around Lake Enare; and some of these may still be tenanted. The last inland resort in southern Norway was deserted many years ago.

As mentioned earlier, most Norwegian resorts of the sea-eagle are by the sea, where the birds can easily obtain the fish and waterfowl on which they depend. Where sea-birds are very plentiful, several eyries may sometimes be found on the one island. Those eagles that in former days bred inland preferred tall, old forests about land-locked fjords or broad lakes. Amongst such surroundings the birds proved more vulnerable than on the great sea cliffs, and there it was that the persecutors of the sea-eagle gained their first successes.

While fully mature sea-eagles appear to be sedentary, the younger birds certainly undertake lengthy journeys. Each autumn numbers of eagles—mostly sea-eagles with a few golden eagles among them—pass down the long chain of islands off the coast of Norwegian Nordland on their way to the most seaward of all, Vaeröy and Röst. There the birds find a mild climate, ice-free seas and an abundance of fish. " The heralds of the dark days ", one island recorder calls the vanguard of these migrants, which appear from the north and east as the first snows of autumn whiten the mainland fells. Other contingents follow when the winter gales set in.

Eagle-trapping was for time out of mind a regular occupation on Vaeröy and Röst, and only when head-money could no longer be claimed for the birds did the practice finally die out. Thome, the Norwegian ornithologist, has left some interesting notes on the simple, almost primitive stratagem employed. Hard by some eagle-haunted fell the trapper dug a pit about a yard deep, around which he built a rough stone hut of equal height, finally adding a roof of stone slabs. The entrance he closed with a large piece of turf. A little distance away was displayed some carrion, usually a sheep's entrails, secured by a cord which led into the hut. On a favourable morning the trapper would begin his patient vigil before daylight. Sometimes he had not long to wait before an eagle appeared. Even when most sharp-set, the bird would always break off its gorging at intervals to look around for possible dangers. Whenever it was so employed, the trapper carefully drew the carrion a little nearer to the hut. So far from showing any uneasiness as the lure moved, the eagle would tear at it the more fiercely. If all went well, the bird would follow its meal right up to the hut, when the trapper, waiting until his quarry's attention was once more distracted, would seize it by the legs and drag it in. Finding itself in the utter darkness behind the turf curtain, the eagle would offer no resistance. If two or more eagles were at the bait together, it sometimes happened that when the first was captured the others continued feeding. With luck, a trapper could catch two or three eagles in a few hours. But his patience often went unrewarded, and there he would remain crouched in the hut until darkness fell. The trappers worked from the end of October until Christmas, the season's catch varying between fifty and a hundred. In the 'eighties and 'nineties an eagle was worth three kroner to its captor, who claimed two-thirds of the sum as head-money, and earned the remainder by selling the wings to be used as brooms.

Disappointingly little is on record of the food of the sea-eagle in Norway, and we must still rely largely on Collett's notes. According to these, sea-eagles prey mainly on fish and waterfowl, chiefly diving ducks, the various auks, and shags, with gulls in the minority. A diving bird is usually gripped as it comes to the surface, and two eagles will combine to tire out the one quarry. Most sea-birds therefore seek safety in flight upon the appearance of an eagle, in striking contrast to their behaviour if a falcon is in the offing, when not one will take to the air. Nevertheless, a sea-eagle can on occasion get the better of a flying bird. A pair nesting on Lovunden preyed on little else than puffins, which were mostly taken on the wing. Once the eaglets are hatched, their parents often bring captured birds alive to the eyrie, first disabling them by crushing their limbs.

A local observer furnished Collett with much original and reliable information on the habits of the sea-eagles breeding on the island of Rodöy. There he found that the eagles procured much of their food by scavenging after otters and gulls. The otters' leavings were mostly wolf-fish (*Anarrhicas lupus*), of which the beasts had consumed only the forequarters, with a few cod and plaice. When an eagle profited by a gull's fishing, the spoil was usually a lump-sucker (*Cyclopterus lumpus*) with its eyes and viscera picked out but otherwise untouched. The eagles themselves seldom caught fish, the biggest catches being small coalfish. On these coasts eiders, mostly old drakes, predominated amongst the birds found about sea-eagles' homes. The bodies of a number of these ducks lay about one eyrie, all still fully feathered, and some far advanced in decomposition, but at another the eagles had brought back all such prey thoroughly plucked and with head and wings torn away.

Konservator Soot-Ryeng has watched the sea-eagle of Masvaër, off Tromsö, despoiling greater black-backed gulls of their catches, again lump-suckers. These eagles also destroyed many of the hares that swarmed about the island.

According to Kolthoff and Jägerskiöld, the fish chiefly taken by sea-eagles off Sweden are the coalfish (*Gadus virens* and *Gadus pollachius*), cod and *Cottus scorpius*. Pike are the commonest scaled prey about inland waters. Schaanning found pike bones under one eyrie in the Pasvik forests, together with the remains of capercaillie, wild geese and a reindeer calf. That sea-eagles will readily gorge themselves on carrion is well known, and in the old days many were shot over baits of offal. From time to time publicity has been given to tales of small children being carried off by sea-eagles, once as recently as 1932. None of these, it need hardly be said, will bear critical scrutiny.

It has become almost a tradition that sea-eagles can be dragged below the surface and drowned by very large fish, or seals, at which they have struck, and it is even alleged that the intended prey has occasionally survived with the eagles' talons locked in its back long after the body of the bird has rotted away. The story finds a place in Collett's *Norges Fugle*, but without a supporting record being cited. One Norwegian told Doctor Blair that he had witnessed such a mishap to an eagle on one of the more remote Finmark fjords. The bird, he said, laid hold of a seal, which instantly dived, taking its assailant with it. Very shortly the eagle reappeared in a dying condition and with its wings broken. Harvie-Brown quotes a Highland keeper as stating that he had seen an eagle killed in this way.[1] He also notes that " about forty years ago a sea-eagle came ashore in Hoy, dead, fast in a fish and another time a halibut was found with an eagle's feet still in its back, the bird having rotted off; the latter case, however, was in Shetland ".[2] Harvie-Brown appears to have had some faith in the source of his information. Saxby clearly thought otherwise, and his opinion of such stories, and their possible origin, it is well to bear in mind.[3]

In the seventies and eighties of the last century, according to the ill-fated Rudolf, Crown Prince of Austria, the sea-eagle was the " best-known " and " commonest " of the eagles occurring in his country. " With the exception of the Alps," he wrote, " every part of Austria is yearly visited by the bird in the course of its wanderings." Up to about 1840 there were occupied eyries in the riverside woods near Vienna, but at the

[1] *Fauna of North-West Highlands and Skye*, p. 152.
[2] *Fauna of the Orkney Islands*, p. 150.
[3] *Birds of Shetland*, pp. 4-6.

time when the Crown Prince undertook the shooting trip chronicled in *Sport and Ornithology* the only breeding stations left within the imperial domains were in southern Hungary, to the east of Budapest. There the birds must have still been common enough, for the Crown Prince and his party visited nineteen inhabited eyries in a few days.

The place where the sea-eagles nested was difficult of access, for open expanses of water alternated with great forests of reeds, half sub-merged thickets, and clumps of tall silver poplars, oaks, willows and elms; fallen stems lay with their highest parts out of the water, and dead oaks, black poplars and wild fruit trees stood isolated among the rustling reed-beds.

All was flooded, and a gentle breeze played over the ripples and the rich verdure in which this exuberant vegetation was decked.

The tree with the nest was on a longish strip of land, nowhere more than twenty yards wide, and though not now under water, the muddiness of the ground showed that the floods had but recently left this more elevated spot. Here stood huge ancient oaks with their thick foliage and dead twisted upper branches, and there were also a few gigantic silver poplars, but the only black poplar was the one on which the nest was placed, and its peculiar form made it conspicuous among all the other trees.[1]

Thirty years later all had changed. R. B. Lodge saw no eagles or any other large bird of prey during a voyage along the same stretch of the Danube in 1907. " It is possible, of course," he comments in *Bird-Hunting in Wild Europe*, " that a few birds may still exist in the more remote parts . . . but it would be quite hopeless to expect to find them in the abundance of thirty years ago."

Farther down the Danube, the sea-eagle continues to hold its own, or at least did so until shortly beyond the recent war. Major W. M. Congreve was rowed to five nests along one Roumanian side-stream of the great river in the course of a day. Southwards of the Danube sea-eagles nest in some numbers throughout the Balkan Peninsula, and particularly in Greece, as well as in Asia Minor.

Habits in the U.S.S.R. : The following notes, sent to me from Leningrad by Madame E. Kozlova, will be of special interest to western readers, as very little has been told of the habits of this bird in the area with which this eminent ornithologist deals. On the small island of Sara near the south-west coast of the Caspian Sea in the vicinity of Lenkoran in Transcaucasia the white-tailed eagle may be seen both in winter and in spring, and in the winter months is numerous, from five to seven being seen within the space of a thousand metres. The birds would sit for hours on pieces of wood thrown up by the waves, on piles of seaweed or simply on the ground, sometimes in shallow water, digesting their last

[1] *Sport and Ornithology*, pp. 38-39.

meal. On this particular island Madame Kozlova found that the eagle fed mostly on dead fish, dead or wounded birds and even dead jackals. Any kind of meat was acceptable to them. The body of a jackal which she had skinned was exposed in an open glade nearby and was soon discovered by three white-tailed eagles, which with much fuss and quarrelling devoured the body in about three hours. On another occasion an eagle attacked a jackal in a trap but Madame Kozlova was not in time to see how the eagle had dispatched its victim. On the approach of a sea-eagle at no great height above the water all ducks and even geese (*Anser anser* and *Anser albifrons*) take to wing in a great hurry to get out of the eagle's path, but although the eagle catches coots with facility, especially those which are very fat and scarcely able to fly, it has never been known by Madame Kozlova to capture a goose.

In the north of its Asiatic range this eagle feeds on lemmings; *Ondatra*; fish, principally pike; birds such as ducks, *Tetrao urogallus* and *Lagopus*; and sometimes mice and water rats.

On Sara Island, where so many had wintered, only one pair remained to breed. Nesting must have begun in this latitude about the end of February, as on 13th March two chicks about two to four days old were found in the nest. The nest was situated in the crown of an old alder tree, about eight metres from the ground. The lining of the nest consisted of pieces of rotten bark, roots and stems of grasses. In the nest were found three *Podiceps cristatus*, one *Larus ridibundus*, one *Fulica cristata* and common coots. The female eagle brooded the young while the male, when not hunting, sat on a dry branch of the same tree. One of the young birds was taken and shortly afterwards the other disappeared. The parents then visited another nest in the vicinity which they were busy repairing for several days but eventually deserted before eggs were laid, and no second brood was reared in this instance. In the Ukraine fresh eggs may be found in March.

To enable a comparison to be made with the breeding dates in northern Russia, Madame Kozlova tells me that a nest with one fresh egg was found on the Kola peninsula—north of the White Sea—on 10th May and a young bird just out of the nest was obtained in the same region on 4th August 1948. A nest of this eagle on the Jamal peninsula (north of the mouth of the River Ob) was first noted in 1913. This same site was occupied by a pair of eagles in 1938, which is proof, Madame Kozlova contends, that one and the same nest, repaired every year, may last for twenty-five years.

For its habitat the white-tailed eagle prefers regions near the sea coast, or near lakes and rivers, especially if there are a few tall trees in the vicinity in which it can nest.

The winter visitors leave Transcaucasia about the middle of March and spring migration is recorded from the valley of the lower Syr-Daria in the second half of March.   First arrivals in the north have been seen on the Kola peninsula on 2nd April 1937 and 29th April 1938, on the Jamal peninsula on 13th April, on the lower Indigirka River on 7th April, and in Anadyr Land in the first half of April.

The return migration begins in the north of Russia at the end of September.   The earliest date of departure of the white-tailed eagle from the Kola peninsula is 25th September, the latest 14th October.   Autumn migrants were noted at Chkalow (formerly Orenburg) in the middle of September and the eagles arrive on the south-western shores of the Caspian Sea about the end of October or the beginning of November to spend the winter in the south.

BREEDING HABITS IN SOUTH-EAST EUROPE :   Sea-eagles' eyries along the Danube and in the Balkans are usually difficult of access. Crown Prince Rudolf was surprised to find one on " a weak oak sapling in the middle of a young cover ", as all the others he knew of were in thick, high trees.   Of the nineteen of which he made notes, six were in oaks, five in white poplars, as many in black poplars, two in beeches and one in a wild pear tree.   In Albania one pair of sea-eagles had resorted to an " immense silver poplar ", while two others preferred huge pollarded oaks (R. B. Lodge).   Of the Roumanian eyries seen by Major Congreve all but one were at heights of from fifty to seventy feet, three in willows and two in black poplars.   The exception was built in a wind-fell tree and was no more than twenty feet above the ground.   On the Greek coasts Captain Cochrane found that the eagles' nesting tree, usually an oak or a chestnut, could often be scaled without any great difficulty.   An old eyrie often includes a good cartload of sticks, and may be six feet across.   Sixteen of the eyries Crown Prince Rudolf saw "were peopled with whole colonies of tree-sparrows ", which recalls the association between the Spanish sparrow and the imperial eagle recorded by Lord Lilford and others.   One long-occupied eyrie on the Greek coast finally became too great a burden for the tree, which lost its foothold and fell from the crag.   Major Congreve was shown an eyrie which had been at one time the refuge of a notorious bandit.

While some sea-eagles are not at all demonstrative at the eyrie, others are very noisy.   Both birds of one pair with hard-sat eggs persisted in returning to the tree although repeatedly fired at (Congreve).   The birds seen by Crown Prince Rudolf, although clamorous enough, were mostly very wary.   One exceptionally bold individual stooped at the Prince's climber, and could easily have been killed " so closely and steadily did it hover like a hawk over the nest, screaming loudly ".   The Crown Prince relates at some length a remarkable experience of his companion, Brehm. The latter had wounded a sea-eagle from a hide, and had sent the keeper who was with him after it.

The man managed to come up with the injured bird and to give it a finishing shot ; but when he was going to lift it from the ground, they both observed another sea-eagle circling high overhead. As soon as this bird saw the keeper pick up its slain comrade it folded its wings and swooped down like an arrow, and the keeper, whose attention was attracted by the noisy flappings of its heavy wings, looked up and saw the eagle only a few feet above his head, with its claws ready extended for attack. The charge was so furious, and the bird was so close, that the keeper, although a perfectly courageous man, was obliged to spring behind the trunk of an adjacent beech tree to guard himself against a fresh assault.

In south-eastern Europe, as in Norway, sea-eagles begin nesting operations very early in the year. The eaglets seen by Captain Cochrane in Greece were at least three weeks old in mid-March, which points to the eggs having been laid shortly after New Year's Day. Four eyries visited by Makatsch in Macedonia held slightly incubated eggs between 13th and 17th February. In Albania R. B. Lodge found incubated eggs in March. Every eyrie which Crown Prince Rudolf's climber reached contained large young at the end of April. On the other hand, those seen by Major Congreve in Roumania all still had eggs, some only slightly incubated, on the 2nd of that month.

BREEDING HABITS IN NORWAY: The sea-eagle becomes sexually mature at the age of five or six years, when it pairs for life. If one of a pair dies, the survivor soon finds a new mate, at least in districts where the species is not on the verge of extinction. Then it has been known for a lone eagle to haunt a breeding station for years after it has lost its partner, like the last of the Shetland birds.

Doctor Yngvar Hagen quotes a vivid account by an eye-witness —again the Norwegian ornithologist, Thome—of the courtship of the sea-eagle. The two birds were circling together at a great height when first seen. At times as they passed each other calling loudly, they would turn on their sides and stretch out their great talons. Every now and then one would dive earthwards in an imposing stoop, its great quills cleaving the air with a sound like distant thunder. Pairing did not immediately follow such a display but took place as much as an hour later. It lasted some ten or twelve seconds, and both birds screamed in a high-pitched tone the whole time.

In Norway a sea-eagle's eyrie is usually built in a precipitous cliff, either on the rock itself on in a pine growing on one of the wider ledges. Most can only be reached by climbers of skill and experience, and some are practically inaccessible. At the other extreme, Chaworth-Musters noted in his diaries that he could walk into one eyrie, and that another was on a small hillock in the midst of a bog on the flat island, Smölen, where Thome visited a similar, if not the same site. In inland forests the birds prefer a tall, sturdy pine, the eyrie being placed as near the top as possible.

A newly built eyrie will be about 1·8 metres across and from ·8 to 1 metre in height. As the structure is occupied and repaired year after year, it may in the course of time be enlarged to a height of as much as 1½ metres. The foundation of the eyrie consists of a firmly interwoven mass of branches and twigs. Above this comes a layer of finer twigs and foliage, both dry and green, and finally a great pad of grass, heather, lichens, moss and the like, with, in the north of Norway, seaweed and wool. One eyrie in Namdal is described by Collett as built of dry pine branches of about a thumb's girth, with a thick inner layer of moss, straw, dry grass, shoots of heather (*Calluna vulgaris*), crowberry-ling (*Empetrum nigrum*) and pieces of seaweed (*Fucus vesiculosus*), the last collected some three miles away.

In Norway sea-eagles are among the earlier nesters. On Onsöy, the last breeding station to be occupied in the south of the country, the first egg was generally laid between 20th and 26th March. On the Helgeland coasts nests contain eggs early in April, while in Finmark laying does not take place until 1st May. Many of the earlier-laid eggs are addled by frost and snow, in which case the birds produce a second clutch about three weeks later. The eggs are laid at intervals of several days, two or, less commonly, three being the normal clutch. A series from Norway varied in length from 70 to 83 mm., and in breadth from 56 to 62 mm., one quite abnormal specimen being 88 mm. long. A fresh unblown egg weighed 140 grams (Yngvar Hagen). In shape these eggs show considerable variation. The more typical are blunt ovate, but some are almost round, while a few are as elongated as those of the geese. Some are rather rough in the shell, while others show a slight gloss. Collett describes these white eggs as being very occasionally and only sparingly spotted with rust-red, but, as Jourdain points out, it is doubtful whether these are true markings. Many eggs show yellow and brown nest stains, and some become almost as deeply coloured as grebes'.

Incubation, which begins with the first egg, is performed chiefly by the female sea-eagle. Estimates of the incubation period vary, some observers calculating from the laying of the first egg to the hatching of the last (seven weeks), others from the laying of the last egg to the hatching of the first (five weeks). Forty days probably represents the true figure. The eaglets are hatched in a greyish-yellow down, which is replaced, after the third week, by a denser, browner coat. They remain about ten weeks in the eyrie, and attempt their first flights at intervals of ten days. The family keeps together for another month or five weeks, after which the young disperse or are driven off by their parents.

REFERENCES : Original Description. *Falco albicilla* Linnaeus, Syst. Nat., 10th ed., 1758, p. 89 : Habitat in Europa. Restricted type locality Sweden.

PLATE 32   **WASP- OR HONEY-BUZZARD**

Pernis apivorus apivorus (Linnaeus)

A Rare and Irregular Visitor to Britain in spring and autumn and a scarce Summer Resident. Formerly bred sparingly. Visits to Scotland in June and July are recorded. To Ireland it is only a rare Vagrant since 1900, but once bred commonly.

IDENTIFICATION : One of the chief distinctions between the honey-buzzard and the common buzzard is to be found in the length of the honey-buzzard's tail (255-275 mm.), which is noticeably longer, but that character is only useful to those who are fully conversant with the silhouette of the more familiar bird. The wings too of the honey-buzzard are narrower and longer, a point which is emphasized in *The Handbook*. Raptorial birds are notoriously subject to many varieties of plumage and the honey-buzzard is quite remarkably so, for not only has it the normal stages to go through before it reaches maturity but it has two quite distinct phases of plumage in addition to the ordinary dress which it may retain throughout its life. It is consequently a tiresome bird to recognize on colour alone.

In all three phases the upperparts are dark brown throughout, with the forehead, lores and cheeks strongly washed with grey, which in old males extends over the crown. The tail is light brown, broadly margined with sepia, and with two other bars of the same purplish-sepia nearer the base. In the normal plumage the chin is white streaked with brown, the rest of the underparts being heavily spotted or barred with brown or blackish on a white ground. The under wing-coverts are dark brown, but the inner lining of the wings and tail is whitish with dark bars or blotches. The wing measures 395-425 mm. (100 mm. is just short of four inches). The bill is black ; the eyes, legs and feet are yellow.

A white phase resembles on the upperparts the plumage already described, but the underparts are either entirely white with a few brown bars on the sides or have a few sepia streaks on the breast ; sometimes the entire head is white.

A dark phase also is not uncommonly met with, in which the entire plumage is brown, varying from rich umber to dark sepia ; but always the white inner lining of the primaries is present.

When handled an unfailing character is the remarkable scale-like feathers of the lores, which are believed to be some protection against the stings of bees and wasps, upon which, and upon the grubs of which, the honey-buzzard largely feeds. The nostrils are fully exposed and are slit-shaped ; the bill is furnished with a sharp hook which overhangs the lower mandible and must be useful when tearing open a wasp's nest, an operation which is aided by using the claws. It should be emphasized that the bird does *not* feed on honey but is always searching for grubs.

LOCAL DISTRIBUTION : This is yet another raptorial bird which has practically disappeared as a breeding species and is now with few excep-

PLATE 32

WASP- OR HONEY-BUZZARD
Pernis apivorus apivorus (Linnaeus)

tions only a rather rare visitor to Britain in spring and more often in autumn. The history of its wanton persecution by collectors of eggs and also of specimens is told by Doctor Eagle Clarke in the 3rd edition of Howard Saunders' *Manual*, still one of the most reliable books that have ever been published on British birds.   This is what Doctor Clarke wrote :

About 1860 it became known that several pairs annually resorted to the New Forest ; £5 soon became the standard price which collectors of " British " specimens were willing to pay for a couple of well-marked eggs ; and nearly £40 was given for a pair of old birds with their nestlings.   By about 1870 most of the birds had been killed ; and it is with difficulty that the few, if any, which still visit this most favoured haunt are preserved.   Elsewhere in Britain it is known to have nested in Hants, Essex, Berks, Oxon, Bucks, Northants, Herefordshire, Warwickshire, Staffordshire, Shropshire, Yorkshire, Durham, Northumberland, Cumberland, Aberdeenshire, East Ross and probably in Cornwall.

It almost certainly has bred in the past in Suffolk.[1]   Mr. Witherby takes up the tale in *The Handbook*, where he notes that it had not been known to breed in Britain since 1911 until 1928, when a pair nested in one locality near the Welsh border up to 1932 ; another pair bred in another locality in the south in 1923 and 1932 " and probably a pair has bred here since in some years ".   That was written in 1939.   If, as almost certain, the bird has nested in recent years it is certainly wise to keep the locality dark, judging from past experience.

As an irregular bird of passage the honey-buzzard is to-day less often recorded than formerly.   September is the month when it is usually observed ; a few are seen in October, very rarely in November.   It occurs also in the spring and early summer from April to July.   To Scotland it is reported to come " not uncommonly " in the months stated and, as the authors of *The Birds of Scotland* observe, " from the number of records in June and July it is quite evidently a bird which if not shot at sight would breed much more often than it has been allowed to do ".   It has in the past been recorded from all but four counties, but is rare in the west.

From the meagre information given in *The Birds of Ireland* (1954) it seems that it is now only a rare vagrant whereas formerly it was, according to Colonel Scroope, " a widespread breeding species ".   It appears that in Ireland it was wiped out as a breeding bird long before this happened in England, for in 1900 Ussher and Warren could list it only as a rare and casual visitor in summer and autumn, occurring on the eastern side of Ireland, never on the western.

On the east coast of Britain it can only be described as a rare and irregular migrant.   In Suffolk Ticehurst has recorded that three or four noted during an autumn implies rather an exceptional visitation of these birds.   It has several times been taken in the North Sea off the East Anglian

[1] C. B. Ticehurst in *A History of the Birds of Suffolk*, p. 231.

coast in September. There was little to show that it passed along the East Anglian coast in spring, according to the records which he kept for so many years. Now that we have regular bird observatories on the east coast its rare visits are likely to be recorded with more regularity.

Between the years 1934 and 1954 there are only five references to the honey-buzzard in *British Birds* magazine, which is some indication of its scarcity as a casual visitor, though the first mention of it was of a brood successfully reared in the New Forest, Hampshire, in 1934. The others refer to an example trapped in Yorkshire in June 1927 (first reported as a goshawk), to one seen demolishing a wasps' nest in Sussex, on 4th October 1944, to a pair seen on the Berks-Hants border in August 1949, and to a bird trapped in Lincolnshire in July 1951.

The honey-buzzard winters far to the south of the British Isles and never remains in northern latitudes. Some notes on its migrations will be given in a later paragraph.

DISTRIBUTION ABROAD : The honey-buzzard has a wide Continental breeding range. The western race *Pernis apivorus apivorus* occurs from southern Norway to the Ural Mountains, and it has been reported from as far east as Lake Baikal, which should be close to the range of *Pernis apivorus orientalis*, a rather larger race. The breeding range of the typical subspecies in western Europe is erratic and may best be understood by the following brief notes on its distribution :

Norway : The headquarters of the honey-buzzard are the districts around the Oslo fjord from Östfold to Telemark. It also occurs locally in the great inland valleys, Österdal, Gudbrandsdal and Valders. To the west it has been found nesting as far as Vennesla in Setesdal. It is of more regular occurrence in Rogaland and has been observed near Bergen, but does not breed in the west. To the north of Dovre it is rare but it has been found nesting as far north as Nordli. Within recent years, Doctor Blair informs me, the honey-buzzard has greatly diminished in numbers. Sixty years ago (about 1895) it was one of the commonest Raptores in Östfold but has almost disappeared from that neighbourhood, largely due to senseless persecution, but it must be remembered that the number of honey-buzzards resorting to a locality varies from season to season regardless of ill-treatment. In some years they are far more plentiful than others.

Sweden : According to Kolthoff and Jägerskiöld the species is distributed over the country and is comparatively common, especially in the central provinces. It has been found nesting as far north as the southern part of Gellivara and north of Kengis (latitude 67° 26′ N.).

Finmark : The honey-buzzard is generally distributed. Here it was that Wolley obtained eggs as far north as Nelivaara in Kittilä (67° 45′ N.) and Kyro (68° N.). Further to the east a nest has been found in Kuusamo (66° N.).

Holland : It is a very rare breeding bird. Its best-known breeding haunt is the Veluwe region of Gelderland, but it has also been found breeding in Utrecht, Limburg, Noord-Brabant and Overijsel. There appears to be only one record of breeding in the western provinces for the past century. Its population seems to be stable but it is often mistaken for the common buzzard. (A. L. J. van Izzendoom in *The Breeding Birds of the Netherlands*.)

Denmark : Here it is recorded as a widely distributed breeding bird, though in small numbers, in most parts of the country, wherever large leafy woods and older heath plantations are to be found. (Paul Jespersen in *Breeding Birds of Denmark*, 1946.)

France : M. Georges Olivier informs me that the honey-buzzard is in 1955 a breeding bird in most forests and wooded areas but is unknown along the Mediterranean coast of France, though exceptions may occur. On the Atlantic seaboard, however, it breeds in the country to the north-east of Narbonne and Béziers, quite near, or on the border of, the Atlantic and Mediterranean zones.

In reply to an enquiry for confirmation of its absence from the Mediterranean zone, M. François Hüe, the naturalist of Pézenas, writes that the only pair which does breed where there are Mediterranean characteristics (ilex, etc.) nests at the base of the Montagne Noire at Saissac (Aude). M. Hüe points out that the dividing line between the two zones[1] is found at that place, which is between Carcassonne and Castelnaudary. As migrants honey-buzzards pass through the Departments of Hérault and Aude in great numbers.

The Iberian Peninsula : The earliest report of the breeding of the honey-buzzard in Spain came to us from the late Lord Lilford, who in May 1876 found it nesting on the frontiers of Santander and Asturias in mountain forests—presumably of the Cantabrian range. Howard Irby also mentions finding it in the same year in the Province of Liebana in Santander and was probably in Lord Lilford's company at the time. From that day to this there has been no definite breeding record in Spain, and though Mr. Hollom and his collaborators in their recent *Field Guide to the Birds of Britain and Europe* (1954) have assumed that the bird nests right across the Iberian Peninsula, there are no other Spanish records to support their supposition. Their map should therefore be redrawn to accord with the proven facts only.

In Portugal, where the late W. C. Tait considered the honey-buzzard an uncommon migrant in the Oporto district of the north, it has more recently (1937-38) been reported to breed in the vicinity of Portel in the Province of Alemtejo (several records) and Abrantes (one record) by the late H. W. Coverley.[2] In his " Nesting Notes from Portugal " he

[1] Méditerranéenne française et du Midi.
[2] *Ibis*, 1939, pp. 149-152.

mentions a female being shot on the nest (*not* by himself), and adds that in his opinion closer investigation would prove that the honey-buzzard is fairly regularly distributed as a breeding species in the southern half of the country. I have doubts if that would prove to be the case, for if it breeds to any extent south of Portel, surely it would have been discovered nesting ere this in Andalusia, where so many British ornithologists have worked in the breeding season.

In eastern and central Europe the honey-buzzard is more generally distributed, extending south to central Italy, and reaching the Mediterranean in Greece, the Balkans and Asia Minor. I have dwelt mainly on the honey-buzzard's distribution in western Europe as it is from that source, if any, that birds visiting the British islands are most likely to come.

The winter range of the honey-buzzard lies entirely outside Europe. The typical subspecies migrates to tropical Africa, ranging on the east to Nyasaland and Natal and on the west to Angola. It has also been found in Madagascar. This buzzard, unlike many European species which have their winter quarters in Africa, is much more numerous in the west than in the east, and especially so in the forest and tree-savanna areas. It has wandered to the Canary Islands on at least four occasions.

Its scarcity on the eastern side of Africa is rather curious. Records from the Sudan are very rare, but it is likely that a few travel south that way, as examples obtained at Semio, Sassa, Niangara and Lukolela may indicate. It has been obtained elsewhere in the Belgian Congo at Avakubi, Luluabourg, Medje and Stanleyville.

West African examples which I have examined have been obtained between 29th September and March from Liberia, the Gold Coast, western Nigeria, the Cameroon Mountain district and the interior of French Cameroon.

The honey-buzzard does *not* breed in Africa, but specimens have been obtained in the tropics long after the others have left for Europe. One was shot in the South Cameroon forests in June and another in the Belgian Congo on 4th July ; the latter was a female with ovary not enlarged.

On passage this buzzard has been procured in the French Sudan at Taberréshat Well in dry country. Dates when it has been recorded in eastern Africa fall between October and April.

The honey-buzzard is a late spring and early autumn migrant to Egypt and Sinai but in small numbers. On passage it has been met with in Iraq and on the Persian Gulf in September, and once in Arabia (three birds) in early April at Hadda. The Siberian race *P. apivorus orientalis* is reported to winter in India, Burma and south China.

HABITS AND MIGRATIONS : Of all the Accipitrine birds so far dealt with in this volume the honey-buzzard is the least worthy to be termed a bird of prey. Its food consists almost entirely of wasps' nests, with larvae and pupae, and sometimes of the wasps as well, and when in its winter quarters it will even attack the wasp colonies of that particularly virulent species *Polybioides melaina*. The name " honey-buzzard " is unfortunate, for in the opinion of one distinguished American naturalist, it does not attack honey bees. In Europe it certainly eats the brood of bumble bees. The pupae of ants are among the other food found in its stomach, and the larvae of lepidoptera and beetles, snails, worms and slow-worms are included in its European diet, but in its winter quarters it sticks to its admirable habit of pillaging wasps' nests of many varieties, for in Africa it does not have to travel far to satisfy its needs.

It is generally stated that the scale-like feathers around the eyes and on the lores of the honey-buzzard serve as a protection from the stings of wasps but in the Congo forests, where the buzzard attacks the venomous species of wasp to which reference is made above, it is the opinion of Doctor Chapin that the feathered lores are not sufficient to explain its apparent immunity to stings.

It seems obvious from examination of stomach contents that in Britain the honey-buzzard prefers to feed on pieces of nest-comb, larvae, pupae and immature workers of the common wasp *Vespa vulgaris* when procurable, but when on passage the bird is not so particular. A honey-buzzard shot in Kent on 17th May had evidently just arrived in Britain, for upon dissection by Doctor James M. Harrison[1] the following surprising assortment was discovered by experts at the British Museum : head and thorax of a beetle which occurs both in Britain and on the Continent ; parts of a weevil which is not a British species ; parts of earwigs, one a British and Continental species, the other an earwig common in France and Belgium but not occurring in Britain ; an ant's head belonging to a central European and Mediterranean species which does not occur in Britain ; and finally a fair amount of grass. Doctor Harrison observes that from the above list it is apparent that the bird had but recently reached our shores.

Nearly all textbooks describe the honey-buzzard as a silent species with rather an indolent nature but Major Anthony Buxton, who studied this buzzard for three years in Switzerland, does not share the general opinion that its actions are sluggish. He suggests that the adjective " deliberate " more accurately describes it, as anyone can judge who catches the gleaming yellow eye which follows everything, especially the flight of a queen wasp. It can certainly move fast enough when necessity arises, and Meinertzhagen has recorded how it can travel with rapidity through thick forest, dodging in and out in heavy foliage. On one occasion in Arabia he witnessed three of these birds diving down to a palm grove from about 1000 feet and after a wide circle round settling in a thick-foliaged tree, where they all sat close together. One of these was in the white phase described, the other two being barred below. The date was 6th April,

[1] *Ibis*, 1931, pp. 772-773.

when the buzzards would be on their way north. In his recently produced *Birds of Arabia* Colonel Meinertzhagen observes that migration occurs by day and in " scattered parties ". This method of travel is employed under certain conditions but more often, when observed migrating, the honey-buzzard is in very considerable numbers, though, in the manner of many large birds of prey, as for instance the black kite, the passage consists of a great many individuals flying together in unison but not bunched together in the manner of waders.

There have been various occasions when " mass migrations " of the honey-buzzard have been witnessed. One of the largest to be described passed over Heligoland in September 1858 and was witnessed by Herr Gätke :

Small groups of three, five and sometimes as many as ten individuals, passed the island in the course of the forenoon. At noon these flights succeeded each other at shorter intervals, while at the same time an increase in the number of individuals took place. From three o'clock in the afternoon, however, until about six in the evening, the migration proceeded in one incessant stream, the numbers of individuals in the successive flocks increasing up to fifty, eighty, or even larger numbers. These made their appearance on the horizon in uninterrupted succession on the east of the island and disappeared from view in the far west. At this time scarcely any gaps occurred between the successive flocks, the van of one band being almost contiguous with the rear of that which preceded it. The weather at the time was beautifully calm, and one might almost fancy that he heard the rustle of their wings, though the mighty horde of wanderers passed on their way silently at a great height above.

Gätke was much exercised in his mind as to the origin of such numbers, remarking that the breeding stations of central and southern Scandinavia could not possibly have produced or accommodated so vast a throng ; only, as he suggests, the endless forests of European and Asiatic Russia could have given them birth. " Even then," he continues, " it remains as much as ever a subject for wonder how so countless a multitude of individuals, whose nests only occur scattered wherever found, could have possibly congregated for migratory purposes on one and the same day."

That this passage over Heligoland which the old naturalist chronicled was not unique has been proved as recently as 1939, when a distinguished successor of Gätke's on this island observatory, Doctor R. Drost, described[1] what took place :

On the 4th September 1939 towards 9 o'clock the start of the migration was observed. About 11 o'clock Honey Buzzards were going over in large numbers. The main body of migrants came through from 11 to 14 hrs. It was an impressive sight to see these masses of Honey Buzzards going past in one unending stream. From the north side of the island at least 100 individuals could be seen at once,

---

[1] " Mass Migration of the Honey Buzzard, *Pernis a. apivorus* (L.), over Heligoland ", by R. Drost, in *Der Vogelzug*, vol. xi, 1940, pp. 191-192.

at times even double that number. They flew over the island from the NNW and vanished in a SSE direction. The birds were flying with a head wind which was blowing moderately from the south-east. They flew low over the water. By 1.30 hrs. the last birds had passed. The total number has been conservatively estimated at 1000, but this is almost certainly too low a figure.

In the face of such a striking phenomenon the question naturally arises : Where did they come from ? Where were they going ? What factors were responsible for this serried migration ? One must believe that other bird observers and naturalists must have noticed this occurrence and would in the ordinary course of events have reported their observations. But—enquiries, even on the German coast, have yielded no results. . . .

In old German literature there are several well-authenticated references to honey-buzzards being seen by various observers in very large numbers. Thus we read that from the afternoon to the evening of 26th May 1874 over 1000 honey-buzzards were observed near Kniphausen (north-east of Wilhelmshaven) flying in almost continuous procession from west to east. Again in the years 1896-97 honey-buzzards numbering some thousands of individuals were seen in north Jeverland (Oldenburg), while another report speaks of many hundreds seen migrating in smaller or larger flocks from 20th to 22nd May over the Hohe Venn in a south-west to north-east direction. A few shot down were said to be " as fat as drakes in autumn ".

Reviewing some of these earlier reports Herr Rudolf Kühk[1] refers to the mass migration of honey-buzzards over Denmark[2] in September 1932. He observes that enquiries were made to ascertain the origin and destination of this large flight but at the time without result. Herr Kühk in the communication cited suggests that it was obviously related to the numbers of migrating honey-buzzards observed on the Mecklenburg coast on 4th September. This wave of migration was later proved to have started almost certainly from south-west Sweden and, reaching its peak on 14th to 15th September, pursued a course from Zealand over the Guldborg-Sund and reached the German Baltic coast in the neighbourhood of the Pomeranian-Mecklenburg frontier, afterwards following the coast-line in a south-westerly direction.

When we consider that the entire breeding population of Europe migrates to Africa and back every year such numbers as I have referred to above cannot be considered remarkable, but we may ask what happens to these migrants ? For how long do they remain in more or less the same formation during their journey to tropical Africa and when do they split up into smaller bands such as Colonel Meinertzhagen believes to be their normal method of travel ? As they proceed south these great flights must be joined by the breeding population of central Europe and their numbers

[1] *Der Vogelzug*, vol. xiii, 1942, pp. 57-58.
[2] *Orn. Beobacht.*, xxx, p. 106.

grow even greater, but how often do we actually see this migration under way, and at what point do they deviate to reach the many scattered areas in Africa where they spend the winter ?

At the Eighth International Ornithological Congress held at Oxford in 1934 the late Professor Lönnberg, when reading a paper on the migrations of Swedish birds, observed that the honey-buzzard migrates to Africa both by the south-western route over Spain and due south over Italy. The birds move quickly, so that some may have reached southernmost Spain or the island of Malta in September, although others have not left the Continent in October. One bird ringed in Sweden in July 1925 was recovered in Cameroon in January 1926 and another in Nigeria. On the other side of the continent there is a record of a north German bird being captured in Abyssinia [1] in November.

The spring passage of the honey-buzzard in the Mediterranean appears to have come under notice more than the return journey in autumn, though the latter is by no means negligible. Irby wrote many years ago that it is to be seen " in swarms " during the spring migration, being at its climax about 8th May, though he noted hundreds passing from the 12th to the 15th between Gibraltar and Malaga.

He noted that once they had passed the water the passage was continued in a gyrating flight of eccentric circles, sometimes very high and as often within shot of the ground. Some eighty years have passed since Howard Irby penned those words and almost to a day the honey-buzzards still make the crossing from Africa in this area, sometimes to the east of Tangier, sometimes to the west of it, as the following communication recently received from Doctor H. M. S. Blair bears witness :

The month of May 1954 opened with fresh easterly breezes bending the growing corn throughout the southernmost provinces of Spain. As some of the heavier gusts attained gale strength, it was clearly not to be expected that many migrants would attempt the crossing from Africa, but in the course of the day the winds slackened and the turtle doves, so eagerly awaited by the local sportsmen, were soon on their way. They swarmed amongst the stone pines along the Guadalquivir the next morning, while the bushes about the fringes of the marismas were as densely thronged with small birds. Then the wind shifted into a more favourable quarter and migrants fairly poured across the narrow seas between the continents. The immigration continued to be most conspicuous along the great river, where waders could rest and feed, but everywhere throughout Andalusia one was likely to come upon a north-bound bird of passage, perhaps a wood sandpiper, an ortolan or, as often as not, a pied flycatcher. Early on 6th May, a calm morning with the sun blazing in a clear sky, one flycatcher took up his temporary quarters in the courtyard of an old house overlooking the Guadalete. Soon afterwards it became evident that a " rush " of honey-buzzards was in progress. At first the big hawks passed over at intervals of half an hour or more, and either singly or in pairs, but in the late afternoon they

---

[1] Ernst Schüz, " Ringfunde europäischer Zugvögel in Afrika und ihre Bedeutung ", *Proc. VIIIth Internat. Orn. Congress*, 1934, p. 540 and Map, p. 541.

followed each other in an almost continuous stream. Often a dozen would be in sight above the tall buildings around the courtyard. More than once three times as many were counted within the same restricted range of vision, and at one moment birds in four different phases of plumage entered the field of the binoculars together. All came into view from the south-west, as if they had made the coast near the mouth of the Guadalquivir, and all travelled at the same height, about two hundred feet above the house and perhaps twice as much again from the riverside orange groves below. They made rather leisurely progress, many loitering to circle together before drifting on towards the peaks of the Sierra Ronda some miles to the north-east. By the time darkness fell some hundreds of honey-buzzards had passed over the old house by the Guadalete.

That the return migration in autumn passes over much the same land and sea is apparent from the experience which on one occasion befell Lord Lilford. In the month of September he witnessed a passage of great numbers of honey-buzzards from Spain to Africa. His yacht was becalmed off Europa Point, and from about noon till dusk the honey-buzzards kept passing over and on both sides of the vessel in flocks of from half a dozen to eighty or more at intervals of a few minutes. The birds were travelling at no very great height above the water, although for the most part out of gunshot of the ship.

The direction and strength of the wind at the time of the passage no doubt influences to a considerable extent the actual sea crossing, and the point of departure and arrival on the opposite mainland must vary from year to year, but there is evidence that the crossing is made on a fairly narrow front. The almost complete absence of the honey-buzzard from the Balearic Islands—and also apparently from Sardinia, where it is rarely seen on passage—points to the correctness of Professor Lönnberg's statement as to the two main routes on the road to Africa. It is to be encountered abundantly in the toe of Italy during the spring migration, and on days when the wind is favourable for the passage of the birds from Sicily every-one in possession of a gun sallies forth to the heights overlooking the sea to await the birds' arrival, or so it was in the days of which J. I. S. Whitaker was writing some fifty years ago. From my knowledge of the Italian peasant it is unlikely that the reception the honey-buzzards receive is any better to-day. In Sicily too they are esteemed as an article of food.

The spring passage of this bird through Malta was studied by Mr. John Gibb[1] for four years, 1942-1945 inclusive, with the result that it was found to occur in two quite distinct waves, the main influx being followed by a lesser one towards the end of May or early June. It is worthy of note that when Despott was recording the ornithology of Malta in 1917 he wrote that he considered the species one which is annually becoming scarcer. The crass ignorance shown by agriculturalists in the Mediterranean area of the benefits which insect-eating birds convey to the land has to be seen

[1] *British Birds*, xl, 1947, p. 78.

to be believed. It has been reckoned that in a perfectly normal breeding season *in Switzerland* a pair of buzzards and two young will consume at least 1000 presumptive wasps in a day, the wasp grubs being varied with those of hornets. Major Buxton computed the number of wasps destroyed by a pair of honey-buzzards with twins during the summer season alone (which takes no account of similar winter feeding) to be in the neighbourhood of 90,000—and the idiots who lie in wait for these birds and succeed in shooting a score or more in a day complain later in the same year that their fruit has been ravaged by wasps.

Of its sojourn in tropical Africa few have left us any notes, and those who have speak of it as did Sir Frederick Jackson in Uganda as a lazy, indolent bird, spending most of its time resting on the bough of a shady tree, occasionally pouncing down upon a large insect which has attracted its attention. Geoffrey Archer was struck by its extreme fearlessness. One bird sat on the top of a large bare tree while his caravan, with much noise and clatter, passed beneath. I have already quoted from Doctor Chapin's observations on its feeding habits in the Congo forests, where wasps' nests supply practically all its needs. He too found it silent and sluggish and it seems that the steaming heat of a tropical forest has much the same effect on a honey-buzzard as it has on a human being !

The probability is that in West Africa, where it is just as likely to be met with in savanna as in forest clearings, it is very often overlooked, for when engaged in my large work on the birds of that region I had difficulty in learning anything about it. Those who learned to know it usually reported that it was very easily approached, being reluctant to fly from any position it had taken up; its natural tameness is encouraged in a land where it is seldom molested. One example collected in Ashanti had its crop crammed with mason wasps. In the great forest country of southern Cameroon the veteran naturalist George Bates met with honey-buzzards between November and March, when they came and perched fearlessly about the native villages.

Breeding Habits [1] : Apart from its attraction in many other ways, the honey-buzzard in the nesting season is a most engaging bird which permits fairly close inspection of its matrimonial life. A charming trait in its character is the care with which it decorates its nest with fresh sprays of green leaves, which are renewed every evening, but of this more will be said hereafter.

The smaller birds recognize its harmless nature and pay little attention to it, in great contrast to the commotion which ensues on the approach of a sparrow-hawk or other predator with similar reputation. Nor do they mob it as they will an owl.

[1] Major Anthony Buxton has kindly allowed me to make full use of the chapter on honey-buzzards in his book *Sporting Interludes at Geneva*. I have also to thank his publishers, Country Life Ltd., for a similar courtesy.

The days have passed when in the month of May we might have looked hopefully for the return of the honey-buzzard to its favourite wood to rear its young in this country. It is a late nester and on the Continent eggs are seldom laid before June or the last days of May. F. C. R. Jourdain considered 10th June to be the date when a full clutch of eggs might be found, but sometimes the full complement is not laid before the end of that month. For its nesting place it chooses a big wood, preferably with tall trees, such as are to be found in the New Forest. Beeches are said to be especially favoured but oaks are often chosen and pine and spruce in areas covered with conifers.

The nest, consisting of intertwined sticks and twigs, is not in itself a large structure, but as it is usually built up on the top of another bird's old nest, such as that of a goshawk, crow or buzzard, its dimensions, including the foundation, may be considerable. On occasions, presumably when no abandoned site is handy, the birds will build a nest of their own on a side branch, in which case the structure is a small one, especially when it is compared with the bulky nest made by the common buzzard. These birds, though both termed " buzzards ", have really little in common, unless it be the display flight in which both species will occasionally indulge.

It was on 19th June, as Major Buxton was passing below a honey-buzzard's nest in Switzerland, that the male bird swept low over his head in a kind of demonstration. The pair then went through a magnificent soaring exhibition, the male leading in great circles up into the sky, his white throat, chest and under surface of his wings glistening as he turned in the sun ; she followed up and up till they were mere specks. Then came a long, steady plane back to the nest, he following her down and sailing majestically round while she settled on what was apparently her first egg. On other occasions a male honey-buzzard has been seen to rise alone to a considerable height before diving steeply down, only to sweep upwards once more and repeat the performance.

Though normally rather silent, the honey-buzzard has a variety of notes, which are heard mainly at the height of the nesting season. Anthony Buxton was able to distinguish four distinct cries when keeping a close watch on a pair near the Rhône valley. The chief call he describes as a soft, long, low whistle, which may be expressed by the word *whee-eee-uh*, adding that if either bird was on the nest the approach of the other was always heralded by this whistle from the sitting bird and answered by the other. Another cry was mistaken for that of a curlew, but as the bird was seen to utter the cry, there was no room for doubt that the honey-buzzard had made the sound while planing down to the nest with a bit of wasp-comb. On the approach of a cat a screeching hiss of anger, or maybe of alarm, was heard, while a distinct bill chattering was made when the parent birds were together, like the light ticking of a machine ; this, it was concluded, was a token of affection.

The obvious pleasure taken by the birds, especially the hen, in keeping the nest decorated with fresh sprays of leaves, of either beech, oak or ash, will endear the honey-buzzard to those with a similar taste for gardening. Major Buxton was convinced that the birds had a passion for fresh green leaves about them, and describes how every evening after the final feed the hen parent would retire a short distance to pull off a large sprig of leaves, generally oak but sometimes ash, which she would carry in either her bill or her claw and lay at the baby's feet in the nest. This she invariably did twice in succession. The reaction of the baby honey-buzzard to this attention was charming to watch.

It was just as delighted with this bouquet of leaves as with a nestful of wasp grubs ; there were the same excited squeals and quivering of the shoulders and, moreover, it played happily with its toy. This little ceremony was enacted daily in addition to the usual decoration of the home and in Major Buxton's opinion the bird decorated the nest just as we decorate our drawing rooms, to make the place attractive. Whatever the reason, however, from the moment the nest was occupied, and before the first egg was laid until the baby flew, fresh green leaves were added every day and in some cases were definitely planted on the side of the nest. Major Buxton concludes his account with the following sentence : " To me this ceremony of the green leaves, conducted in the half light of a summer evening, with the birds' heads against the sky, was the most impressive of all the scenes we witnessed."

The young honey-buzzards are particular to keep the nest as unsoiled as possible and the food which they consume helps materially to that end. At first they are fed exclusively on wasp grubs. The male parent, having discovered a wasps' nest, will tear it from its hole and carry back in his claws portions of the comb, about as large as a man's fist, to the sitting hen, who in turn picks out the young grubs and pops them into the mouth of the nestlings. Now and again this diet is varied by a peeled frog, the parents skinning the frog with their bills while the head is held by a claw as neatly as a skilled taxidermist would hold it.

Eventually, as the chicks grow older, the frogs are delivered whole. The approach of a meal is heralded by squeals, for the youngsters have the true eye of a hawk, spotting the parent at a great distance. Of all the food brought to the young a bumble bees' nest causes the greatest excitement and the honey from these combs is evidently looked upon as the supreme thing in delicacies. A point of much interest discovered by Major Buxton was the addition of fruit to the diet in the shape of the ripe red berries of "lords and ladies" (*Arum maculatum*), which are generally believed to be poisonous to birds.

Honey-buzzards usually lay two eggs, occasionally one only, and exceptionally three. They are described very fully by Oates in the *Catalogue of Birds' Eggs in the British Museum* as short ovals or ellipses and occasionally almost spherical in shape, smooth, and with a considerable amount of gloss.   The ground is white or cream-colour, but is in many cases almost entirely concealed by the markings, which are deep reddish-brown, plain brown, chocolate-brown and sometimes blackish-brown.   The disposition and size of the markings varies greatly.   Some specimens are blotched chiefly on the larger half ; others have a broad cap at the large end, the remainder of the shell being merely speckled and spotted ; others again have about three-quarters of their surface covered with confluent blotches and smears ; and a certain number are entirely covered with a deep rufous wash, more or less mottled with dark brown or black.

The series in the British Museum measured from 1·9 to 2·22 inches in length and from 1·5 to 1·7 inches in breadth.   Jourdain gave the average of twenty-five British eggs as 50·22 × 41·39 mm. and the average of 100 Continental eggs as 50·82 × 41·09 mm.

During incubation, which begins usually with the first egg and lasts from thirty to thirty-five days, the sexes take turn and turn about, but in most instances the female takes the major share, and she it is who feeds the young at first from the combs brought to her by her mate.   Later both birds go off hunting and both bring food to the nest.   Forty to forty-five days is the usual fledging period but longer and shorter periods are instanced by Jourdain.

When the young birds are ready to fly they are put through a period of semi-starvation.   Major Buxton found that six days before a youngster actually made its first flight no food was given to it all day until after five o'clock in the afternoon.   The baby, however, made no move, and normal feeding was resumed for five days, when the starvation experiment was repeated, this time successfully.   After much hesitation the young bird sailed off for twenty yards to a bough, and during the day made a number of trial flights.   For several days the parents continued to bring the food to the nest and called the baby back.   The process was reversed, and when the baby had learned to balance on one foot and hold the comb in the other it was encouraged away from the nest to receive its food.   During the whole period when the young bird was learning to fly it was kept short of food. The first short flight was made on 5th September and the whole family apparently left for good on 14th September.

As honey-buzzards are so distinctively marked it is possible in certain cases to recognize the same bird from season to season, and little individual traits of character soon betray a particular bird to an astute observer.   In the case of the pair whose nest Major Buxton kept under observation in Switzerland the same birds undoubtedly returned to that valley *for three years in succession*.   Had it been possible to continue to watch for their return for a fourth year, the same birds would probably have been seen again.   This surely points to the honey-buzzard pairing for life, and the pair must keep together not only during the flight to Africa but also during the months spent in winter quarters. It seems that in this species we have a bird of prey as faithful to a particular valley in which to breed as are the swallows and house martins which return year after year to the same district or even to the same house. What a joy it would be to watch for their return.

This essay would be incomplete without reference to the account[1] which Mr. C. H. Gowland gave to the British Oological Association at their meeting in September 1932 of a pair of honey-buzzards nesting for five years in succession (from 1928 to 1932) in a wood " somewhere in England "; these birds he succeeded in saving from the keeper's gun. For thirty years previously, as F. C. R. Jourdain remarked on that occasion, the honey-buzzard's eggs had not been taken in the British Isles, though many birds which might well have bred had fallen victim to keepers. The first nest found was in a tall beech : " The nest appeared to be an old crow's nest, renovated and built up with many small leafy twigs of beech, quite fresh, having evidently been added within a day or so." In 1929 they bred again in another beech about forty yards from the first site ; two eggs were found about the end of May. In 1930 the nest was fairly accessible, in an old squirrel's drey in an oak, but the two eggs, unlike those in the earlier nests, were very poorly marked. In 1931 the nest was in an old crow's nest in a fir tree. In 1932 the actual nest was not discovered but the adults with two youngsters were seen, so that Mr. Gowland inferred, no doubt correctly, that for five successive years a pair of honey-buzzards had successfully reared two young each year in this same wood.

At the same meeting of the Oological Club it was disclosed by Mr. Nethersole-Thompson that a second pair of honey-buzzards had been located in another wood in the year 1932 and that this pair had reared a single young one.

From observations which Mr. Gowland made when watching these birds he noted that before nesting they seemed to spend much time on the ground, but prior to the actual choice of a site were more often circling and wheeling about in the air. Afterwards they remained much in the tree-tops, or were seen gliding just over the trees, probably in search of likely sites. He remarked that the fresh supply of green leaves appeared to be added daily, thus corroborating Major Buxton, whose account I have already quoted. Both sexes took part in incubation and in feeding the young. When incubation had just begun the female would fly to meet her mate on his approach, but when incubation was advanced she did not leave the eggs until the male bird was alongside the nest. As the above account describes one of the very few occasions when observations have been made on a British nesting pair, I have given it in some detail.

---

[1] I am indebted to my friend Mr. Clifford Borrer, for many years Hon. Secretary of the Oological Association, for enabling me to see volume xxxv of the *Bulletin of the B.O.A.*, 1932, in which Mr. Gowland reported his discoveries.

The latest account of a pair successfully breeding in this country and rearing two young has been sent me by Major W. M. Congreve. This pair had used the remains of an old sparrow-hawk's nest, which had been considerably added to and was situated on the tallest spruce in the wood. The year was 1947. After leaving the nest the young were taken to a clump of enormous beeches about 200 yards away, and were present during the whole of August, answering the calls of their parents and moving from tree to tree. Major Congreve's wide experience leads him to believe that the honey-buzzard is likely to nest yearly in one or more of the afforested areas of Britain. The nesting localities to which he drew my attention are intentionally omitted, but are not confined to southern England.

I will end this essay by quoting the final sentence of Major Buxton's account : " Surely," he wrote, " a bird that comes all the way from Africa to eat ninety thousand of our wasps in a season is worth something more than a charge of powder and shot."

REFERENCES : Original Description. *Falco apivorus* Linnaeus, Syst. Nat., 10th ed., 1758, p. 91 : Europe ; restricted type locality Sweden.

Family AEGYPIIDAE

Genus *GYPS* Savigny

GRIFFON VULTURE   PLATE 33

Gyps fulvus fulvus (Hablizl)

An Accidental Visitor

IDENTIFICATION[1] : This is one of the large vultures, with a huge wing spread, and as it is almost uniform brown in plumage, it is a bird which is fairly easily identified. The sexes are alike. The head and neck are creamy-white and are covered with down ; the ruff at the base of the neck is also creamy-white. The rest of the upperparts shows some variation from pale brown to dark brown, sometimes with a greyish tinge. The underparts vary from sandy-brown to rufous-brown. The tail, like the primaries of the wing, is almost black. The nostrils are slit-shaped and the iris is brown to golden-brown.

In immature birds the ruff is composed of long lanceolate fulvous feathers and the whole bird is slightly pinker than the adults. Nestlings are covered in white down. The griffon takes at least three years to reach maturity. An adult bird weighs about eighteen pounds[2] and the expanse of wings varies from eight to nine feet.

[1] After Meinertzhagen, but not verbatim.
[2] On the testimony of Willoughby Verner.

OCCURRENCES IN GREAT BRITAIN : The only example which has been obtained in Britain was an immature bird caught alive on the rocks near Cork harbour, Co. Cork, in the spring of 1843, and is now preserved in the National Museum, Dublin. In addition to this Irish record, there are three sight records in England which rest on the testimony of individuals. The first is recorded in Howard Saunders' *Manual*. To quote Doctor Eagle Clarke, who edited the third edition, "an eminently cautious ornithologist, who is familiar with griffons, informed Saunders that some years since he had watched one soaring near Southampton water ". That seems pretty poor evidence, even though of such a huge bird, but as this vulture has now been seen again by three other observers, Doctors Sadler and Hollick and Miss Hollick, who appear to have had an excellent view of two griffons soaring over Ashbourne, Derbyshire, on 4th June 1927, we may perhaps accept all three sight records as having been in all probability of birds reliably identified.

DISTRIBUTION ABROAD : Griffons do not breed in any numbers nearer to the British Isles than the Pyrenees. A very few still retain a precarious footing in the Tarn Department of southern France (of which more will be said later), and further west it is to be found in the Cantabrian Mountains of north-western Spain. In the Peninsula as a whole it occurs in many of the sierras but is especially numerous in Andalusia. It is reported now to be rare in the Apennines and Etruscan Alps.

In the Mediterranean area it breeds in Sardinia and Sicily (but not in the Balearics) and fairly generally in the mountain systems from Albania and southern Jugoslavia eastwards, ranging through Asia Minor to Palestine and Sinai. There are breeding colonies also in Crete and Cyprus ; thence the range extends to Turkestan and the Himalayas. It is sure to breed in Arabia, though colonies in that country have not yet (1955) been located.

South of the Mediterranean the griffon breeds in Egypt (south of Suez), in the Libyan Desert and in scattered colonies through all the North African countries bordering the Mediterranean where suitable mountains occur. Breeding colonies are isolated and uncommon and are mainly restricted to the northern ranges. There is, however, one known nesting place in the extreme south of Tunisia.

South of the Atlas ranges, where the desert extends to the foot of the mountains, griffon vultures are only exceptionally seen but with their immense powers of flight they may sometimes be encountered very far from their normal habitat or nesting caverns.

I have no information on this vulture's presence in the Great Atlas. Although I have crossed these great mountains on four occasions I have never seen any sign of a griffon, though the bearded vulture is well known. It has, however, been obtained in that range. I doubt if a breeding colony exists so far south, as in all my travels in Morocco I have encountered the griffon only in the mountains which rise near the Mediterranean shores. It is recorded, however, from the Middle Atlas by Admiral Lynes among others, and in East Africa is known to be resident and fairly common on the Red Sea plains and hills.

Griffons are resident wherever they are found, but naturally wander far afield. The bird has strayed once to Central Africa, where a specimen, now in the British Museum, was shot during the Denham-Clapperton Expedition, probably in the vicinity of Lake Chad. It has also been recorded in the non-breeding season from countries of East Africa[1] north of the Equator : Abyssinia, the Sudan, Eritrea, British Somaliland and —in the west—the French Sudan. Subspecies are recognized from India (*fulvescens*) and from Turkestan (*cinnamomeus*).

THE GRIFFON IN FRANCE : Thirty years ago[2] a French writer, M. le docteur A. Rochon-Duvigneaud, published an account of a visit to the haunts of the griffons which nested in the famous Gorges du Tarn,[3] the breeding place of this vulture nearest to Britain. Apart, however, from a scenic description of the locality and a depressing picture of the griffon's declining numbers, the author has little to record. He computed that some forty years previous to his visit in 1925 the high walls of the ravines of the Causses held a really numerous population of vultures, but to such an extent had the numbers decreased that at the time of his last visit he was able to count only half a dozen birds where three or four years before it had been possible to meet with a dozen or more. It seems that the lack of food in the vicinity has hastened the decline of this once thriving colony and that, despite the valiant efforts of the Société Nationale d'Acclimatation, the last breeding colony of griffon vultures in France to exist *north* of the Pyrenees is verging upon extinction.

In reply to an enquiry as to its status to-day M. François Hüe (of Pézenas) writes under date 16th March 1955 :

Il reste encore pas mal de vautours *Gyps fulvus* en France dans les Pyrénées et j'en vois toujours quand je fais des excursions dans cette région montagneuse. Il existe en particulier une bonne colonie près du col du Tourmalet et dans beaucoup d'autres endroits comme le Cirque de Gavarnie.

Pour les Causses *il y en a encore*, mais très peu. J'en ai vu dans la vallée de la Jonte voilà une dizaine d'années, mais je n'y suis pas revenu depuis. Plus bas dans les Cévennes *depuis 1950* j'en vois chaque année trois ou quelquefois quatre ensemble aux stations suivantes : Cirque de Navacelles, St. Guilhem le désert et près de Montpellier au Pic St. Loup. On les voit aussi l'hiver. Cette faible densité est dangereuse pour l'espèce, mais il y en a davantage car on en a tué plusieurs ces années-ci jusqu'au bord de la mer.

HABITS : The griffon vulture was first described from the mountains of northern Persia, and though attempts have been made to distinguish

[1] Grant and Praed, *African Handbook of Birds*, 1952, i, p. 131.
[2] This essay is written in 1955.
[3] *L'Oiseau*, vi, 1925, pp. 182-184 and pp. 260-272.

between birds inhabiting Sardinia, the Pyrenees and Algeria (*occidentalis*) on the one hand, and Dalmatia and Turkey (*orientalis*) on the other, no stable characters exist for the separating of any of the European population, which are rightfully all referred to-day to the typical subspecies.

A first encounter with this bird outside a zoo is sure to remain fixed in one's memory. The experience fell to me in the Tell Atlas of Algeria when wandering up a narrow glen leading from the great Gorge du Chiffa, famed for its semi-tame Barbary apes. A passing shadow directed my gaze upwards and there, floating majestically above the high walls of the defile, were five griffons which I had inadvertently disturbed from their ledge. The breadth of their wings with pinions upturned and the short widespread tails at once proclaimed their identity, though I had never seen one before under such circumstances. As they peered down their light-coloured ruffs were clearly visible to the naked eye but soon they were mounting higher and higher, with barely a tilting of the great wings, until they had reached such a height that I could barely follow them with binoculars. I have seen griffons in many lands since that day and under many different circumstances but that first view of these huge birds at comparatively close quarters has never faded from my mind.

Griffons love the sun and hate the rain, and when caught in a downpour present rather a miserable appearance as they crouch on boulders with draggled wings and feathers. I well remember one February morning coming upon a party of thirty-five in the hills of Andalusia when on the road to Tarifa. The sun had come out after a heavy shower and the huge birds were sitting about the rock-strewn hillside drying their feathers in the sun. Some had their wings outspread in the manner of a cormorant which has emerged from the sea to dry its wings on a fish-trap. Under such circumstances griffons on the ground make an attractive picture but equally they can be repulsive when engaged in feeding, and a too close scrutiny of their behaviour at such times can make an observer feel quite sick.

Feeding largely on carrion, as do all of their family, griffons are a distinct asset in lands where a dead camel, ox, mule or dog is permitted to lie where it falls, and were it not for the carrion-eating birds the carcasses would soon be offensive. The speed with which a dead or dying animal is discovered is quite remarkable, the keenness of a vulture's eyesight being phenomenal. No sooner has it been located by a soaring griffon than others come from all directions, drawn to the spot by the action of the first bird to make the discovery, for griffons keep their weather eyes as much on their companions as they do upon the ground below. Meinertzhagen has estimated that vultures may be drawn to a kill from a radius of as much as fifty miles, and describes with what speed a camel can be cleaned out. " When feeding, the eyes and soft parts are attacked first, then the abdomen is pierced and the intestines are swallowed ; the solid meat is the last to be consumed from an opening made in the abdomen, some birds getting right inside the camel."

The same authority has stated (*Birds of Arabia*, p. 381) that both the griffon and the cinereous (or black) vulture will hunt tortoises on the ground and extract the meat from the carapace. In Cyprus, where I have seen both these vultures tearing to pieces a dead dog, the two species seemed to be on equal terms, perhaps because in that island the griffon so greatly outnumbers its larger relative. Normally the black vulture keeps the griffon in its place, and Meinertzhagen relates seeing a griffon with blood pouring from its neck because it had presumed to share a dead camel. Eighty years earlier Colonel Verner had also remarked the black vulture's dominance over the griffon from observations made in Spain. Griffons are cowardly birds and are easily driven off by a pariah dog. To such an extent will they gorge themselves on putrid flesh that if suddenly disturbed at the feast they have great difficulty in rising. It is well known, as Cyril Mackworth-Praed has emphasized in his useful *Handbook of African Birds*, that griffons will not touch an animal if it shows the slightest sign of life. It is all the more remarkable that it will hunt and presumably kill tortoises as Meinertzhagen has described. Large animals are usually allowed to lie for some time, until putrefaction has set in.

To all appearances the sexes of this vulture are alike but when a number are gathered together they exhibit a surprising difference in colour. This may be partly explained by bleaching and by the staining of the feathers by soil, and not least by their repulsive feeding habits. A cinereous (or black) vulture among them stands out fairly clearly from its paler brethren. A griffon takes four seasons to gain its completely adult plumage and at each successive moult exhibits some difference from the former stage. Juvenile birds are darker on their upperparts than adults and have a pinkish rather than a sandy tone but the moults of this bird are very difficult to follow and it is not surprising that in a congregation of old and young many varied forms of dress are to be seen.

Should a griffon experience exceptional cold it appears to become half paralysed. Joseph Whitaker tells the tale of an uninjured bird being easily captured near Palermo by someone throwing a cloak over its head during a snowstorm, the latter event being sufficiently rare in Sicily to cause the griffon to lose its power of action !

Although Andalusia is the land in western Europe where griffons can be seen in their greatest numbers—B. W. Tucker counted 150 at one carcass—there are many other localities in Spain where the birds have long-established colonies. The western end of the Sierra de Gredos not far from Madrid is one of these places. There Harry Witherby observed so many griffons that they must have formed a considerable colony. " From the King's shooting hut at 6500 feet the mountain drops very steeply towards the south, forming a range of cliffs and crags between here and the peak of Almanzor. Standing on the edge of this steep drop on 21st June, we could see numerous griffons coming up from the plains below, and also some coming up from the north behind us and descending in to various points in these cliffs where they were evidently nesting in some numbers." That account by a distinguished ornithologist is typical of the surroundings in which the griffon makes its home, though in Andalusia the landscape is more wooded and the breeding places—at any rate near Gibraltar— less easily located. Abel Chapman reported years ago that griffons were rarely seen in the Sierra Nevada, but from that great range I have no recent information. In Andalusia and around Arcos de la Frontera the birds hang round their nesting cliffs all the year round.

In the delightful books which he wrote about Spain the late Abel Chapman has numerous references to the griffon, and in the last book[1] he published he gives an account of the griffon colony in the great cliffs at Arcos, on the summit of which was perched the ancient Roman castle which eventually passed into his possession. The castle itself occupies the apex of the ridge, its ramparts rising from the very verge of crags 312 feet in vertical height. These crags formed—and still form—the ancestral home of a horde of huge griffon vultures whose eyries are in the caverns or on the long open ledges of the stratified limestone cliffs. From a look-out post in the castle these cliffs, and the vulture colony, could be kept under close observation. On winter mornings, when mist overspreads the lower land, the vultures make no attempt to set forth on the day's work before ten or even eleven o'clock, and their returning forms are to be seen again about four in the afternoon. On wet or fog-bound days never a vulture quits the eyrie at all. The whole crowd sit huddled up on their ledges, for an enforced fast in no way incommodes them, used as they are to going without food for days at a stretch. On bright and sunny mornings on the contrary, all is hustle and activity, the giant birds presenting an imposing spectacle as they pass and repass along the cliff almost within reach of a stick. These morning manœuvres may continue for half an hour or more, the vultures rising ever higher at each repeated circuit. Then for no reason all may return to the ledges, or, on the initiative of certain leaders, the whole company will strike out a bee-line in one direction or another and within brief seconds all will be lost to sight.

The return of the vultures in the evening affords another striking spectacle which Chapman describes with his inimitable pen. Between three and five o'clock, the hour depending upon visibility, the skies above the castle become punctuated with soaring forms whose varied methods of descent are delightful to watch. Some continue wheeling around with set pinions but in ever-descending circles. Others drop vertically earth- wards, the great wings just sufficiently tilted upwards and backwards, the body under perfect control. At first it appears as a mere speck, then

[1] *Retrospect*, pp. 281-291, from which I have compiled my account.

momentarily its size increases till one realizes this speck is a vulture falling through space at amazing speed. The dive may be prolonged over 1000 feet or more, then the wings extend once again, a horizontal attitude is regained and, with a hurricane header, the vulture vanishes within its eyrie. Another and most graceful mode of descent practised by some individuals is by an interrupted spiral—dropping in a series of exact mathematical half-circles, the wing-action at each reversing point being masterly beyond words.

Abel Chapman records in his account how the first arrivals all make for the caverns, until all available space therein is occupied, the later comers contenting themselves perforce with a perch on some projecting buttress, or on the long open ledges already described. Even here congestion is soon apparent and some individuals are forced to find lodging elsewhere. On the first arrival of the vultures scores of rock pigeons are driven out of the caverns by the disturbances made by the returning vultures. These cliffs are tenanted by other birds as well : ravens, falcons and the great eagle-owl, to say nothing of the many lesser kestrels which arrive in February, tiny hawks as Chapman describes them, " so elegant and so chastely hued that the sunlight seems to shine through their gossamer figures ".

After Abel Chapman's death the famous Castle of Arcos de la Frontera passed into the hands of the well-known artist, the late W. H. Riddell, whose delightful pictures illustrate in colour Abel Chapman's last book. Riddell was an excellent observer and an ornithologist of acute perception. He and I corresponded for many years but never met. He was always enchanted by the griffons which lived below his windows and I will end this account of the Arcos griffons with a quotation from a letter which he wrote to me on 21st November 1929 :

Our vultures are in full force. I counted one evening 98 coming in to roost. One day too they had a feast (dead mule) upon the plain below. It was towards evening time and they struggled with great difficulty back to their precipice after the meal with scarlet heads. Next morning they finished the fragments that remained. The vulture is very strictly diurnal. They had all left the carcase well before sunset (though unfinished) and did not return till an hour after sunrise to continue the feast. He is not so gluttonous a bird as some people would have us believe.

Mrs. Riddell is still resident at El Castillo as I quote these lines from her husband's letter.

In many parts of Andalusia vultures have been disturbed roosting about rocks near their breeding places, being influenced, we are told, in their choice of position by the prevailing wind. It was Irby who found them also roosting in some numbers on cork trees on the side of a sheltered valley in the Sierra Retin. At another nesting place in the great cliffs of the Ciscar Willoughby Verner watched as many as eight together taking shelter in a large sandstone cavern on the lee-side of the mountain.

Both Abel Chapman and Irby raise the question of how these great birds manage to find a living in winter and spring. Then, in contrast to the parched summer months, when numbers of domestic animals die from thirst and from the excessive heat, the griffons must be hard put to it to find sufficient food. Chapman considers that the solution can only lie in the bird's powers of flight and of speed which baffle conception. These enable the vulture day by day to survey in detail vast areas of semi-savage regions. Moreover, it does not necessarily require a meal a day. In fact, after gorging itself on putrid meat it is content to go foodless for some time.

From the accounts of those best able to judge the griffons in Spain are stationary, but the question arises whether or not there is any regular migration overseas. Those who are familiar with Irby's *Ornithology of the Straits of Gibraltar* will recollect that the author quotes Favier, the old naturalist of Tangier, as saying that the griffon occurs commonly near Tangier *on passage*. That statement has never been corroborated and it is inconceivable that a bird of its size should pass regularly unnoticed. Heim de Balsac [1] claims without much evidence in support that the griffon winters in the French Sudan, and in Mauretania, etc., basing his assumption on a few sight records, mainly of his own. The only definite evidence which he can produce is the reported capture of a griffon by a compatriot at Atar in Adrar in November, but we are not told whether this example was preserved.

There would be nothing remarkable about griffons occasionally reaching the Adrar or the Rio de Oro, as there are breeding places of the griffon in Africa north of the Sahara, and what more likely than that these birds with their great powers of flight should travel far afield in the season when nesting no longer occupies their time?

NESTING HABITS: There is still much to be learned regarding the breeding biology of the griffon vulture and no study of it has been made on modern lines. The griffon is by nature a colonial breeder, building its nest for preference in the caverns of precipitous cliffs or, failing these, on ledges such as were described in the last section. Although the nests are usually difficult of access and dangerous to reach, there are many exceptions when it is possible to reach one without a rope or without a hazardous climb.

Abel Chapman is, I believe, the only naturalist who has found a regular colony of nests in trees.[2] That was many years ago in the Sierra Moréna but, as he himself suggests, this colony was presumably due to the lack of suitable crags which elsewhere form the griffon's invariable nesting place. Unfortunately, he gave little description of the nests, which F. C. R. Jourdain, from his remarks in *The Handbook of British Birds*, evidently considered were abandoned nests of other birds. The griffon has also been

---

[1] *Alauda*, xix, 3, 1951, p. 159.
[2] *Unexplored Spain*, pp. 163-164.

reported by A. C. Stark to have nested on one occasion on the ground near the summit of a hill in Spain.

On ledges and in caverns the nests are often placed close together, depending no doubt on the number of birds in the colony in comparison with suitable nest sites. Different opinions have been expressed as regards the nest itself, some writers recording that it is " of the scantiest description "—to quote *The Handbook*—a few sticks or twigs, mixed with grass and palmetto husks. Other nests, such as the ones depicted in the excellent photographs illustrating Mr. Robert Atkinson's *Quest for the Griffon*, prove to be fairly bulky structures, just as that author has described in his text. The truth was probably expressed by Colonel Verner when he wrote [1] that few birds seem to hold more divergent views on the subject of the size and shape of their nursery than do griffons. After long experience Verner formed the opinion that griffons varied in their ideas of comfort and cleanliness almost as much as human beings. According to this authority, typical nests have a foundation of big sticks, dried branches of trees and heather, the platform varying from two to four feet in diameter. Some have a neatly formed basin about fifteen inches across lined with dried tufts of grass, palmetto, etc., while others have little more than a central depression amid a collection of stiff quill feathers gathered from an adjacent griffon's roost.

Griffons are capable of breaking off branches from an ilex, olive or cork tree with their powerful beaks and these they carry in their beaks to the site of the nest. It was found that the birds continued this habit after the young were hatched, the parent birds providing their offspring with fresh bedding in the form of newly cut branches of green ilex and heath placed on the top of the dirty and much used nest. Verner emphasizes the point that griffons may frequently be seen flying to the cliffs holding big sticks, straw, tufts of grass and sundry other objects in their feet, and when thus occupied their legs are stretched out behind instead of being retracted.

In southern Spain Verner found that the birds lay as a rule early in February, sometimes even earlier ; fresh eggs may be taken in March and April but rarely in May. Eggs laid in April and May are considered second layings should the first egg be taken. This vulture is single-brooded.

It was Colonel Verner's opinion that cliffs much frequented by griffons as nesting sites are pervaded by a pungent smell of death and decay but somewhat different views have been expressed by Abel Chapman, who states that the nests are usually, if not always, clean, as the griffons feed their young by disgorging half-digested food from their own crops.

---

[1] *My Life among the Wild Birds of Spain*, from the account of the griffon in which much information here quoted has been obtained. As a young man the present writer was invited to visit the author in his cottage in Andalusia but to his lasting regret the opportunity was missed of being introduced to Spanish ornithology by such an authority.

Consequently there is no carrion or putrefying matter lying around to give forth an offensive smell.

If suddenly disturbed the young bird—no matter what size it may be—has a habit of instantly shamming death by throwing itself flat with its head lying in a dislocated fashion on one side ; it will remain motionless for some time. Even when nearly full grown birds have been known to feign death in this extraordinary fashion. A less pleasant habit and one guaranteed to get rid of a human intruder in the minimum of time is used as a last resort—the bird recovers from its " faint " and after a series of polite bows brings up the whole of its last putrid meal. This action usually wins the day for the young vulture and the climber beats a hasty retreat before he follows the example of the bird.

At the nest griffons are anything but aggressive and the statement made by a young naturalist that he had been " attacked " by a griffon when attempting to photograph it came in for severe criticism by F. C. R. Jourdain (*Bull. B.O.C.*, lix, p. 129). The most a bird will normally do is, as Verner relates, to strike a series of threatening attitudes and to emit a loud hissing noise resembling escaping steam. But in fairness to the undergraduate so characteristically "jumped upon " by the Rev. pastor, Verner himself once encountered a pugnacious bird which sailed close to him in most threatening manner with a mighty swish of its wings, well-nigh dislodging him from the cliff. A wounded bird, however, will not hesitate to bite. Apart from furious conflicts with their own kind over a disputed carcass the griffon is not an aggressor and should it be attacked prefers retreat to combat. The occasion described by Verner when he witnessed a griffon attacked by a bearded vulture until both became inter-locked and fell vertically at least a hundred feet must be almost unique.

The griffon lays a single egg and cases when two have been reported are the result of some abnormality or else, and more likely, a mistake has been made by the finder. Jourdain has pointed out that on cliff ledges nests are sometimes close together and there is room for error unless very careful observation can be made. Almost always the egg is unmarked, but on very rare occasions an egg will be found with a few spots, streaks or smears of dark red on the shell. Probably no one has examined more griffon's nests than the late Willoughby Verner and in the account of his experiences he observes that in over thirty years, in spite of the many scores he has seen, he only came across three eggs with any pretensions to markings ; two of them were discovered on the same day. Moreover, never in his life did he find more than *one* egg in a griffon's nest.

The average of sixty Spanish-taken eggs measured by Jourdain is 92 × 70·1 mm. Max. 101·2 × 73·8 and 94 × 75 mm. Min. 81·5 × 65 and 85 × 64·5 mm. Heinroth's estimate of the incubation period as fifty-one to fifty-two days seems to be extraordinarily long.

As very few naturalists have made a study of the nesting habits of

PLATE 33

GRIFFON VULTURE
Gyps fulvus fulvus (Hablizl)

EGYPTIAN VULTURE
Neophron percnopterus percnopterus (Linnaeus)

the griffon it was with particular interest that I received the following notes from Mr. Frank Taylor, who had kept the nest sites of several pairs of griffons under observation in 1952, 1953 and 1954 in Cyprus.

Building or nest repairing was seen to be going on at a site near the Koronia Forest Station on 12th February, when two nests were located. The parent birds were sitting closely on untidy nests of fresh pine branches on 26th February, though it was impossible to see an egg as the parent birds refused to move. It was not until 8th April that Mr. Taylor had his first view of a chick, which he estimated at that date to be two or three weeks old, and lively enough to shuffle about the nest. It was covered in white down and had probably been hatched between 18th and 25th March. Whenever uncovered by the hen the youngster " chirped ". On 26th April the chick was still in down, but less white and growing rapidly. A week later, on 3rd May, a considerable change had taken place ; the chick had developed considerably and was growing its wing feathers. The hen was very devoted and attentive to the chick, which appeared to be less active. By 17th May this youngster was quite big and well feathered, but did not attempt to stand. On that day the parent flew off the nest to join four other adult birds which had been disturbed from the nesting cliff. Visits to the nest on 14th and 21st June showed that the young bird was almost fully grown and feathered and was standing upright and alone in the nest.

From the end of June onwards Mr. Taylor visited the nest site almost daily in order that the young bird's first flight might if possible be witnessed. Daily the young griffon stretched its wings and spent much time preening its feathers and sunbathing with wings outstretched, but it made no attempt to fly. Towards the end of July it was seen to make a vertical jump of a foot or more with wings half-spread but nothing more ambitious occurred until 3rd August, when the nest was found to be empty, and the parent was located sitting alone some twenty feet above the nest. Darkness intervened before Mr. Taylor could locate the young, but early next morning, 4th August, the parent bird on being disturbed from its perch above the nest flew across a deep ravine and landed by its offspring some 200 yards from its nest. As the sun reached the rock on which the young bird stood the latter spread its wings ; it remained in that position so long as it was possible to watch it but never stirred. On 6th August it had mysteriously reached a ledge high above its nest place and from there Mr. Taylor at last saw it launch itself into the air, when it flew round for two or three minutes, to land clumsily on a crag above its nest. Later it made a stronger flight of five minutes' duration.

During the remainder of August it took daily flights and towards the end of the month was flying strongly in much the same majestic way as its parents, but its landing was inexpert, with legs dropped long before the old birds dropped theirs. It would sometimes pitch on a tall pine and sunbathe there with wings spread for half an hour. Mr. Taylor noticed that early in September the nest in which this youngster had been hatched had been rebedded with fresh pine branches and twigs.

Supposing that this egg had hatched around 18th March, it was not until 3rd August that the young bird had taken its first flight. During the period the young was in the nest feeding took place entirely by regurgitation, and the clamour and excitement which accompanied the feeding process from the time the chick was a few weeks old struck Mr. Taylor as remarkable. Its sudden alertness and gaze into the sky would indicate the approach of the old birds and in some way it was able to distinguish either parent, while high in the air, from other adult birds. The young one, squawking loudly, would be prostrate with wings half-spread and head down on the floor of the nest as the parent landed beside it, then with heads down and close together amidst continued squawking, regurgitated food was passed to the offspring.

This method of feeding was continued long after the young bird was fully grown and could presumably have fended for itself. Mr. Taylor instances two occasions, one on 9th September, the other on 3rd October, when the feeding of the young by the parent was witnessed—the latter an extremely late date. On the former occasion one of the parents was perched alone on the nest site. A few minutes later the young bird approached, crying loudly and excitedly, legs dangling, made its clumsy landing on the nest and grovelled with outspread wings and head down as described earlier. The feeding lasted for almost five minutes and the noise—not unlike the squealing of a small pig—would have been audible three or four hundred yards away. The old bird flew off immediately after feeding the young one.

Naturalists with any experience of griffons have always been struck by the length of time the young appear to remain in the nest, but from Mr. Taylor's observations, the accuracy of which I can vouch for, it seems that the young are in the nest *much* longer than was suggested by Mr. C. S. Webb when lecturing before the Zoological Society of London on this very point. Mr. Webb estimated that in Spain the young griffon remained up to twelve weeks in the nest before attempting to fly, but from Mr. Taylor's experience it appears that the fledging period, from the date the egg is hatched to the day of the first flight, may be as much as 130 to 139 days. Mr. Webb found that a young bird in down will weigh as much as twelve and a half pounds and one with body feathers showing fourteen pounds, the full development of the wing being required to sustain the weight of a bird before it dare launch itself safely into the air.

If future investigation shows that a period of well over four months is spent by the young griffon in the nest before it makes its first flight, and that the bird watched so carefully in its nest in Cyprus, from which that estimate was made, behaved in the normal manner, then Mr. Frank Taylor may be congratulated on having made a substantial contribution to the breeding biology of a bird notoriously difficult to study in its nesting site.

REFERENCES : Original Description. *Vultur fulvus* Hablizl, Neue Nord. Beytr., 4, 1783, p. 58. Mountains of Gilan, Northern Persia.

Genus *NEOPHRON* Savigny

EGYPTIAN VULTURE

PLATE 33

Neophron percnopterus percnopterus (Linnaeus)

An Accidental Visitor

IDENTIFICATION : An Egyptian vulture in adult plumage is unmistakable by reason of its entirely white body plumage and the black terminal portion of the wings ; the primaries are black with the basal portion of the outer webs brownish-grey. The chin, throat, forepart of the crown and sides of the face (as well as a patch on the upper breast) are bare of feathers and the skin is yellow, the back of the crown being white. At the nape and on the sides of the neck lanceolate pinkish-buff feathers form a ruff. The bill is yellow and slender with a black tip ; the feet are yellow and the iris is dark orange.

At close quarters it will be noted that the upperparts and underparts, including the tail, are white to creamy-white washed with pinkish-buff on the middle of the back and on the belly and thighs. In comparison with the griffon it is a much smaller bird, with a wingspan of about five feet.

The slow stately walk and ungainly appearance when on the ground contrast poorly with its buoyant flight, for once airborne the Egyptian vulture is a delight to watch as it soars in ever-widening circles without visible motion of its wings.

Both adults and young have a wedge-shaped tail, conspicuous in flight, and as the bird carries its head tucked in between the shoulders its silhouette is unmistakable.

The young *Neophron* resembles its parent in size but in its first year is sombrely clad in dark brown, the feathers tipped with buff or fulvous. As the bird progresses in age the feathers become brownish-white, a number of buff feathers appear and gradually, with successive moults, the white feathers are assumed.

The sequence of moults has been discussed by Professor Stresemann, who observes that the young Egyptian vulture leaves the eyrie in brown plumage and begins to change this dark dress in March of the following year ; it exchanges it for a very similar dark dress, which presumably lasts over another year, while the primaries are renewed for the first time. In the third calendar year it assumes a colouration which already resembles fairly clearly the adult plumage, though it is far from being white in effect. White Egyptian vultures, therefore, are as a rule at least four years old.

Stresemann points out that as long as the Egyptian vulture shows any colouration of plumage it appears to be incapable of breeding, for it is rare for a bird not entirely white to return from Africa to Europe in the spring. Irby, Tristram and Lilford all confirm this. It follows then that the immature Egyptian vulture of European origin (young birds of two or three years) wanders about Africa at all times of year.

OCCURRENCES IN GREAT BRITAIN : There are two records of this vulture having been obtained in England. The first was taken in October 1825 near Kilve, Bridgewater Bay, Somerset, and was an immature bird ; the second, also immature, was obtained on 28th September 1868 at Peldon, Essex.

At the meeting of the British Ornithologists' Club held in November 1917 the first of the two specimens mentioned above was exhibited. It is an example of great historical interest and the full history of its capture is given by Mr. W. L. Sclater in the *Bulletin of the B.O.C.*, xxxviii, p. 13.

DISTRIBUTION ABROAD : The Palæarctic range of the Egyptian vulture extends through southern Europe from the Iberian Peninsula to Palestine and Sinai and in northern Africa through the lands bordering the Mediterranean from Morocco to Egypt, in which last country it is now reported to be scarce though formerly abundant. Thence it ranges east to southern Russia and through Arabia and Persia to north-west India.

The range of the Egyptian vulture in eastern Africa north of the Equator was summed up by Professor Stresemann, after a thorough investigation, in the following paragraph :

The N. African region, which to the north merges with the southern European and to the N.E. with the Asiatic region, occupies the whole northern rim of the continent and stretches in many places south to ca. 14° N. or even a little further south ; in N.E. Africa, however, it follows the mountain ranges and rocky semi-desert areas and approaches much nearer to the equator. Not only does it include Abyssinia and Somaliland, but stretches out a tongue in the neighbourhood of Lake Rudolph as far as the Mt. Kenya district and therefore crosses the equator itself. It was fairly common in the bare rocky regions in the north of the former German East Africa. Doctor G. A. Fischer (*J.f.O.*, 1885, p. 121) gives its most southerly point (breeding place ?) as Usaramo ca. 7° S. Bohm and Reichardt saw several *Neophron* in the quite isolated locality of Lake Itambe (between Lakes Moero and Upemba).

I have myself dealt elsewhere with the range of the Egyptian vulture on the western side of Africa, where there are resident colonies in both the Canary and Cape Verde archipelagos. The former is in the Palæarctic, the latter in the Ethiopian Region. On the mainland the bird has a number of breeding places in Morocco, and according to Balsac is regularly distributed beyond the Anti-Atlas in the whole of the coastal zone as far as the mouth of the Dra. It occurs certainly in the Spanish zone, and in a few of the oases in the direction of the Bani. An odd pair or two breed at

Zemmour. The *Neophron* is reported to be totally absent from the Adrar and from the Sahel as a breeding bird.

In the central Sahara it almost certainly nests in the Hoggar Mountains area (Meinertzhagen) and has been found to do so in the Aïr Massif (Buchanan); in northern Nigeria Paludan found many adults and young birds in the vicinity of Zinder.

It seems evident that this vulture nests wherever it finds suitable environment as far south in western Africa as the border of the forest area. There is another breeding area where the *Neophron* bred very sparingly, *i.e.* in South Africa, but from all accounts it has now practically disappeared as a nesting species. In 1944 Professor Stresemann wrote as follows of its former status in the Cape[1] :

In earlier times the Egyptian Vulture had a wide distribution in the south and east of Cape Colony, right down as far as the near neighbourhood of Cape Town. In the eastern half of South Africa it was distributed northwards to the Transvaal or to Matabeleland, where it has been scarce for decades, but can still be seen in the Kruger National Park. There are clutches from Hogefield (Malmesbury District) and Colesbury in the South African Museum. In 1860 it was not uncommon in the west of South Africa in Great Namaqualand and Damaraland. Its days there seem numbered, however, and it will share the fate of the Lammergeyer, which is already extinct in South Africa. That bird of prey expert, Finch-Davies, wrote in the *Ibis* in 1920 that he had seen the Egyptian Vulture now and again in the south-eastern districts of South Africa (*e.g.* in Pondoland) but had never encountered it in S.W. Africa, neither had he ever seen a young or immature bird. Hoesch also never saw it in S.W. Africa, though Niethammer saw a specimen in Damaraland on 30th Sept. 1938, and Bradfield colletced an immature female there on the 17th February 1923 (*J.f.O.*, 1940, p. 162).

The autumn migrations of the European *Neophron*, and the wandering habits of the African population, will be referred to later in this essay.

In the Indian peninsula a subspecies, *Neophron percnopterus ginginianus*, takes the place of the typical race.

HABITS : This is a vulture with which I am thoroughly familiar through long acquaintance with the bird in the Canary Islands. In the two principal ports of that archipelago, Las Palmas and Santa Cruz de Tenerife, one's ship has barely cast anchor before the traveller is aware that Egyptian vultures are soaring overhead. Both ports offer many allurements in the way of garbage thrown overboard from ships to attract these useful scavengers and it is seldom that three or four of these striking birds cannot be seen either over harbour or town or walking along the sea-shore in their ceaseless hunt for refuse cast up by the waves. In the latter case they can be approached quite closely.

Altitude is no barrier to the Egyptian vulture and when encamped on Grand Canary at 6000 feet I have had the birds around the camp ever

[1] *Orn. Monatsber.*, lii, 1944, p. 146.

ready to dispute a discarded morsel with the ravens, but never venturing too near, however hungry they appeared to be.

Over mountain and valley, forest and plain the Egyptian vulture will sail, ever watchful for a dying goat or mule, the feast of all others which really satisfies its wants. I have disturbed as many as forty at a carcass in a mountain ravine, the birds quarrelling among themselves for the choicest entrails and tearing at the flesh. When the last morsel has been picked from the hideous skeleton and the head often severed from the trunk, the overloaded vultures struggle to the nearest perch, where they will remain digesting the putrid meal, almost too lethargic to move, though at other times they will brook no close approach. Of all the vultures it has ever been my fortune to see, the Egyptian is the most loathsome feeder. Nothing foul comes amiss to it—carrion of all kinds, preferably putrid, fish entrails and offal, garbage swept up by the sea, street refuse, maggots, beetles and human excrement, which it appears to relish. I have skinned only one of these vultures in my life and the experience was not to be repeated. But, on account of the good offices which it performs, the bird is rightly protected almost wherever it is found.

How different does the Egyptian vulture appear in one's eyes when seen in its immaculate white plumage with black primaries widely extended, soaring against a cloudless blue sky. Watch it steadily mounting to the heavens, tilting now one wing, now the other, to catch the air currents, and with each widening circle growing smaller and smaller until the tiny speck is lost in space. It is difficult then to remember how repellent it can be at close quarters, when the bare yellow neck and forehead give it an almost obscene appearance.

I have watched one of these vultures in Grand Canary quartering a euphorbia-covered hillside in much the manner of a harrier. The bird was sailing along not far above the ground with its head turning this way and that, keenly on the look-out for prey of some kind, but whether lizards (which abound) or locusts, upon both of which it preys, I was unable to discover. In the eastern islands of the group, where carrion in the shape of goat, donkey or camel is by no means plentiful, the Egyptian vulture has become a regular insect-eater. Two birds which Captain Polatzek shot in Lanzarote had their crops crammed with large green grasshoppers, and at those times when the migratory locust arrives from the Sahara it is consumed by the vultures in great quantities. It is on record that *Neophrons* have been seen flying low over the ground opening and shutting their beaks and rising and falling in their flight, just as if they were capturing insects on the wing, and if this action is correctly interpreted, it is an acquired character which, so far as I know, has never been observed elsewhere.

In contrast to such low flying it has been recorded that during the last war an Egyptian vulture was fired upon by an aircraft-gunner at 5000 feet, being mistaken for an enemy plane.

Except when gathered at a kill or in the vicinity of a slaughter-house, these vultures are not normally gregarious. In the country they are more often encountered singly or in pairs, and even at their roosting places, when a number repair to the same cliff, each pair has its own particular ledge to which it goes as evening approaches.

I have never seen any large roosts in the Canaries such as Colonel Meinertzhagen describes from Port Sudan, where he saw over 200 roosting on telegraph poles in the evening and many more roosting on the ground. There are, of course, nothing like such numbers in the Canaries. In Arabia Meinertzhagen found a communal roost in an acacia tree, twenty-five sitting together and coming in well before sundown.

Egyptian vultures pair for life and European birds are said to continue their attachment when migrating overseas.

It is a remarkably silent bird ; I have never heard it utter any cry under any circumstances even when suddenly startled. Usually it is of a peaceable nature but Polatzek observed two instances of a vulture attacking a raven. In the first case the bird was seen to pounce upon a raven, which was prevented from rising until the vulture continued its flight. When released the raven gave chase to the vulture and attacked it from in front, whereupon the vulture struck back violently with its wing and quickly put the aggressor to flight. On another occasion a vulture was seen to swoop upon two ravens flying beneath it until the latter were almost forced to the ground ; the vulture then ascended and repeated the performance until the discomfited ravens managed to escape.

It is always dangerous to judge the habits of a bird solely from its behaviour in one locality, for birds, like humans, will adapt themselves to their environment and to the circumstances in which they are at the time. I have often been struck by the comparative shyness of birds in one area, whereas in another they are particularly fearless, and this applies to vultures as well as to many other groups of the feathered world. In parts of East Africa the Egyptian vulture shows no more sign of fear than the turkey buzzard in Jamaica or the black vulture in Trinidad which wander around scavenging in the streets.

When a native kraal is moved the vultures move along with it for what they can pick up, and as their tastes are utterly depraved, the occupants of the village benefit to no small extent from the attendance of these birds.

Along the coasts of the Red Sea and the Gulf of Aden the Egyptian vulture is abundant, and it has been described by Sir Geoffrey Archer as ubiquitous in Abyssinia and Somaliland :

Wherever in Somaliland there are villages and the prospect of offal or refuse of any sort, there the Egyptian vulture will be found. . . . It will permit of extremely close approach before taking wing, and will then merely flap away to the nearest tree or settle on the ground a few yards distant. It is the pariah of the bird creation, but withal vastly useful as a scavenger in tropical countries. At Aden rows of these birds may be seen lining the rocks in the vicinity of the Parsee Tower of Silence, where they gruesomely await the laying out of the human remains.

My personal acquaintance with the *Neophron* in North Africa has been confined to the area between southern Tunisia and the Atlantic coast of Morocco, and more especially to the crossing of the desert (February and March) south of the Great Atlas from Ouarzazate to Colomb Béchar in Algeria. In this desert area it was not rare but we never encountered more than a pair together. Those birds which had spent the winter south of the Sahara had evidently not begun to come north by the middle of March.

MIGRATIONS: Unlike the griffon, which is for the most part a stationary bird, the Egyptian vulture is to a large extent migratory. In southern Europe and Asia Minor, and even in Palestine, this vulture is seldom seen in winter, almost all migrating to warmer climes, some in August but the majority in September and the late stragglers in October. The breeding population of Tunisia, Algeria and Morocco—at any rate those which nest north of the Atlas—disappears for the colder months, not to return until March or April, though I have seen them in the vicinity of the Great Atlas range as early as 20th February. It has been pointed out by Stresemann that the principal winter quarters of this vulture seem to lie on the southern edge of the desert and just south of the Sahara, and it is to be expected therefore that migration would take place across that vast desert in the early spring and during the autumn. As the birds usually wander in pairs and not in large flocks they would be little noticed and all the less, as Stresemann emphasizes, as there are many places in the desert where Egyptian vultures breed.

When encamped in Darfur Admiral Lynes was struck by the variation in numbers of this vulture at different times, but this, as Stresemann suggests, may be attributed to the arrival from Europe of northern breeding birds. In autumn and winter it was very common at all towns and villages from El Obeid to Fasher, while in spring and summer the numbers were much reduced. It would seem that the African winter quarters in the southern Sudan of the European Egyptian vultures roughly coincide with the breeding area of the African resident birds. The latter occupy every place that is suitable for an Egyptian vulture, rocky gorges and the terraced cliffs of the dry zone, provided there is enough to eat in the neighbourhood. It follows that when the migrant birds have departed the numbers of the Egyptian vulture in this area will be smaller in summer than in winter, when their numbers are reinforced from the north. Moreover, as Stresemann has shown, there will be a higher percentage of coloured birds, for only the fully adult vultures go north to breed, the immature non-breeding birds wandering about Africa. Stresemann writes :

In the whole southern half of its distribution area in the Northern Hemisphere the Egyptian vulture is both sedentary and bird of passage, namely in the Sudan,

Abyssinia, Somaliland and Kenya, in Arabia and in southern Mesopotamia, as also in Lower Egypt and in the Sinai Peninsula. . . . The Egyptian vulture in S.W. Asia behaves exactly the same as in Europe. There too it is a bird of passage in the cold regions, arriving in March and leaving again in September or October, probably for N.W. India. The young appear to be stationary in the south (N.W. India ?), for they are not seen in the more northerly regions, just as in Europe.

As to how the European birds reach their winter quarters by crossing first the Mediterranean Sea and then the barren waste of the Sahara, Professor Stresemann points out that :

On its flights to Europe and back to Africa the Egyptian Vulture endeavours as far as possible to avoid crossing the Mediterranean at its broadest points ; it uses chiefly all the straits which offer : Straits of Gibraltar, Straits of Messina and the Dardanelles. It seldom uses the Aegean, and the 10 birds which Despott (*Ibis*, 1917, p. 484) knew from Malta were significantly all found in the autumn ; evidently *Neophron* avoids the stretch of sea from Tripoli to Malta, which is considerably longer than that from Sicily to Malta.

The desert, on the other hand, seems to hold no terrors for the bird, for travellers have met with it in the very heart of the Sahara.

BREEDING HABITS : After years of studying the nesting habits of the Egyptian vulture in southern Spain Colonel Willoughby Verner wrote that the favourite site for the nest is in a cavern or on a shelf protected from the rain by an overhanging rock. This was my experience in the Canary Islands, J. I. S. Whitaker's in Tunisia and Sir Geoffrey Archer's in Somaliland, and I have no doubt that in more recent days ornithologists have found the same. In nine cases out of ten the nests are extremely difficult to reach, some in fact inaccessible to the most experienced rock climber, but now and again an absurdly easy site is selected, usually in a wild place where the bird relies on the inaccessibility of the area rather than of the nest site itself. Twice in his considerable experience Verner came across nests built in a crevice amid big boulders on a hillside within a few feet of a path used only by goats and cattle. In southern Spain there are hundreds of similar valleys overgrown with giant heath and cistus and dotted with similar big grey rocks in all directions, and such a situation would appear a safe place in which a vulture might rear its young with impunity.

In the Canary Islands I have spent many hours stumbling up the rock-strewn bed of a barranco whose precipitous walls, studded with innumerable caves and ledges, came closer and closer as one ascended into the interior, until one found oneself in a narrow gorge hemmed in by precipices. Few except goatherds ever followed the course of the torrent— dry for most months of the year—and the vultures were fully aware of the fact, for both roosting and nesting sites were situated well inland wherever the coastal area was populated, and often when it was not. The breeding places were quite inaccessible from the cliff summit to anyone without a rope. In some of these caves the mortal remains of the Guanches have been discovered, the ancient race which inhabited the Canaries in the fifteenth century. How the bodies of the departed Guanches ever reached such an unapproachable burying place as these caves, situated three-quarters of the way up an unclimbable precipice, is a mystery to present-day minds. It is in the smaller caverns in such a situation or under the shelter of an overhanging ledge that the vultures in Grand Canary and Tenerife rejoice to rear their young. Single nesting sites are the rule but I have several times found what appeared to be a number of nests within easy distance of one another. Altitude does not trouble this vulture in the Canaries. One pair had their nest in a niche of Los Pechos, the highest point of Grand Canary, while I have seen others almost at sea-level in the sea cliffs.

I have never in any land seen an Egyptian vulture's nest anywhere but in a cliff, but a tree nest has been recorded; the nest of another bird of prey had been utilized, the vulture altering it to suit its own requirements and taste. Verner describes such a site : a nest freshly built by a snake-eagle, *Circaëtus gallicus*, in the cork woods near Gibraltar, but to-day one would have to go a long way from the Rock to find a situation such as this bird had selected.

Other instances of tree nests have occurred but only very exceptionally.[1] Sir Geoffrey Archer found an Egyptian vulture nesting in a fig tree in Somaliland on 23rd February 1921, but in that country the great buttressed cliffs surmounting the Golis range provide a regular and favourite breeding haunt among the ledges and crannies in the rocks, where the bird has for company kestrels, fan-tailed ravens and chestnut-winged starlings. In his note in *The Handbook of British Birds* F. C. R. Jourdain observes that the Egyptian vulture formerly bred on buildings in Turkish towns, but now it apparently does so less frequently.

The late Hugh Whistler has recorded that in India the Egyptian vulture places its nest " on rocky precipices, earthy cliffs, buildings *and trees*, often in very exposed and frequented situations ". He further adds that it has no fear of man, and perches on buildings and trees in the most crowded bazaars, or stalks sedately about open spaces, graveyards and camping grounds, looking in gait and appearance much like a large, disreputable old hen. That description of the vulture's behaviour in India is a pretty good illustration for the warning given earlier in this essay that it is inadvisable to judge the habits of a bird in one locality from its behaviour in another. *Neophrons* which I have encountered in Spain and in North Africa have certainly not resembled " Pharaoh's chickens ", though in the Canaries they are " tamer " than I have found them elsewhere.

[1] In parts of Spain, such as the plains of the Guadalquivir, where rocks are absent Colonel Willoughby Verner was informed that the Egyptian vultures had made use of trees but he evidently never verified the tale himself. In any case that record is many years old and no recent instance has come to my knowledge.

There is one characteristic of these birds, apart from their disgusting feeding habits, which is exemplified the world over—their amazingly dirty nests. Probably no bird in existence has such unclean habits when nesting, and as the immaculately clad downy young are hatched amid filth, so in their turn do they rear their own offspring under similar conditions. Such is the force of parental example!

The same site may be used year after year, and in consequence some nests reach a considerable size. Both sexes take part in the building, or rather in making the collection of material which forms the unsavoury nest. The foundation is of sticks and twigs—in the Canaries dried branches of euphorbia are utilized—and the bowl, if that term can be used of such an untidy flat structure, is warmly lined with wool, goat's or clotted camel's hair, or some other handy material. No nest is complete without rags, the dirtier the better, and the list of articles found in or by the nest is inexhaustible. One naturalist alone, with exceptional experience, confesses that setting aside human excrement, he has found in nests which he has examined kittens, rats, hedgehogs, tortoises, snakes, lizards, toads, frogs, the remains of foxes, dogs, fish and young birds, all in various stages of putrefaction, in addition to a motley collection of old rope, filthy rags and paper, dried animal's dung and a bag of flour crawling with meal worms.

The eggs are sometimes surprisingly beautiful, and unlike the griffon the Egyptian vulture lays a pair, occasionally even three; single eggs have also been found. To describe first eggs which I have examined from the Canary Islands: the commonest type has the entire shell smeared with deep reddish- and purplish-brown. Others are almost entirely white with rather pale purplish-brown blotches and spots gathered round the obtuse end. Typical of the more handsome series are eggs in which the broader half is covered with a confluent mass of deep red-brown, varying to almost black in patches but pale on the cap; the pointed end is creamy-white, speckled sparingly with various shades of brown and having underlying markings of lilac. In Spain clutches have been taken which can vie with the most handsome eggs of the osprey.

In addition to the nine eggs from the Canaries there is in the British Museum collection a considerable series from Spain and elsewhere. Examination of the whole collection shows that the eggs of this vulture are very varied. The ground colour is white, cream or rufous-buff and the predominating markings are brown. A few eggs have only a few reddish-brown spots and blotches but the majority have the entire surface covered with confluent masses of deep reddish-brown to such an extent that hardly any of the ground colour is visible. Every variation between these two extremes exists. Some specimens have a heavy cap of rich reddish-brown covering the broad half of the egg; others are almost uniform reddish-brown all over. Lightly marked eggs are unusual but one examined had the shell almost entirely white, with rather pale purplish-brown blotches and spots gathered round the obtuse end.

Jourdain has published the measurements of 100 eggs of *Neophron percnopterus* as : average 66·18 × 50 mm. Max. 76·4 × 51·7 and 68·1 × 56·1. Min. 58·2 × 50 and 64 × 43 mm.

The end of March is the earliest date when eggs may be found in southern Europe but many birds have not reached their breeding places until that month is well advanced and it is not until April that eggs can be sought with impunity, preferably in the middle of the month. In the British Museum series of the Egyptian vulture's eggs, taken in southern Spain, Greece, Algeria, Egypt and Palestine, dates when they were obtained vary from 22nd March (Malaga) to 15th May (Algeria), while those in the Meade-Waldo collection from the Canary Islands range from 21st March to 12th April, layings being no earlier than in southern Europe though not apparently prolonged into May. In British Somaliland the nesting season of the Egyptian vulture begins in January and extends into April, the second and third weeks of March being perhaps the best period in which to find nests with eggs. Sixteen eggs in Sir Geoffrey Archer's collection from that country averaged in size 66 × 51 mm. Max. 71 × 53, min. 62 × 49 mm.

Incubation is reported to be shared by both sexes, but as the parents are exactly alike it is a point which it is difficult to verify, short of shooting the bird which leaves the nest. There is an interval between the laying of the two eggs which Verner has described as " considerable ". Incubation begins with the first egg laid. *The Handbook*, without quoting its authority, gives the incubation period as *circa* forty-two days. The fledging period does not appear to have been ascertained.

REFERENCES : Original Description. *Vultur perenopterus* (misprint for *percnopterus*) Linnaeus, Syst. Nat., 10th ed., 1758, p. 87 : Egypt.

PLATE 34

OSPREY
Pandion haliaëtus haliaëtus Linnaeus

Family PANDIONIDAE

Genus *PANDION* Savigny

OSPREY[1]   PLATE 34

Pandion haliaëtus haliaëtus (Linnaeus)

An uncommon Passage Migrant; formerly bred in Scotland on various lochs, and rarely in England. Now exterminated as a breeding bird, though may re-establish itself.

IDENTIFICATION : This grand bird is about the size of a buzzard but very different in appearance. It is conspicuous from afar by reason of its shining white underparts, relieved by an area of light brown on the crop with some dark streaks. Very noticeable too is the head, the crown being white, heavily streaked with blackish and having a broad band of dark brown passing from below and behind the eye down the sides of the neck. The feathers on the hind part of the crown are tinged with russet and are lengthened to form a short crest which the bird can raise. The rest of the upperparts is dark brown, including the tail. The axillaries and under tail-coverts are white. The eye is bright yellow, the bill black and prominently hooked, the cere greyish-green and the legs and feet greenish-yellow. The feet are very powerful, the toes furnished with immensely strong curved sharp claws and with sharp prickly scales on the underside. The outer toe is reversible.

Immature birds have the upperparts not so dark as the adult and many of the feathers are tipped and edged with white. The band on the crop is paler and almost negligible, so that the whole underside from chin to under tail-coverts appears white with only faint pectoral markings. The tail is lighter and has bars on the outer web, while there is much more white at the tip of the rectrices.

Some additional notes on the appearance of the osprey in the field will be given when discussing its habits. The total length of the osprey as given by Seton Gordon is twenty-three inches, while the wing expanse is just over nineteen inches.

OCCURRENCES IN GREAT BRITAIN TO-DAY : The description in *The Handbook*, " rare but regular passage migrant ", probably fits the bill so far as Scotland and England are concerned, but as there have been only fifteen occurrences in Ireland since 1900, *i.e.* in fifty-five years, it cannot be termed a regular visitor to that country. As a migrant it is rarely seen in Wales but on the east coast of England it can fairly be termed of regular occurrence, especially in Norfolk. On occasion it is also met with on inland lakes and reservoirs, but it is a bird which attracts the attention of the

[1] It should perhaps be emphasized that the " osprey " plumes, so fashionable at one period in ladies' dress, have nothing whatever to do with the bird of that name. These ornamental plumes are found only on certain species of the heron family—especially the egret—and are grown only during the breeding season. The true osprey has no ornamental feathers on its body.

PANDIONIDAE 336 OSPREY

casual gunner and each year one or more are shot or trapped. The status
of the osprey in Scotland at the present day (1955) may be gathered from
the final paragraph in the account of the osprey in *The Birds of Scotland*,
where Miss Baxter and Miss Rintoul sum up the situation in the following
words [1] :

As the Osprey is a summer visitor to Northern Europe it has always occurred on
migration in Scotland and still continues to do so. . . . It occurs on the west side of the
mainland, but more regularly on the east coast and is very uncommon on the Islands.
. . . It has occurred on Islay and Skye, but only once in the Outer Hebrides. It
has been reported on a few occasions in Orkney, Fair Isle and Shetland, and on the
Isle of May we have twice seen Ospreys passing over to the northward in May. The
principal autumn movement is in September, with a few records in August and
October, while the usual spring dates are in May and June, though it has been
recorded in April. Single birds only are usually recorded, so the occurrence of a
party of eight [2] in the parish of Carmunnock, Lanarkshire, on March 27th, 1946, is
very remarkable.

When discussing the status and disappearance of the osprey as a
breeding bird from Britain in the 3rd edition of Howard Saunders'
Manual which he edited, the late Doctor Eagle Clarke correctly states
that the osprey has never been known to nest in Ireland. Surprising as
that fact may be, it is necessary to emphasize it, for, as the late H. Kirke-
Swann pointed out in a letter to *British Birds*,[3] the osprey was much confused in Ireland in olden days with the sea-eagle, *Haliaëtus albicilla*,
and references to the osprey breeding in Ireland most certainly refer to
the former bird.

There is no doubt that as a migrant the osprey appears regularly on
the east coast of England and in some years is much more commonly
reported than in others. In 1930 for instance several were recorded during
the autumn passage.

PAST HISTORY IN BRITAIN : It is not my intention here to give a
complete account of the osprey's former habitats in our islands, or to
chronicle in detail the various lochs upon which it has been reported to
nest in former days. That it once bred in the Lake District of England
is now generally recognized. The last breeding place south of the Border,
Doctor Blair assures me, was Whinfield Park, Westmorland. The evidence
is reviewed and discussed by MacPherson in his *Vertebrate Fauna of
Lakeland*.[4] There was also a site in the Ullswater crags mentioned by

---

[1] The third line of this quotation has been altered slightly from the original by Miss
Baxter herself to read more clearly.

[2] Reference to this occurrence is made in *British Birds*, xxxiv, 1946, p. 218, by P. A.
Clancey, who appears to have been the witness of this passing flock which Miss Baxter
and Miss Rintoul mention.

[3] *British Birds*, xv, 1922, p. 220.

[4] Pp. 214-217.

Richardson.[1]   When these two sites were abandoned is uncertain, but they were occupied apparently up to the end of the eighteenth century.

The history of the osprey's status north of the Border before its final extirpation as a breeding bird has been told by Miss Baxter and Miss Rintoul in their recently issued *Birds of Scotland* (1953), which is available to everyone interested in this melancholy subject.   The tale of greed, theft and cruelty which surrounds the last pairs of ospreys attempting to breed year after year, and as regularly having their eggs taken, is sickening to read.   One or other of the old birds was time and again wantonly shot from the nest[2] and one reads of the survivor of a pair returning alone to the nesting site for as many as five years in succession before finally giving it up as hopeless and deserting the place for ever.

Whether the osprey was ever quite as common as some would make out seems extremely doubtful, as many of the lochs and rivers in our country are incapable of supporting a pair of ospreys and their young.   It is true that certain lochs were regularly favoured by the birds but what chance had they of survival under the circumstances described ?

One of the most famous of the old nesting places was on Loch an Eilein, where breeding took place yearly up to 1899.   The story of the osprey's nesting in that locality from 1808 until its extermination is given by C. G. Cash in the *Scottish Naturalist*,[3] a story, as the author admits, " of such ruthless persecution and of such altogether inadequate protection that the wonder is that the ospreys survived so long ".

The pair which bred at the very beginning of the nineteenth century on an island of Loch Lomond—reputed by Robert Gray to have been Inch Galbraith—were finally slaughtered by one John Colquhoun, who is reported to have said that though their eggs were taken every year they never forsook their eyrie.   The latter was built at the side of a chimney on an old ruin.   No osprey has bred since on this famous loch.   There were eyries on Loch Awe, on the Lake of Menteith, on Loch Tay, on the beautiful but little known Loch Ordie, above Dunkeld, on Loch Morlich and on Loch Maree, to mention a few of the better substantiated localities where the ospreys attempted to rear their young in olden days.   In 1867, according to Robert Gray, quoting H. J. Elwes (President of the B.O.U. in 1921-22), there were " at least three or four " breeding stations in Ross-shire which to his knowledge were " strictly protected ".   Ospreys also nested on Loch Luichart in Cromarty, and there were several others in Inverness-shire ; two pairs bred at Guisachan and a pair at Loch Insh, among other localities. In Sutherland the birds were exterminated on Loch Assynt in 1848, since when they have apparently deserted the locality.   In *The Birds of*

---

[1] In a short essay contributed by him to Hutchinson's *History of Cumberland*.

[2] See the description given by Charles St. John of Elgin in his *Natural History and Sport in Moray*, which contains an account of his exploits in 1848 : pp. 127-131 and 148-153.

[3] 1914, pp. 149-158.

Scotland the authors name other Inverness-shire lochs upon which the osprey bred, but observe that by 1867 Harvie-Brown believed the bird to be extinct as a breeding species in that county, though there have been unconfirmed reports of it breeding there since the date quoted and to my knowledge one eyrie at least has been built.

The breeding of the osprey in south-west Scotland rests largely on the testimony of Robert Service, the Dumfriesshire naturalist, who wrote that beyond any doubt it bred on the islets of Lochs Skerrow and Grennoch in Kirkcudbrightshire, and also on one or other of the Glenhead group of lochs till 1860—a year, or maybe two, sooner or later. There must have been a number of other localities, some well known, others less so, where ospreys bred in Scotland prior to 1900 but since that date the eyries which have existed can be counted on the fingers of one hand.

Up to 1908 ospreys bred yearly on Loch Arkaig in Inverness-shire. *The Handbook* stated that breeding ceased there in 1902, but a letter[1] from Cameron of Lochiel corrected the date to six years later. The eyrie on the island was on the top of an old oak tree and was occupied continuously every year. From 1909 a single bird returned annually up to 1913. A second pair at one time (about 1899 or 1900, according to Lochiel's recollection) nested on a tree on the south side of the loch near the foot of Glen Camagarry, though the eggs apparently were stolen. The latter eyrie, Lochiel has estimated, was not occupied after 1900.

In the letter to *British Birds* from which I am quoting, Cameron of Lochiel adds that he had seen an osprey on two or three occasions since 1913 but just a passing bird fishing, which he took to be one of the birds which he understood were nesting on Loch Loyne on the Glen Garry estate, where he was informed that a pair of ospreys continued to nest for some time after the pair had left his own estate on Loch Arkaig.

Confirmation of the above has been given me by Mr. Patrick Sandeman, who, in his capacity of Hon. Secretary of the Rare Birds Protection Committee for Scotland, has taken a special interest in the history of this species. Mr. Sandeman was definitely informed by the head keeper of the Lochiel estates that the osprey had bred on Loch Loyne in 1916, and if that is correct it is the last occasion when a wild pair have bred in the Highlands.

Although breeding has been reported on various subsequent occasions, once as recently as 1926, as mentioned in *The Birds of Scotland*, no definite proof was forthcoming. It is only fair to add that the 1916 nesting, if a fact, must have been kept a very close secret, for even men in the privileged position of Sir Norman Kinnear had no knowledge of it then or since.

In the early 1920s it became known to a few bird-lovers that ospreys were being reared " with protective supervision "[2] in woods by the River

[1] *British Birds*, xxxvi, 1943, p. 184.
[2] To quote from *The Scottish Naturalist*, lxv, 1953, p. 54.

Deveron, near the line dividing the counties of Aberdeen and Banff, but the fact was not made public. It so happened that in July 1925 Mr. J. Murdoch Henderson was staying in the vicinity of Loch Riach[1] and observed that from the last week of July, and during every morning for more than a fortnight, four ospreys—*at least some of them obviously juveniles* —came to the loch. There was no evidence to show where these birds had been bred, whether they were from some unknown breeding place, or whether, as was most likely, they were the result of the introduction to the woods of the Deveron to which reference is made above, but that they were Scottish-born ospreys seems to be a sound deduction. Mr. Henderson further reported that from the latter half of the spring of 1929 one bird, presumed to be an adult and possibly a breeding bird, fished the same loch until it met its inevitable end at the hands of some callous wretch who wounded it, despite all the efforts made to preserve it. No subsequent occurrence of an osprey at Loch Riach has been reported.

Referring to the occurrences of the osprey in Scotland since 1950 Mr. Patrick Sandeman tells me that about six single birds are brought to his notice annually, though in 1954 as many as eight were reported from widely different localities between 15th May and 30th June. To the best of his knowledge the osprey has not bred successfully since—at latest— 1916, apart from the breeding of the introduced pair in north-east Scotland in the early twenties. A pair frequented a Scottish loch in 1955, as I learn from another source, but nesting has not been confirmed.

DISTRIBUTION ABROAD : The breeding range of the osprey in Europe is influenced very much by the suitability of the terrain, the bird preferring isolated lochs and freshwater lakes in which it can fish undisturbed. Rocks off-shore and precipices overlooking the sea are also favoured in some localities, but water is essential to it as well as peaceful surroundings. In consequence there are large areas in western Europe where ospreys are only seen passing through on migration, for the bird is imbued with a very strong migratory instinct ; the northern birds which breed in Norway, Sweden, Finland and the Baltic States regularly pass south in autumn to winter in the Mediterranean countries and islands and in North and tropical Africa. Its northern breeding range extends as far as the birch growth does, *i.e.* to about 70° N. In Britain we know that it has ceased to nest and the same must be said of Denmark, where it was formerly a fairly common breeding bird, especially on the islands of Zealand, Lolland and Falster, from which it had already disappeared by the end of the nineteenth century.

The eastern range extends to western Siberia, to the Altai. The osprey does not breed in France, Holland or Belgium and is absent from the greater part of Spain and Portugal except for the Mediterranean coastal area of those countries and the south-west of Portugal. Absent from the mainland

---

[1] An artificial reservoir known locally as the Broch Dam which supplies the burgh of Fraserburgh.

of Italy, it breeds, however, on some of the islands and in Sicily, Corsica and Sardinia, as well as in the Balearics, where it nests on the cliffs and outlying rocks of all the islands in that group.

South of the Mediterranean it breeds on the coasts of all the countries bounded by that sea but only sparingly. It also breeds in the Canary Islands and in the Cape Verde archipelago, and I suspect that it breeds on an island off Dakar. No nest of the osprey has been reported as yet from the West African mainland, but ospreys are said by van Someren to have bred on Lake Naivasha. Its nesting on an island of Lake Victoria has been disputed, however. In eastern Africa it has been found nesting on the islands off the coast of Somaliland, and it is abundant on the islands off the Red Sea coast. It nests too at Port Sudan.

In southern Africa, where the osprey is a widely dispersed migrant, it has been found nesting once on the Berg River in a high poplar by Austin Roberts.

In northern Europe and Asia the osprey is a summer resident only, the birds from the former continent wintering in the Mediterranean area and in Africa south of the Sahara, while those from Asia are reported to winter in India and the Malay archipelago. In the large series of specimens in the British Museum collection the osprey is represented from many parts of tropical Africa and it is reported to reach the Cameroons on the west and Natal on the east. Whether the birds found in the vicinity of the Cape Province are actually migrants from Europe appears to me to be doubtful, in view of Doctor Austin Roberts' statement that both birds and eggs in South Africa show smaller measurements.

The species is almost cosmopolitan, for although only the typical race occurs in Europe and Africa, except possibly at the Cape, several other races have been separated, the best known being *Pandion h. carolinensis* from the Americas and *Pandion h. cristatus* from Australia.

HABITS : When discussing this species in my *Birds of West and Equatorial Africa*, I wrote that the osprey may be recognized from afar by its white head and still whiter breast, but it is by its actions rather than by its colour-pattern that it will best be identified, for in its graceful flight and in its manner of hanging poised in the air with beating wings on the watch for its slippery prey it is unlike any other bird. The sea-eagle of Europe and the river eagle of Africa both have different methods of capturing their victims. The former, though it will occasionally plunge like the osprey, may usually be seen flying low over the water capturing fish which come up to the surface, or it will remain motionless on some stump or rock for hours on end, and has even been seen wading in shallow water. Slightly different is the method of the African river eagle. Though it too attacks fish near the surface, it does so by making a long gradual swoop from some height, throwing forward the feet and talons at the last moment to scoop up its prey. The glide upwards follows without the slightest pause, the captured fish dangling from the eagle's feet. That is not the method employed by the osprey. Watch it as I used to do in the Canary Islands flying in leisurely fashion down the coast at a good height above the sea, never going far from the land, but with head inclined downwards, the sharp eyes searching for any movement in the clear water below. Now it will pause in its flight and, not unlike a kestrel on a wind-swept hillside, will remain hovering over the spot where its quarry has been sighted. If the fish is within reach the osprey plunges down *feet first* to disappear among a cloud of spray, sometimes completely submerging. Within seconds it reappears shaking the water from its head, but now heavily laden, a good-sized fish held in its talons. With legs fully outstretched it makes its way slowly shorewards, usually to some ledge or cliff if one is handy, there to devour its catch.

When flying thus laden over the blue sea, the osprey makes a delightful picture, the wet silvery scales of the fish gleaming in the sunlight below the snow-white belly of the bird. When living on one of the uninhabited islets of the Canary group I have constantly seen it thus engaged and never tired of watching it from a vantage point on the cliffs where the birds had their eyrie. In the daytime this pair would often fly to a mass of basalt peeping above the waves known locally as the Roque Infierno, and the day that I first landed on this wave-lashed rock the two ospreys were sitting composedly on the highest block of lava. Mistaking me for a fisherman, they remained sunning themselves until I was within about forty yards, so tame was this pair through never having been molested.

It was in the same group of islands that E. G. B. Meade-Waldo to his astonishment came upon an osprey sitting among a number of gulls waiting for scraps thrown away by a party of fishermen temporarily encamped on the beach. It has been stated by Captain Munn when resident in the Balearic Islands that ospreys will there enter the harbours to fish, plunging on to their prey without paying any attention to the boats and fishermen around.

Amongst many different surroundings the ospreys may be seen in Sweden or Finland on the great lakes which are such a feature of those countries, and there one would look for them perched on some prominent tree growing for choice on an island in the middle of the lake. A dead tree so situated affords an ideal look-out, just as Mr. Lodge has portrayed in his picture, painted from a sketch made in Norway. In contrast, the last osprey I happened to see was perched on a post protruding from a stream meandering to the sea through the Rinçon marshes, between Ceuta and Tetuan. Either a winter visitor or a passing migrant to Spanish Morocco, the bird in question was very shy and quickly made off at our approach. Two days later it was back again on the very same post and this time accompanied by its mate, for the date was the third week of March, when the ospreys in the Mediterranean basin would be thinking of returning north.

Those who, like myself, have had opportunities of seeing this lovely creature in its native haunts must needs curse the day when through the greed of collectors it was banished from our Scottish lochs. I have always been a firm admirer of Charles St. John, who lived over one hundred years ago, admiring him for his prowess as a sportsman and fisherman, for his love of the Highlands and for his undoubted all-round knowledge of the habits of the wild creatures in his native land, but admiration turns to disgust when we read in his own diary of the decisive part he and his friend Dunbar played in the year 1848 in hastening the extinction of the osprey as a breeding bird in our country. Our Scottish lochs are the poorer, and never again are we likely to witness the scenes which St. John portrays with such a facile pen [1] :

May 28 (1848). My peregrinations in Sutherland were most amusing. I started from Bonar Bridge in a light boat on wheels drawn by my old gray pony. We went *via* Oykel, Inchnadamph, Scourie, Durness, Aultnaharrow, and back to Bonar, through a most wild and extraordinary country ; launching our boat here and there, sometimes dragging it over the hills where horse could not go, in order to get at nests of the osprey, black-throated diver and wild geese. The eagles' nests had been already robbed by the shepherds, who have found out their value. We, however, procured six eagles' eggs, beside peregrine falcons'. A shepherd told us of an osprey's nest, or, as he called it, an " eagle fisher ", on an island in a loch near Scourie. We started at daylight over bog and rock, dragging our boat with us, and on reaching the loch I was delighted beyond expression at seeing the two ospreys, one of them on the nest, and the other soaring above, uttering cries of alarm at our approach.

The nest was placed in a most curious situation. About a hundred and fifty yards from the shore there rose from the deep water a solitary rock about ten feet high, shaped like a broken sugar-loaf, or truncated cone ; on the summit of this was the nest—a pile of sticks of very great depth, evidently the accumulation of many breeding seasons, as the osprey returns year after year to the same nest. How this heap of sticks withstood the winter gales without being blown at once into the water, puzzled me. In a crevice of the rock was a small tuft or two of green, otherwise it was perfectly bare and steep.

Many naturalists will know the country which St. John here describes, a country known to the writer which can have changed but little in a hundred years. The lochs are there, the conical-shaped rocks some 200 yards from the shore which the ospreys loved to choose as their nesting place, and the old ruined castles at the water's edge which held such a fascination for the " eagle fisher " and upon the crumbling battlements of which the osprey once built its huge nest. Only now the birds are missing. Shall we ever again listen to the shrill cries echoing across the water when the male returns from his fishing to feed his mate on her nest far out on some inland loch, tucked away among the Scottish hills ?

[1] *Natural History and Sport in Moray*, Chapter the Sixth.

Normally the osprey feeds almost entirely on fish but there are exceptions to that diet as F. C. R. Jourdain pointed out in a contribution to a German periodical,[1] though it is probable that only inability to procure its natural food will turn its attention to small mammals, mice, coots, sandpipers, small duck, jackdaws and—as instanced by Captain Munn—the little grebe. Frogs too have been taken occasionally, but in the case of birds in general it seems that only those which have met with some accident are taken as prey. An apparent exception to this is recorded by C. M. Swaine,[2] who observed a bird which he identified as an osprey drop to the ground and rise with a half-grown lapwing in its talons. Rapidly gaining height, the osprey disappeared from view still carrying its victim. Stress of hunger must surely have been the explanation of this extraordinary episode, even though it took place in Wales in June.

In our Highland freshwater lochs trout were evidently the staple diet but other fish, such as roach and carp, are definitely recorded, while many kinds of surface-swimming sea fish are taken, mullet being a special favourite of the osprey. Indeed, so partial is the osprey to that species that a pair of ospreys which lived beside Loch Arkaig, a freshwater loch in which trout are plentiful, did almost all their hunting on the sea lochs Eil and Linnhe, returning nine times out of ten to their eyrie with a mullet in their talons.[3] That its partiality for that fish is not prompted merely by local circumstance is proved by its love of the cefalo or grey mullet in Sicilian waters which has earned for it the name of " cefalaru " or mullet hawk.

In the Canary Islands I have watched the osprey hovering over the irrigation tanks in which goldfish are often kept but never saw the bird make an attempt at capture. Captain Munn in Majorca was more fortunate, for there he observed an osprey capture a big goldfish in a tank, only to be much alarmed at the appearance of its prey, which it attempted to shake off. Its claws, however, were so firmly fixed in the goldfish that they could not be immediately disengaged, so osprey and fish flopped to the ground ; on the goldfish coming free the osprey took wing, leaving the fish behind.

It is seldom that an osprey fails in its plunge to capture its prey but Munn recounts how one bird made five attempts on a fish which twice escaped by jumping. When an osprey is carrying a fish in its talons the fish is held lengthwise with its head pointing forward, gripped by the talons on either side. Immediately before alighting one foot is disengaged and stretched forward to assist the bird in its perching. So particular is the osprey about carrying its prey with head pointing in the direction of its flight that a bird has been seen to turn a fish round in mid-air to bring its head to the front. This is a provision, Seton Gordon suggests, to reduce

[1] *Beitr. Fortpfl.-Biol. Vög.*, xv, 1939, p. 27.
[2] *British Birds*, xl, 1947, p. 252.
[3] Seton Gordon, *Hill Birds of Scotland*, p. 56.

wind resistance to a minimum when laden with a heavy fish. There are tales of ospreys striking fish so heavy that it is impossible for the bird to lift them, and then the claws must be quickly freed before the osprey is dragged below the surface and loses its life.

Though in general the osprey lives a peaceful existence, a pair have been known to stoop repeatedly at a black vulture, though leaving it quite undisturbed. A more serious combat has been reported by Seton Gordon, a desperate conflict which took place in home waters, near an ancient nesting site in the Scottish Highlands. The origin of the battle was not discovered but it was believed to be rivalry over a solitary hen. For an incredible length of time the combatants struggled fiercely above the surface of the loch, until at length one gained the advantage and, forcing his adversary to the water, kept him pinned below the surface until he drowned.

In his book *The Home Life of the Osprey* Mr. C. G. Abbott from ten years' experience of the huge American colony points to the fact that ospreys are of a peaceful and sociable nature, seldom molesting other birds but allowing themselves to be pursued and harassed by assailants not one tenth their size, and quotes an occasion when he saw an osprey driven from her nest by a tern three or four times within a quarter of an hour. Perhaps the American osprey is more cowardly than his European cousin, for we read in Irby's *Ornithology of the Straits of Gibraltar* how that observant naturalist saw an osprey give a gannet which had ventured too near its nest " a great buffeting, knocking him about and chasing him for half a mile ".

The osprey is most abundant in the Straits in winter, and indeed all along the Mediterranean coast the resident birds have their numbers augmented. Migratory ospreys are said to arrive in North Africa in October and November and that there is a partial migration to tropical Africa in winter seems to be certain. The mouth of the Gambia River is a well-known haunt of the osprey in the winter months but whether the birds are migrants from Europe or visitors from the archipelagos of the Canaries and the Cape Verde Islands, in both of which groups the osprey breeds, it is impossible to say.

Professor Einar Lönnberg has stated[1] that Swedish ospreys after breeding in that country travel towards the Mediterranean directly south, or with a south-westerly twist that takes them over the Danish islands and farther to southern France and northern Spain perhaps by the month of September. One was seen fishing at the Lipari islands off Italy in October. Ringing has shown that some are rather late in returning north, as was proved by a four-year-old osprey having been shot on 27th April in the Department of Lozère, southern France. We have naturally no ringing returns from Britain, but occasionally a Swedish osprey is recovered in

[1] *Proceedings of the VIIIth International Congress*, p. 612.

this country on its way to or from its northern home.[1]   That some pass through Britain very much later than the end of April is apparent from Miss Baxter's observations on the Isle of May, where she and Miss Rintoul saw single birds passing over to the northward on 17th May 1921 and 21st May 1926.

Ospreys are so seldom seen actually during passage that the late Charles Bird's record of an osprey flying up the coast of Rio de Oro on 16th April is worthy of notice here.

There are no known breeding places of the osprey on the *West* African mainland, but as has been shown already there are colonies in Somaliland and along the Red Sea coast, which makes the assessment of migrants from Europe a more difficult matter.   In Kenya van Someren has stated that a fair number visit the Colony and are particularly common on Lake Victoria and Lake Naivasha during the winter, where specimens have been collected between November and March.   Loveridge eventually discovered a pair nesting on Naivasha, but that was an unusual instance and there is little to contest the statement, confirmed by Sir Frederick Jackson, that the osprey is a migrant to both Kenya and Uganda, though Sir Frederick gives the arrival date as September.[2]

As for the Belgian Congo, we learn from Doctor Chapin [3] that it is not at all numerous in the Congo basin, but he has observed it more or less regularly along the Uelle, Kibali and Ituri Rivers from August to April inclusive.   All were excessively wary, which points to the fact that they are migrants from the north.

BREEDING HABITS :   Most accounts available in this country dealing with the nesting of the osprey are based on information supplied in American literature.   The American osprey, *Pandion haliaëtus carolinensis*, can be studied at close quarters in the huge colony on Gardiner's Island, off Long Island, which is reputed to contain between 200 and 300 nests.   It appears from the account in Mr. Cleveland Bent's *Life Histories of North American Birds of Prey* that the race which breeds on the other side of the Atlantic is much more addicted to nesting in large colonies than are ospreys in other parts of the world, but in other respects it is unlikely that the habits of the races vary to any appreciable extent.   Certainly in western Europe and in the Mediterranean basin it is sometimes possible to find two or three nests in the same stretch of cliffs, but no big colony has ever been discovered to compare with what exists in North America.

In Scotland, where seldom more than one pair frequented the same loch, the ospreys of the past had a choice of three quite distinct sites upon which they habitually built their huge nests.   Charles St. John of Elgin, who had probably visited—and robbed—more ospreys' nests than any

[1] E. P. Leach, *British Birds*, xli, 1948, p. 177.
[2] *Birds of Kenya Colony and the Uganda Protectorate*, pp. 227 and 228.
[3] *Birds of the Belgian Congo*, i, p. 536.

man living in his day, affirmed that ospreys arriving in the country to nest sought a conical-shaped rock rising from the water at about 200 yards' distance from the shore upon which to build. He found that on all the lakes which he visited where this singularly shaped rock was to be seen, there, sure enough, would be the nest of an osprey, the birds trusting to their isolated situation for safety.

Another site, favoured by a number of ospreys and particularly by the pair which bred for years on Loch an Eilein, was on the battlements of a ruined castle—in the case in point on an island eighty yards from the shore. Seton Gordon, in his *Hill Birds of Scotland*, has stressed how interesting it was to discover how often the ruins of some Highland chief's castle were chosen as the site for an eyrie, adding that a nest had even been found built upon the remains of a disused shooting lodge.

A third site—one sometimes selected in the past by Scottish ospreys— was on the summit of a tall tree. Such was the eyrie described by Cameron of Lochiel at Achnacarry, where the birds had chosen to build on the top of an old oak tree on a small island adjacent to Chapel Island at the east end of the loch [1] ; a second nesting place on the south side of the loch was in a similar situation.

The tree usually selected by the osprey in Scotland was an old pine, upon the very top of which the bird would build, but tree nests were *not* preferred (despite the statement in *The Handbook of British Birds*) where small rocky islets or ruined buildings were available. It may readily be imagined that the latter sites were much more secure against the severe winter gales normally experienced on these Highland lochs, and as the same nest is used year after year by the same pair, the structure eventually reaches very large dimensions and is liable to be blown over. It is stated in American literature that although the bird sometimes builds in dead trees, in most cases the tree is killed by the weight of the nest or by the saline character of the nesting material and of the birds' food. Mr. Cleveland Bent [2] knew of many cases where the tree had died or fallen after the ospreys had built on it.

Although I have been unable to find an instance of a cliff nest having been seen in Scotland it would be surprising if none existed in the days when ospreys were not so very rare. In southern Spain it is probably to this day the most favoured situation. Seventy years ago a pair or more regularly had their eyrie on the east side of the Rock of Gibraltar, but according to Colonel Tuke (1953) the ospreys no longer nest in what must have been a wonderful situation. These cliff nests were well-nigh inaccessible even to the most experienced climber.

In Morocco, before that country was as accessible as it is to-day, there is reputed to have been an osprey's eyrie on every headland, and I can speak from personal experience that in the Canary Islands, where ospreys

[1] *British Birds*, xxvi, 1943, p. 184.
[2] *Life Histories of North American Birds of Prey*, p. 356.

are common enough, they invariably choose the sea cliffs upon which to rear their young.

On the other side of Africa, on the low-lying sandy islets off the Somali coast, the osprey makes its nest very near to sea-level, the nests being placed on or near a mound in the absence of a better eminence. These nests, standing often four feet high, and weighing as much as 400 pounds, can be seen a mile away. On some of the islands in the Red Sea the ospreys come very near to being colonial builders; Admiral Lynes has reported that several pairs will build in close proximity. We also hear of it nesting off the Arabian coast in stunted mangroves.

The material of which the nest is built varies according to locality, but sticks when available are preferred for the foundation. That was certainly the case in Scotland, where some of the sticks were quite a load in themselves. Heather stalks were woven in among the heavier material and the usual collection of seaweed, moss and débris of various kinds was eventually added to the bulk. The bowl was lined with finer material such as dead grass and moss. Some old nests measured as much as five feet across, while others were about three feet; the size depends much upon the age of the nest, as it is constantly being repaired and used year after year. In contrast to the above, Sir Geoffrey Archer described nests on the coast of British Somaliland as being built of sticks, driftwood, plant stalks, sea-lavender, sponges, fish bones and any flotsam and jetsam that can be picked up along the shore. It will be remembered that the osprey which breeds in Somaliland and along the Red Sea belongs to exactly the same race as that which formerly bred in the British Isles.

Osprey's eggs are among the most handsome laid by birds of prey. The clutch is normally two or three, four eggs being exceptional. Oates has described them well in the *Catalogue of Birds' Eggs in the British Museum* in the following words : " The eggs of the osprey are generally of a perfectly oval form, coarse in texture and possess a very small amount of gloss. The ground varies from cream-colour, sometimes tinged with yellow, to pinkish-buff. The markings are bold and consist of spots and huge blotches of the richest reddish-brown and chocolate-brown. These are usually confluent and seldom cover less than half the surface of the egg. Some specimens are smeared and blotched with yellowish-brown and a certain number exhibit underlying blotches of violet-grey."

F. C. R. Jourdain gives the average of 100 eggs of the typical subspecies as 61·59 × 46·37 mm. Max. 69 × 46 and 68·4 × 50·3. Min. 50·4 × 41·3 and 55·2 × 40·2 mm.

The breeding season in the British Isles used to extend from the end of April and the beginning of May onwards. Both sexes take part in incubation, which begins with the first egg, the hen taking the greater share. The incubation period is said to be thirty-five days and the fledging period lasts from eight to ten weeks.

Mr. Seton Gordon points out that the osprey was quite six weeks later than the golden eagle in beginning the duties of rearing a family when it bred in Scotland ; this is a not unnatural difference when it is remembered that all the ospreys which still breed, or bred formerly, in northern latitudes are summer migrants, whereas the eagle is with us all the year round. The nesting season also varies to some extent according to latitude. Eggs may be found in the south of Spain as early as the middle of March (Irby and Verner), and as late as May if first clutches are taken. In Finnish Lapland, on the other hand, Steward took eggs but slightly incubated on 16th June.

It is from Scandinavian sources that we must hope to attract the passage migrants—all too few in number—which wend their way south after the short northern breeding season has drawn to a close. The migratory instinct is very strong in these birds and although we do not know as yet exactly how far south they proceed to pass the winter, their homing instinct is so strongly developed that it will be only the merest chance if a pair elects to visit one of the old nesting places in Scotland. Loch Arkaig and Loch an Eilein come to mind as the two most likely to tempt a passing pair to tarry in their old haunts. It would be a red-letter day indeed if such a miracle came to pass and future generations could hear again the wild cry of the osprey among our Scottish hills and watch again a pair at their fishing on Loch an Eilein as in the halcyon days of old.

REFERENCES: Original Description. *Falco haliaëtus* Linnaeus, Syst. Nat., 10th ed., 1758, p. 91 : Europe ; restricted type locality Sweden.

INDEX

PRINTED IN GREAT BRITAIN BY
OLIVER AND BOYD LTD.
EDINBURGH